LOST HERITAGE

Also by Henry Savage, Jr.

SEEDS OF TIME: *The Background of Southern Thinking*
River of the Carolinas: THE SANTEE

~ By Henry Savage, Jr.

LOST HERITAGE

~ William Morrow and Company, Inc.

New York   1970

From concept to index this book has been a joint enterprise with my wife, Elizabeth. In recognition of the part she has played in its creation, this work is dedicated to her—with a very deep bow.

PREFACE

In developing the accounts of the group of naturalists who are the subject of this book, a liberal use of quotations from their own journals and other writings has been made in order to give flavor and accuracy to their stories, particularly in reporting their observations of the American wilderness to which they gave their dedicated devotion. Inconsistencies of style and spelling which may be noted in various quotations attributed to the same person in most cases result from the fact that edited and published versions are often the only surviving or accessible source. In the case of the Michauxs, the quotations represent translations from the original French, sometimes those of the author, sometimes those appearing in published versions.

ACKNOWLEDGMENTS

The work on this book has been, for the most part, for me and for my wife, who has shared its burdens and rewards, a happy and enriching experience for which we are indebted to many persons now living and to those from the living past with whom the book is concerned. During the years of reading, writing, and rewriting, one of our principal pleasures has been the daily companionship with the seven remarkable men whose tale this is. Obviously and properly the principal sources of the book are the works of these men, their writings, paintings, journals, and letters.

For the opportunity to study indispensable source material as well as related works, we are deeply grateful to the following persons and institutions:

The libraries of the University of South Carolina, which possess an outstanding collection of rare books in this field; Mr. Alfred Rawlinson, for permission to use the libraries freely; Mr. E. L. Inabinet and his staff of the Caroliniana Library, for generous assistance and for access to their original editions of Catesby's *Natural History* and *Hortus*, Lawson's *New Voyage*, Bartram's *Travels*, and the *Flora* of Michaux, the elder, as well as other relevant materials; Mrs. Davy-Jo Ridge of the Treasure Room at the McKissick Library, for the opportunity to work with the eight volumes of Wilson's *Ornithology* and the *Sylva* of Michaux, the younger, and to examine the magnificent paintings in the elephant folio of Audubon;

Miss Virginia Rugheimer and her staff of the Charleston Library Society, for the use of the files of the *City Gazette* of 1804, the only published source in this country, so far as we know, of De Leuze's memorial account of André Michaux;

Mrs. Granville T. Prior of the South Carolina Historical Society, for the opportunity to examine unpublished letters and other papers, and for many useful articles in their magazine;

Mrs. Gertrude Hess of the American Philosophical Society, for valuable suggestions. To her and her staff we are indebted for the privilege of examining the unique notebook journals of André Michaux, presented to the society by his son, as well as an opportunity to look at rare books and paintings in their possession;

The libraries of Harvard University, where preliminary research on this book was done, and where opportunity was given to examine copies of Wilson's *Foresters*, a copy of Michaux's *Flora*, annotated by Asa Gray, manuscript journals of Audubon, and a manuscript copy of John Bartram's 1743 journal, as well as the unpublished work of John Abbot;

The libraries of Yale University, especially the Beinecke Rare Book Library, where we were permitted to examine a copy of André Michaux's book, *Histoire des Chênes de l'Amérique. . .* ;

The libraries of Columbia University, for the facilities of Butler Library. Especially I wish to thank the personnel of the Special Collections divisions who made it possible for me to examine their volumes of Wilson's *Ornithology;*

The Historical Society of Pennsylvania, for opportunity to examine manuscript letters of Alexander Wilson and manuscript material of John and William Bartram, including the manuscript copy of the 1765–66 journal of John Bartram;

The library of the New York Botanical Garden, for permission to study relevant material and to examine their horticultural collections;

The library of Duke University for free access to the stacks and reference rooms.

In addition, we would like to thank Mr. and Mrs. Richard Lloyd for the use of rare books in their possession, Miss Sallie B. Anderson for sharing the results of her personal research in this field, Mrs. Emily Cheston and others of The John Bartram Association, and Mr. John Baher, guardian of the Bartram house and garden.

Our thanks go to our friends and to our children for their interest and encouragement, to our daughter, Virginia, for her research at Harvard University, to our daughter, Helen, for finding for us an indispensable source book, and to many others, in particular the staff of my law office, my law associates and our secretaries, for patient forbearance with my eighteenth-century absorption, as well as for substantial assistance.

I am deeply indebted to my friend Harry Shaw, of Fairfield, Connecticut, for consultation and advice, and to Mrs. Helen King, of William Morrow and Company, for her indispensable aid and the kind of creative criticism that every author hopes to receive from his editor.

Specifically, we wish to thank the American Philosophical Society for permission to quote from John Bartram's diary of 1765–66, published in their *Transactions of 1942*, from the original manuscript in the files of the Historical Society of Pennsylvania. For permission to quote a 1737 letter from Peter Collinson to John Custis, we wish to thank the American Antiquarian Society, of Worcester, Massachusetts.

For permission to reproduce prints of original drawings and paintings in their possession, we are grateful to the following: the Caroliniana and McKissick libraries of the University of South Carolina, the libraries of Columbia University, in New York, the American Philosophical Society, in Philadelphia, the Independence National Historical Park Collection, in Philadelphia, and the British Museum, in London.

CONTENTS

ILLUSTRATIONS

LOST HERITAGE

~∿ Chapter 1

THE ROOT OF THE MATTER

Its lands are lofty and in it are many sierras and very high mountains. . . . All are most beautiful, of a thousand shapes, and all accessible,
and filled with trees of a thousand kinds and tall, and they seem to touch the
sky; . . . and some of them were flowering, some with fruit. . . . All there
were singing the nightingale and other little birds of a thousand kinds in the
month of November, there where I went. There were palm trees of six or
eight kinds, which are a wonder to behold on account of their beautiful
variety; . . . therein are marvelous pine groves . . . and many kinds of
birds and a great variety of fruits.

So wrote Columbus on his return to Spain in the spring of 1493, extravagant in praise of the new world he had found on his westward
voyage.

The news of his discoveries, and the exotic productions of nature
which he brought back in support of his glowing words, kindled the
imagination of awakening Renaissance Europe. Others soon followed the
sea path he had blazed to the west, some to seek such treasures as the
New World might offer, others to search for a passage through the
newly discovered continents that might lead to the Orient. The names of
these men are written in bold letters across the pages of American history: Verrazzano, de Ayllón, Ponce de León, Cabot, and Hudson, followed, in a later period, by Drake, Raleigh, Champlain, and John Smith,
to name but a few of those of most significance to North America.
Their discoveries were momentous, but they were mostly navigational,

largely confined to the coastline, and superficial in relation to the land and the life that lay beyond. Nevertheless, the enthusiastic, sometimes marvelous reports they carried back, acting in concert with imperial rivalries, were sufficient stimuli to bring into being seaside settlements from Maine to Florida in the century centered on 1700. Still, however, the great wilderness beyond the narrow strip of settled coastline remained, an alluring, mysterious, and formidable world of which little was yet known. Even after many of the beachhead colonies had become well-established communities, the question was still being asked: "If the Porch be so beautiful, what must the Temple be?"

This book is about some of those who undertook to answer that query. They were "curious" men, as those of inquiring mind were then described. They were intrepid men, undaunted by the hazards of their mission, stubborn men for whom discouragements were but stimuli to greater effort. Above all they were dedicated men, as dedicated as their more famous predecessors in the world of discovery. Their dedication, however, was to the discovery of America in depth and detail. Theirs was not a search for an elusive Northwest Passage, nor was it for silver and gold or for any mythical El Dorado. Their El Dorado was the great green wilderness of eastern America and the myriad creatures it harbored. To that El Dorado they became the ambassadors of the day, and the reports of their missions remain so alive and pertinent in the twentieth century that, in effect, their missions have assumed a degree of immortality.

Today there is also, it seems to me, in what these wilderness naturalists found and reported, a new urgency for us and a greater currency than ever. Modern life has become so complex and artificial and so remote from nature that it all but completely obscures our fundamental relationship with the green world. It is essential for our survival that we never lose awareness of that basic kinship and our total dependence on it.

Only yesterday a constant awareness of that dependence came naturally with the warming fire from the logs dragged in from the forest, with the hay, pregnant with last summer's sunlight, pitched to old Dobbin as fuel for transportation. It is far more difficult to visualize the sunlight-storing action of chlorophyll in heat delivered through pipes and wires; it is well-nigh impossible to feel the dependence on the action of green leaves long dead that is inherent in the volatile fraction from their fossil remains, when it drives one's automobile over a turnpike, surfaced with other fractions cracked from the debris of plants dead and buried millions of years ago. The things upon which all these things and even life itself depend are generally forgotten. Only intellectually is it possible to see chlorophyll's part in the daily life of modern man and the essential part it plays in providing every mouthful of food he consumes, every stitch he wears, even the life-giving oxygen in every breath he takes.

Now, with most of the magnificent, teeming, and flowering wilderness that was our heritage all but obliterated from the landscape and the little that remains sorely threatened by human carelessness and the ever mounting pressure of population, there is urgent need for us to look back to the glory of eastern America before it was severely manhandled. There can be no better guides for us into that green and wonderful wilderness than those who knew it as virgin country, who appreciated its magnificence, who left us their personal record of a world of fabulous beauty now well-nigh lost to all but memory. Through their letters, and journals, and books, we can travel with them on their lonely pilgrimages, over our mountains, down our rivers, through forests whose only paths were those of Indian or buffalo, under the burning sun of southern summers or the biting frost of northern winters, as they journeyed to discover an America that remained almost unknown to western man.

When the Europeans established their earlier colonies along the Atlantic seaboard, their new-found home was a land of incredibly rich fauna and flora, unrivaled anywhere else in the temperate zones of the earth. Perhaps had it been less rich we might never have developed into a nation of wastrels. All across our land the abundance of fauna in the American wilderness is memorialized in place names—memorials to creatures which, with few exceptions, are now long gone from the land, leaving only their names—footprints of history, implanted on the mind. Long gone are the stately, great-antlered elk from Maryland's turbulent Elk River, from Elk Valley in the Cumberlands of Tennessee, and from Pennsylvania's Elkland. Along the Buffalo Creeks and Buffalo Rivers all across the East, from the Great Lakes to Florida, in Buffalo Cove and along Buffalo Ridge, herds of buffalo once browsed commonly enough to leave their name inscribed there before they fell victim to the leaden balls of the white interlopers in paradise, covetous of hide and hair of the great beasts, and hungry for boiled buffalo tongue.

No longer do whooping or sandhill cranes haunt the forests and waters around Alabama's Crane Hill, and no more is there much chance of finding eagles nesting at North Carolina's Eagle Rock, or along the Eagle Creeks of Kentucky or Tennessee, although there remains an outside chance of finding a pair at Florida's Eagle Lake.

Among the first to give way in the face of the white man's invasion were the big cats. First to go was the magnificent, secretive jaguar, known to the vanguard settlers under the Old World soubriquet of tiger, who lingered after the coming of the white predators only long enough to leave his name on a river of the Carolina Piedmont, before retreating westward. Soon the lithe, tree-loving panther (alias puma, mountain lion), unjustly considered a threat to life and livestock, was all but extirpated by the settlers, knocking out in the process an invaluable spoke in the wheel of life in the American forests, for at the same time his fellow predator, the American wolf, was meeting a like fate. Now never of a winter's night does the howl of a wolf drift across the waters of Illinois' Wolf Lake, or through the forests along Mississippi's Wolf River.

It has been many a year since anyone traveling the Inland Waterway through North Carolina's Alligator River has seen an alligator sunning on the bank; neither is he apt to come on a fishing bear on Bear Inlet farther down the waterway. In fact, among the dozens of Bear Creeks and Rivers, Mountains and Wallows, only a few can claim a living bruin. For the countless Turkey Creeks it is much the same story— never a strutting turkey cock to be seen or heard. And for the even more numerous Beaver Creeks, a beaver dam, in this country, is a rare exception.

Never again as long as the world lasts will the passenger pigeons darken the sky over Pigeon Mountain, in Georgia or New York, or regale themselves by the millions on the acorns along Pigeon Creek in Alabama, or roost in the forest giants of the Great Smokies and drink from the crystal waters of the tumultuous Pigeon River there. Never more will those swift and graceful birds, with their iridescent plumage, look upon any of their geographical namesakes. Despite their former multitudes, they are gone from the earth forever. Nor will anyone ever again delight his eyes with the sight of the brilliant-feathered, red, yellow, and green Carolina parakeet, for he, unfortunately, had a taste for the seed of apple and pear, a "vandal" taste, which civilized man could not tolerate.

Gone, too, down the road to near extermination, is the noblest offering of the American wilderness, the American Indian, who, for at least a dozen millenniums, was an integral part of its web of life, a predator but, like his fellow predators of lower orders, a dweller in essential harmony with his fellow creatures of the wilderness. And, just as did his fellow creatures as they bowed out, so did the Indian indelibly write his evocative and mellifluous names across the land, from sea to sea: on its flowing waters, from the Merrimac and Penobscot to the Yazoo and Pascagoula, from the Chattahoochee and the Tallapoosa to the Illinois and Kankakee; and on its still waters from Huron to Okeechobee; on its great mountains, Appalachians, Alleghenies, and Adirondacks; its forest trails, such as the Mohawk and the Natchez Trace; on regions that became states, Kentucky, meaning dark and bloody ground, Mississippi, great river, and Michigan, great lake.

The vanished world of the unravaged American wilderness can be seen by us most clearly now through the eyes of pioneer naturalists. Some used the pen to paint what they saw in eloquent words, written often by lonely campfires; others, the artist's brush, to portray the shapes and colors of that vivid and varied landscape and its creatures; but pen and brush alike spoke with such accuracy and care that they have preserved forever for us their vision of a land of natural beauty and healthy abundance which can not only fill us with nostalgic longing but can inspire us to cherish before it is too late what still can be salvaged of our natural and primal glory.

Among the many pioneer naturalists of America to whom our history and culture owe so much, the seven, who in this book lend us their eyes and share with us their understanding of the American wilderness in the eighteenth and early nineteenth centuries, are a varied group, representing in the range and variety of their personalities, abilities, and experiences, all the marvelous diversity and dramatic contrasts of the new continent. They themselves were men of singular fascination, each with his separate and very personal love affair with his demanding mistress, Nature, and his own way of singing her praise.

The first is John Lawson, gentleman, charming, impulsive, dynamic, who came from England to the Carolina colony in 1700, with mystery in his past and martyrdom in his future, to become, in his eleven crowded years in America, lively diarist, adventurous promoter, and enthusiastic pioneer naturalist of the Southern colonies.

He is followed by Mark Catesby, artist and naturalist, who began his American adventures as a more or less casual visitor in 1712, but who fell so deeply under the spell of the natural beauty he found here that he spent the rest of his life in painstaking labor to portray in his magnificent *Natural History* the enchantment he had experienced.

The next two, John and William Bartram, father and son, were Quaker farmers, whose names are revered today wherever botany is cherished as a science or loved as an art. Rooted as they were in the rich soil of their native Pennsylvania, they made the whole world of nature their study, the green world their special province. The personality and character of John Bartram, revealed in his letters and journals, are as essentially American as the thousands of seeds and plants he collected and shipped to the gardens of Europe. His sturdy and practical nature met its complement in the romantic and artistic William, whose dedication to natural history found lasting expression in his famous *Travels*.

The last part of the eighteenth century brought another father and son to America, sent on a botanical mission from France, a country whose early explorers from Florida to Canada had been among the first to awaken interest in the flora and fauna of the new continent, and who now faced, on all frontiers, the menacing competition of rival European powers. André Michaux and son, François André, are the first professional botanists in our group. America was but one chapter in the life story of André Michaux, which reads like a botanical odyssey, but the chapter is of great significance in American natural history. François André Michaux, inheritor of his father's unfinished mission in America, is known today as the father of American forestry in recognition of his original and important work on American trees.

The last naturalist in our group is the artist-ornithologist, Alexander Wilson, a man of passionate devotion to the birds he studied and painted. Indeed, he himself was a bird of passage, fleeing from a youth in Scotland as harsh and lonely as its landscape. Romantic and poetic by nature, with more than a hint of Celtic melancholy, Wilson is in many ways the most personally appealing of the seven.

This book is an attempt to evoke virginal America through the eyes and often in the words of these wilderness naturalists, who knew and loved it well. Strikingly dissimilar in personality and character though they were, their geniuses had a common focus. Adventurers all, they harkened to the same wild music.

However, although the main purpose of this book is that it should shed more light on a strangely neglected facet of the history of the discovery of America and to that end it is largely concerned with men whose dedication was to the discovery of America in depth and detail, beyond that purpose is the intent, with the aid of their testimony, to contrast an undespoiled America with what we have today.

Americans are wont to take pride in the conquest of the wilderness, which those men knew and loved, a wilderness that had flourished for hundreds of years before the first white man's footprint on these shores signaled its doom. Now we are awakening to a realization that perhaps that conquest was a Pyrrhic victory at best. There is widespread apprehension abroad today, particularly among the more thoughtful, an apprehension that our great conquest has been so ruthless, so devastating, and so complete that nature may be mortally wounded. There is growing suspicion that there is more shame than pride inherent in the awful extent of that conquest. Was not the victim our earth mother, the placenta of all life on earth?

Deplorably, the misconceptions, ignorance, and selfishness which motivated such excessive destruction continue to dominate modern man's relationship to nature.

Few Americans today can be wholly unaware of the blight across our nation's landscape, our maimed and dying rivers, their waters polluted, their once lovely banks unsightly and barren, our poisoned air where the pall of gasoline and other noxious fumes grows steadily more deadly, our plundered countryside, where urban sprawl and encroaching concrete nibble away inexorably at the last green oases. But all too few are aware of the vital relationship between the health of our natural environment and the existence of life on earth. Few realize that the sickness of our natural environment is rapidly and literally becoming a sickness unto death.

Even while man's inability to live in rational amity with his fellowman, of whatever ideology, race, color, or nation, threatens our species with extinction through war, simultaneously the survival of life on earth is seriously jeopardized by man's inability or unwillingness to live in harmony with nature and in obedience to her laws. Unfortunately, it is far easier to arouse human beings to war against their fellow-men than to battle against their own greed, ignorance, stupidity, and carelessness. Yet in this crusade for reform the trumpets must be sounded with no uncertain note if life is to continue on our troubled planet.

On almost any cluttered highway one may come upon the familiar sign, nailed to a tree or painted on a boulder: "Repent and be saved." This exhortation, implicit with warning of imminent doom and hope of salvation in a better world, may have earthly implications when the sign is seen in the context of our ravaged landscape. Dismayed at the appalling extent to which signs, trash, junkyards, and shoddy and ugly structures have invaded and elbowed from view the green countryside, few will deny that there is ample cause here for repentance on the part of present-day Americans for the way they have superficially butchered their once lovely land. The majority, however, are unlikely to see a deeper, unintended relevance to modern man in that warning, "Repent and be saved," the imperious necessity that modern man repent and reform his spendthrift, ruthless, and predatory ways all across the land, extending far beyond that manhandled road, and reaching into every aspect of his natural environment.

Yet Americans today are not so much guilty of deliberate assault upon their natural environment as woefully ignorant of the basic truths of ecology. We have been taught neither the inexorable laws of nature nor the penalties of infringement. For the most part we have gone about our work of destruction wholly unaware of the unity of all life on earth, of the awesome truth that "Thou canst not stir a flower without troubling of a star."

Intent upon his role as lord of the earth, man has tended to forget that he himself is an integral part of nature, his very life dependent on the health of his natural environment.

At first glance, the urgent need for conservation and ecological reform, to be discussed in more detail in the last chapter of this book, may seem to have little relation to a study of explorer-naturalists out of the American past. It is true that the early naturalists, though opposed to the wasteful practices already current in the colonies, were not conservationists as we use the term today. The imperatives of ecology were not recognized until long after their deaths. Their constant awareness of man's oneness with nature, however, and their dedication to the green world give them a special relevance to our problems today and make them helpful guides as we grope toward a more harmonious and essentially practical relationship with the earth and its products. Furthermore, in the hard struggle to bring back this country's natural environment to a state of radiant health—a struggle for survival itself—the still unravaged, green and flowering wilderness, seen through their eyes, remains a permanent inspiration to us, a lost glory we can never wholly regain but may, in time and in some measure, restore.

Chapter 2

JOHN LAWSON

∽ 1

In the year 1709, in the city of London, a book was published with the following title: *A New Voyage to Carolina; Containing the Exact Description and Natural History of that Country: Together with the Present State Thereof. And a Journal of a Thousand Miles, Travel'd thro' several Nations of Indians. Giving a particular Account of their Customs, Manners, etc.* The author was John Lawson.

It is strange that, significant as this book was in the natural history of America, nothing at all is known of the author's life before 1700. In the spring of that year, fate, in the form of a chance meeting in London, turned him westward to the New World, as he himself tells in the introduction to his journal:

In the year 1700, when People flock'd from all Parts of the Christian World, to see the Solemnity of the Grand Jubilee at Rome, my Intention, at that Time, being to travel, I accidentally met with a Gentleman, who had been Abroad, and was very well acquainted with the Ways of Living in both Indies; of whom, having made Enquiry concerning them, he assur'd me, that Carolina was the best Country I could go to; and, that there then lay a Ship in the Thames, in which I might have my Passage. I laid hold on this Opportunity, and was not long on Board, before we fell down the River. . . .

We are interested at once in this impulsive and adventurous young man. We are eager to learn more about him. Who was the much traveled gentleman accidentally encountered, perchance in coffeehouse or tavern? What was his name and business? Who, indeed, was John Lawson? For all that history knows, it is as though his very life began on that spring day in London. Cloaked in mystery, he comes without introduction, credentials, birth certificate, or known ancestry, projected, as it were, into recorded history with his departure from England and his arrival, nearly three months later, in Charleston. Though his eleven years in the colonies, broken only by one short visit back to England, were crowded with experience and achievement, thrusting him into prominence in America and in Europe, no scrap of reliable data of his life before 1700 has ever been discovered.

One may search his writings in vain for the missing facts. It is not surprising that his journal and natural history have no personal revelations of his past for he seems not to have been an introspective man. There seems, however, in his writings a more than casual reticence, a deliberate secrecy. Nevertheless, here and there straws of information are dropped, which may be gleaned and sheaved into a meager bundle of fairly reliable speculation. His professed English-gentleman status is supported by his obvious familiarity with the ways of the gentry of his day and his good education by seventeenth-century standards. His awareness of the color of Dutch ditchwater, his discussion of the French methods of pruning vineyards vis-à-vis that employed in Italy, and other such references, indicate an acquaintance with the Continent and some travel there. His frequent use of the physical aspects of Yorkshire, as standards of comparison for his American observations, suggests a North of England background. On the other hand, he speaks with such intimate knowledge of London that one suspects he may have lived there for some time before abandoning the city for the Carolina wilderness.

Perhaps it is not too fanciful to suspect that John Lawson was not his real name. Men walked warily amid the shifting loyalties and deadly intrigues of seventeenth-century England, and many a hard-pressed youth sought a new life in the New World with a new name as well.

However that may be, the John Lawson who stepped ashore in Charleston in the late summer of 1700, after a long and arduous sea voyage, brought to the New World a character singularly well adapted to its challenges: an observant eye, an inquiring mind, physical stamina, courage, and, withal, a youthful zest and energy akin to the vitality of the as yet unspoiled country. He had only good to say of Charleston, barely twenty years old, which he describes as the "Metropolis of South Carolina," but it was not here that his destiny lay. Before the waning year had passed he was off to adventure in the Carolina wilderness.

Characteristically, he tells us nothing of the purpose of his expedition, nor does he name or identify his companions other than by nationality. Surely it was somewhat quixotic to set out in the depth of winter, in a cypress canoe, for an unknown destination, through uncharted and dangerous lands. But we are left, as with the story of his sudden decision to quit London for the Carolinas, wavering between an impression of romantic, almost wayward, impulse and a grimmer hint of sudden and desperate urgencies.

He set out in late December with five other Englishmen, three Indian men and one woman, wife to the Indian guide, and Lawson's spaniel bitch, all in a single cypress dugout canoe, and headed north along the marsh creeks behind the sea islands, aiming for the mouth of the Santee River. Their trials began even on the first night, which they spent at Bell's Island, where they were attacked, in spite of the season, by "thousands of Musketoes and other troublesome Insects tormenting both Man and Beast." The second day they ran aground on a sand bar exposed to the surf but finally "by God's Blessing, got off safe to Shore."

They arrived, in the afternoon of the next day, at Bulls Island, now, for birds and bird watchers, the most popular part of the Cape Romain National Wildlife Refuge. It is interesting, in the light of the island's destiny as a bird refuge and its continued popularity as a winter spa for waterfowl, to read Lawson's account of "in the Season, good Plenty of Fowl, as Curleus, Gulls, Gannets, and Pellicans, besides Duck and Mallard, Geese, Swans, Teal, Widgeon, etc."

Their first night on the island was again troubled: "Although it were Winter, yet we found such Swarms of Musketoes, and other troublesome Insects, that we got but little Rest that Night." However, next day, after a gale had driven them back onto the north end of Bulls Island when they tried to cross over to the mainland, they set up camp there to await more favorable weather. They crossed the island to the beach where they were particularly interested in the quantities of jellyfish stranded on the sand and the large pen shells which Lawson called Spanish oyster shells. "At our Return to our Quarters, the Indians had kill'd two more Deer, two wild Hogs and three Racoons, all very lean, except the Racoons. We had great Store of Oysters, Conks, and Clanns, a large sort of Cockles. These parts being very well furnish'd with Shell-Fish. . . ."

Two days later they entered the Santee which was then in flood, its waters spread out for miles into the bordering forests where grew the "vast Ciprus-Trees of which the French make Canoes, that will carry fifty or sixty Barrels." The weather was bitterly cold and their progress against the flood current painfully slow, but for a man of Lawson's "curious" mind the watery wilderness was a constant source of wonder:

As we went up the River we heard a great Noise, as if two parties were engag'd against each other, seeming exactly like small Shot. When we approach'd nearer the place we found it to be some Sewee Indians firing the Canes Swamps, which drives out the Game, then taking their particular Stands, kill great Quantities of both Bear, Deer, Turkies, and what wild Creatures the Parts afford.

This was Lawson's first introduction to the Indian method of fire-hunting, which he explains in detail later in his account of the Indians of North Carolina, describing the careful selection of suitable terrain for the temporary hunting quarters where "they have their Wives and Ladies of the Camp, where they eat all the Fruits and Dainties of that Country, and live in all the Mirth and Jollity which it is possible for such People to entertain themselves withal." The Indians in their natural setting seemed to fascinate John Lawson who saw them as a part of the native wildlife, their numbers already greatly diminished, their existence constantly menaced be the whites, even by mere contact with them: "These Sewees have been formerly a large Nation, though now very much decreas'd, since the English hath seated their Land, and all other Nations of Indians are observ'd to partake of the same Fate, where the Europeans come, the Indians being a People very apt to catch any Distemper they are afflicted withal . . ."

The gratuitous afflictions which Lawson saw as the nemesis of the Indians were smallpox and rum, to both of which they had little resistance. We know now that measles and whooping cough and other diseases common in Europe were probably equally deadly to the American Indian. These scourges had been decimating them since the first ships with the Maltese cross on their sails dropped anchor on American shores. Two centuries had passed since then, and now but a fraction of their earlier numbers remained. At village after village the Indians told Lawson of their former greatness and lamented their bitter fate. Miles and miles of deserted Indian fields, which the travelers crossed, seemed to Lawson stark evidence of the destruction already suffered by the highest creature of the American wilderness, presaging the doom of this proud people in the years to come.

After a brief visit to the newly established French Huguenot settlements along the south bank, Lawson's party crossed the swollen river, abandoned their canoe, and started up the Indian path which ran generally along the edge of the swamp.

There being a deep Run of Water in the Way, one of our Company being top-heavy, and there being nothing but a small Pole for a Bridge, over a Creek, fell into the Water up to the Chin; my self laughing at the Accident, and not taking good Heed to my Steps, came to the same Misfortune: All our Bedding was wet. The Wind being at N.W. it froze very hard, which prepar'd such a Night's Lodging for me, that I never desire to have the like again; the wet Bedding and freezing Air had so qualify'd our Bodies, that in the Morning when we awak'd, we were nigh frozen to Death, until we had recruited our selves before a large Fire of the Indians.

In the account of even this trivial episode there is again the by now familiar echo of purposeful evasion. His luckless companion is merely "one of our Company," and it is even so that he consistently speaks of the companions of his travels. Who were they? What had impelled them all to undertake this long and hazardous voyage, in an inclement season, with, as develops later, no planned route or destination? Beyond the remark that one had formerly been a trader with the Santee towns, there is no answer to these questions.

One wonders, too, what were John Lawson's own qualifications for such pioneering? Whence came his equanimity and savoir-faire on what appears to have been his maiden trial in a new and strange environment?

Apparently none the worse for their ordeal by water and cold, the travelers continued up on the river: ". . . we set towards the Congerees, leaving the Indian Guide Scipio drunk amongst the Santee-Indians. . . . We met in our Way with an Indian Hut, where we were entertain'd with a fat, boil'd Goose, Venison, Racoon, and ground Nuts. We made but little Stay; about Noon, we pass'd by several large Savannah's, wherein is curious Ranges for Cattel, being green all the Year; they were plentifully stor'd with Cranes, Geese, etc. and the adjacent Woods with great Flocks of Turkies."

Two or three days farther along they reached an Indian town, probably the one which once stood beside the large mound still standing on the shore of Lake Marion, known as Fort Watson since its use as a fortified point in the Revolutionary War. There they tried unsuccessfully to employ their Indian host as guide:

He was the tallest Indian I ever saw, being seven Foot high, and a very strait compleat Person, esteem'd on by the King for his great Art in Hunting, always carrying with him an artificial Head to hunt withal: They are made of the Head of a Buck, the back Part of the Horns being scrapt and hollow, for Lightness of Carriage. The Skin is left to the setting on of the Shoulders, which is lin'd all around with small Hoops, and flat Sort of Laths, to hold it open for the Arm to go in. They have a Way to preserve the Eyes as if living. The Hunter puts on a Match-coat made of Deer's Skin, with the Hair on, and a Piece of the white Part of a Deer's Skin, that grows on the Breast, which is fasten'd to the Neck-End of this stalking Head, so hangs down. In these Habiliments an Indian will go as near a Deer as he pleases, the exact Motions and Behaviour of a Deer being so well counterfeited by 'em, that several Times it hath been known for two Hunters to come up with a stalking Head together, and unknown to each other, so that they have killed an Indian instead of a Deer, which hath happened sometimes to be a Brother, or some dear Friend; for which Reason they allow not of that Sort of Practice, where the Nation is populous.

Lawson, of course, was mistaken in believing in the Indians' ability to preserve the eyes of deer. It is now known that the large polished seed of the American horse chestnut was used for this purpose, hence its common name, buckeye.

Again their way proved arduous. In freezing weather they waded through "a prodigious wide and deep Swamp, being forc'd to strip stark-naked; and much a-do to save our selves from drowning in this Fatiegue." Perhaps this hardship was too much for one of the travelers, for, though the route improved next day, Lawson laments "one of our Company tir'd, being not able to travel any farther; so we went forward, leaving the poor dejected Traveller with Tears in his Eyes, to return to Charles Town, and travel back again over so much bad Way. . . ." It is easy to sympathize with the "poor dejected Traveller" and to wonder if his tears were of disappointment for the trail abandoned or dread of the one to be retraced; and again one is given no further clue to identity than "one of our company." Had he continued for a day or two more his spirits might have risen with the terrain for, as they approached the first hills, the ridges of the High Hills of Santee, travel became much less difficult.

That they might the sooner reach this hill country, Santee Jack, the new guide, urged them to forgo the day of rest they had planned.

. . . so we mov'd forwards, and about twelve a Clock came to the most amazing Prospect I had seen since I had been in Carolina; we travell'd by a Swamp-side, which Swamp I believe to be no less than twenty Miles over, the other side being so far as I could well discern, there appearing great Ridges of Mountains, bearing from us. W.N.W. One Alp with a top like a Sugar-loaf, advanc'd its Head above all the rest very considerably; the Day was serene, which gave us the Advantage of seeing a long Way; these Mountains were cloth'd all over with Trees, which seem'd to us to be very large Timbers.

Though these "mountains" are considered today mere bold hills, they must have loomed mightily in the distance to Lawson and his companions after long travel in flat forest country or swamp. More accurate were his observations on the wide alluvial plains which border the rivers of the Southeast where they cross the coastal plain, which Southerners usually refer to as "swamps" although they have little resemblance to the bog swamps common in more northerly regions.

The Swamp I now spoke of, is not a miry Bog, as others generally are, but you go down to it thro' a steep Bank, at the Foot of which, begins this Valley, where you may go dry for perhaps 200 Yards, then you meet with a small Brook, or Run of Water, about 2 or 3 Foot deep, then dry Land for such another Space, so another Brook, thus continuing. The Land in this Percoarson, or Valley, being extraordinary rich, and the Runs of Water well stor'd with Fowl. It is the Head of one of the Branches of Santee-River; but a farther Discovery Time would not permit; only one Thing is very remarkable, there growing all over this Swamp, a tall, lofty Bay-tree, but is not the same as in England, these being in their Verdue all the Winter long; which appears here, when you stand on the Ridge, (where our path lay) as if it were one pleasant, green Field, and as even as a Bowling-green to Eye of the Beholder; being hemm'd in on one Side with these Ledges of vast high Mountains.

Here the wildlife was as myriad and bountiful as the plant growth of the rich alluvial swamp.

When we were all asleep, in the Beginning of the Night, we were awaken'd with the dismall'st and most hideous Noise that ever pierc'd my Ears: This sudden Surprizal incapacitated us of guessing what this threatning Noise might proceed from; but our Indian Pilot (who knew these Parts very well) acquainted us, that it was customary to hear such Musick along that Swamp-Side, there being endless Numbers of Panthers, Tygers, Wolves, and other Beasts of Prey, which take this Swamp for their Abode in the Day, coming in whole Droves to hunt Deer in the Night, making this frightful Ditty 'till Day appears, then all is still as in other Places. . . . Near the Seaboard, the Indian kill'd 15 Turkeys this Day; there coming out of the Swamp, (about Sunrising) Flocks of these Fowl, containing several hundreds in a Gang, who feed upon the Acorns, it being most Oak that grow in these Woods. There are but very few Pines in Those Quarters. . . . Some of the Turkeys which we eat, whilst we stay'd there, I believe, weigh'd no less than 40 Pounds.

It had now been a little over two weeks since the travelers had started out, but all signs of civilization had long since been left far behind, since the settlers as yet held only a brave fringe along the coast. A traveler in this area today may have difficulty in realizing how quickly and completely Lawson and his companions were plunged into a strange wilderness world. It was a world prodigal and generous, in even winter mood, and John Lawson responded in kind with all his being.

We do not know when he decided to keep a detailed journal account of all he saw and experienced, or where or how it was written, whether in notes taken along the way and later expanded into the lively prose of the published diary, or written in full, night after night, by campfire or moonlight, and only revised for printing. It seems, however, that the young man, who left Charleston, on what seemed a foolhardy adventure of impulse or escape, to travel the unknown Carolina backcountry, emerged at the end of the trail a committed man, a lover and student of the Carolina wilderness, and dedicated, as both lover and student, to the task of describing its wonders. A careful reading of the journal reveals the confidence, the sustained and eager interest, the fervor of the artist who has found his medium.

He had far to go yet before his journey's end on the coast of North Carolina. After leaving the teeming region of the Santee River swamp, the party continued on up the trading path paralleling the Wateree River, visiting a Congaree village along the way. These Indians kept cranes as domestic fowl. One of these, either a sandhill crane or a white ibis, is described by Lawson as "scarce less than six Foot in Height, his Head being round, with a shining natural Crimson Hue, which they all have." Along the way Santee Jack shot a "Tyger [puma or jaguar?] that crossed the Way" but apparently did not hurt him for he continued to watch the party, with, Lawson thought, designs on his spaniel bitch. All along the way he kept noting the quantity of "marble" sometimes as freestone, sometimes as outcroppings. What he was seeing was not marble at all but granite, the igneous remains of the now almost eroded away oldest mountains of the earth, the remains of which make up the Southern Piedmont, one of the few areas on earth which show no signs of having been submerged and which could have no marble, a stone which has its origin in the residuum of sea creatures.

After a few more days' travel northward along the Indian path, which at this point lay a few miles east of the Catawba River, the weary travelers had reached the neighborhood of the present Charlotte, North Carolina, where the Waxhaw Indians lived. There they met such warm hospitality that they stayed several days. In honor of his visitors the Waxhaw "king" staged a great celebration which Lawson described in detail with remarkable vividness, from the ceremonious reception, where formal and traditional protocol was strictly observed, to the elaborate feasting with "great store of Loblolly, and other Medleys, made of Indian Grain, stewed Peaches, Bear-Venison, etc. everyone bringing some Offering to enlarge the Banquet, according to his Degree and Quality," followed by music—"the Burthen of their Song was, in Remembrance of their former Greatness, and Numbers of their Nation, the famous Exploits of their Renowned Ancestors, and all Actions of Moment that had (in former Days) been perform'd by their Fore-fathers"—the whole accompanied by dancing, which, interspersed with eating and music, went on until late in the night. "When the Dancing was ended, every Youth that was so disposed, catch'd hold of the Girl he liked best, and took her that Night for his Bed-Fellow, making as short Courtship and expeditious Weddings, as the Foot-Guards us'd to do with the Trulls in Salisbury-Court."

One is impressed by the intensity of Lawson's interest and his close observation not only of the appearance of the Indians and their habits but of every facet of their lives and characters. Much that he notes about their history and traditions could not have come from personal observation but must have been gleaned from conversation. Though in time he was to prove himself an eager student of Indian dialects, on this first journey he could have picked up a few phrases at most; how then did he communicate, at length and in depth, with each tribe? Elsewhere he mentions that one of his fellow travelers had been a trader among the Indians, and it seems reasonable to assume that he may have served as interpreter. However, the actual means of communication is often left obscure in many of the early naturalist chronicles.

After leaving the Waxhaw town Lawson's party continued on their way, following a great arc across the North Carolina Piedmont which took them near the present High Point, Hillsboro, and Durham, crossing as they went the Yadkin River and tributaries of the Cape Fear and the Neuse. Along the way, ever alert, Lawson noted the use of plants by the natives in effecting cures which seemed remarkable to him. The sweating treatment, which was in common use among them, employed, as an integral part of the treatment, the plant we call life everlasting or rabbit tobacco, still popular in rural Carolina for a variety of ailments. He marveled at the Indians' success in treating "one of our company" for lameness by scratching the sore limb with a comb of rattlesnake fangs and applying a dressing of dried and ground sassafras root, binding it up well. The patient recovered completely in a day or two.

More intriguing are those which appear to anticipate later developments in Western medicine. Oil extracted from acorns, according to Lawson, worked wonders in curing burns, anticipating latter-day ointments of tannin and grease. To cure infected lesions the Indians employed methods which strongly suggest the agency of penicillin-like molds. They sprinkled the infected part with "nothing but the rotten doated Grains of Indian Corn, beaten to Powder, and the soft Down growing on a Turkey's Rump. This dry'd the Ulcer up immediately. . . ."

In this hill country game was even more plentiful. He was struck by the beauty of the multicolored wood ducks, which he accurately described, and with the quantities of woodcock they encountered along the way. But it was the now extinct passenger pigeons near the Sapona town of Yadkin River that were the highlight of his bird encounters:

. . . we went to shoot Pigeons, which were so numerous in these Parts, that you might see many Millions in a Flock; they sometimes split off the Limbs of stout Oaks, and other Trees, upon which they roost o' Nights. You may find several Indian Towns, of not above 17 Houses, that have more than 100 Gallons of Pigeons Oil, or Fat; they use it with Pulse, or Bread, as we do Butter, and making the Ground as white as a Sheet with their Dung. The Indians take a Light, and go among them in the Night, and bring away some thousands, killing them with long Poles, as they roost in the Trees. At this time of the Year, the Flocks, as they pass by, in great measure, obstruct the Light of the day.

Day after day as the party moved across the hill country the Indian and his ways seemed to absorb less of Lawson's attention, which was increasingly directed toward the plants and animals they encountered. The Indian, so exotic in his native surroundings, must have appeared to him at first simply a part of the forest tapestry, but closer acquaintance revealed him, to Lawson's quick intelligence and responsive nature, as primarily a human being, more brother than alien, sharing alike man's poignant fate, and with much to teach the stranger who had the wit to learn, from ancient wisdom and philosophy to practical matters such as hunting skills and plant lore. An Indian doctor showed Lawson a "great Quantity of medicinal Drugs, Produce of those Parts," telling him the maladies they cured. The honey locust and chestnut came in for special attention, as did the beaver population which the Indians were trapping, and the wolf that interrupted their sleep when it came into camp.

In one valley they crossed, the forest was superlative:

This Valley afforded as large Timber as any I ever met withal, especially of Chestnut Oaks, which render it an excellent Country for raising great Herds of Swine. Indeed, were it cultivated, we might have good hopes of as pleasant and fertile a Valley, as any our English in America can afford. At Night we lay by a swift Current, where we saw plenty of Turkies, but pearch'd upon such lofty Oaks, that our Guns would not kill them, tho' we shot very often, and our Guns were very good. Some of our Company shot several times, at one Turkey, before he would fly away, the Pieces being loaded with large Goose-shot.

The path they had been following for some days was that known as the Virginia path. To go to the North Carolina coastal settlements one had to leave this path in the neighborhood of the present Hillsboro. Lawson writes: "This Morning, most of our Company having some Inclination to go straight away for Virginia, when they left this Place; I and one more took our leaves of them, resolving (with God's Leave) to see North Carolina. . . ." Presumably he meant the seaside region of North Carolina. Again he is as unrevealing about his English companions and himself as he is explicit about the Indians and even an occasional traveler met along the way. His account of one such meeting, three days after the party had decided to separate, is particularly tantalizing:

"As soon as it was day, we set out for the Achonechy-Town, it being by Estimation, 20 Miles off, which, I believe, is pretty exact. We were got about half way, (meeting great Gangs of Turkies) when we saw, at a Distance, 30 loaded Horses, coming on the Road, with four or five Men, on other Jades, driving them. We charg'd our Piece, and went up to them: Enquiring, whence they came from? They told us, from Virginia. The leading Man's Name was Massey, who was born about Leeds in Yorkshire. He ask'd, from whence we came? We told him." But what did they tell him? It would be interesting to know.

After they left the Virginia path their route eastward lay near the present Durham, Raleigh, and Goldsboro to the lower Neuse River and thence northward to Washington on the Pamlico River. As their guide through this little-traveled country, they engaged an Indian, recommended to them by trader Massey, known as Eno Will, who was henceforth to be Lawson's devoted friend and travel companion. Reluctantly they prepared to leave the beautiful and fertile hill country, from which the English settlements were separated by the warlike and unfriendly Tuscaroras. "The Savages do, indeed," says the journal, "still possess the Flower of Carolina, the English enjoying only the Fag-End of that fine Country."

From there on for a fortnight their way lay across the flat country of tall pines and green savannas, of moss-draped oaks, and cypress swamps where the slow-flowing water had a brown color "much like the Sluices in Holland," where even the small rivers became wide estuaries as they entered the great inland sea behind the Outer Banks. The lower reaches of the Neuse River, beautiful even today in spite of the depredations of industry and commerce, must have been breathtakingly lovely to the travelers approaching their journey's end, and to this area Lawson was soon to return, to build a cabin for himself and, later, to lay out for Swiss emigrants the town of New Bern.

As two of the company, who had turned aside to go to Virginia, had rejoined Lawson and his companions, there were now four Englishmen and several Indians who took their way across the pine flats between the Neuse and the Pamlico estuaries, toward the English plantations. It was late February. They slept on the last night under a bark shelter at the foot of a large oak tree. "There fell abundance of Snow and Rain in the Night, with much Thunder and Lightning." Next day, however, under clearing skies they came safely to the hospitable home of Richard Smith on the Pamlico River.

There ended John Lawson's historic, midwinter, six-hundred-mile voyage (which he called one thousand) through the Carolina back-country, two months of adventure and excitement that to a remarkable degree epitomize his ten-year life in America. Like the weeks of his journey, his remaining years in America were years of ceaseless activity and new experiences, of study and apt learning of Indian ways and Indian tongues, of farming and surveying, of promotion and business deals, and, most of all, of a consuming and pervasive interest in the natural history of his adopted home. But though the activities of these years were to push him into increasing prominence, a persistent aura of mystery remained.

Now, in February, 1701, fortune seemed to smile upon him. He resolved to stay for some time in the Pamlico settlement—"Pleas'd with the Goodness of the Country," and "well receiv'd by the Inhabitants," one of whom was a girl named Hannah Smith, presumably a member of Richard Smith's family. Hannah Smith was soon to become Lawson's devoted companion, his "Beloved Hannah," and the mother of his children.

Charged with his characteristic energy and inspiration, he seems almost immediately to have launched his scientific career with a plan to make natural history collections for interested persons in England and, only a few weeks after his arrival at the Smiths', he wrote to James Petiver, offering his services as collector of vegetables, and animals, shells, fish, butterflies, and other insects. James Petiver, London apothecary and botanist, member of the Royal Society, insatiable collector of exotic productions of nature from all over the world, was one of the first and most significant of those Englishmen who sponsored and encouraged a study of the flora and fauna of colonial America. Lawson had chosen well, as Petiver seems to have been not only a brilliant botanist but a generous and conscientious patron.

At the same time Lawson was planning other enterprises, for the next we hear of him he is back in the region where the Trent River joins the Neuse, the site of the Indian town he had visited on his way from the interior. There he bought land and built for himself a house beside a stream, still known as Lawson's Creek, where he lived with "a young Indian Fellow and a Bull-Dog" as companions. Soon he discovered he had as close neighbor an alligator, who had built his den directly under the house, with an entrance in the creek side below the bank:

I was sitting alone by the Fire-Side, (about nine a Clock at Night, some time in March) the Indian Fellow being gone to Town, to see his Relations; so that there was no body in the House but my self and my Dog; when, all of a sudden, this ill-favour'd Neighbor of mine, set up such a Roaring, that he made the House shake about my Ears, and so continued, like a Bittern, (but a hundred times louder, if possible) for four or five times. The Dog stared, as if he was fright'ned out of his senses; nor indeed, could I imagine what it was, having never heard one of them before. Immediately again I had another Lesson; and so a third. Being at that time amongst none but Savages, I began to suspect, they were working some Piece of Conjuration under my House, to get away my Goods; not but that, at another time, I have as little Faith in their, or any other working Miracles, by diabolical Means, as any Person living. At last, my Man came in, to whom when I had told the Story, he laugh'd at me, and presently undeceiv'd me by telling me what it was that had made that Noise.

Although to the end of his life Lawson continued his association with the Neuse-Trent area, most of his interests were on the Pamlico where the Smiths lived. He bought a plantation there and an interest in a smaller tract on the north side of the river's estuary, where it is joined by Adams Creek. There in 1705 he laid out the town of Bath, North Carolina's first municipality. For himself he purchased the most choice of the lots, from which one could look through the cypress trees growing along the water's edge, all the way down the Pamlico to the eastern horizon out in the great sound beyond. There, as the old plats show, he built his house on the edge of the street which ran along the high riverbank. To it he brought Hannah, and there little Isabella Lawson played away her early years.

It was to this house by the river that John Lawson kept returning after surveying expeditions out into the wide country north of the Cape Fear River, from long forays to collect specimens to ship to James Petiver, from longer, unaccountable absences in such places as the Rappahannock region of Virginia, or from conferences in Williamsburg to plan for the survey of the dividing line between Carolina and Virginia. Here he found home and welcome after his long voyage back to England in 1708 to supervise the publication of the book which would make him even more widely known in Europe than in Carolina.

~∂ 2

John Lawson had been eight years in America when he set out for England to attend to the publication of his book. He had with him not only his account of his 1701 journey from Charleston to Pamlico but copious notes on the geography of Carolina, the Indians and their several languages, the agriculture, actual and potential, the industries and fisheries of the region, and a variety of other subjects. His observant eye and incredible industry had provided him with an amazing array of natural history data covering almost the entire spectrum of the living world: mammals, birds, reptiles, fish, trees and other plants of interest. Unless he had come to this country with a familiarity with natural history, as his writings suggest, it would seem impossible for anyone busy as he was with other affairs to have accumulated knowledge of American natural history as fully and accurately as he did during those crowded years.

His book, *A New Voyage to Carolina,* can be described by a term Lawson liked to use for the potpourris of meat, vegetables, and nuts, boiled together, which the Indians often served: a medley. The account of his voyage is followed by a description of Carolina and its state at that time; then comes his natural history of Carolina, occupying some eighty pages. The book closes with an equally long account of the Indians of North Carolina, containing a five-page, three-column comparative glossary of several of the native languages of the region.

Considering the relatively short interval between his arrival in England and the appearance of this book, it is a reasonable assumption that most of the work, in addition to the 1701 journal, was written before he left Pamlico in January or on board ship to England. In any event it is easy to believe that he was, either in fact or in memory, sitting on the east porch of his home in Bath, with the wide sweep of the Pamlico River in view, when he wrote the first few paragraphs of his description of Carolina:

. . . indeed, most of the Plantations in Carolina naturally enjoy a noble Prospect of large and spacious Rivers, pleasant Savanna's, and fine Meadows, with their green Liveries, interwoven with beautiful Flowers, of most glorious Colours, which the several Seasons afford; hedg'd in with pleasant Groves of the ever-famous Tulip-tree, the stately Laurel, and Bays, equalizing the Oak in Bigness and Growth; Myrtles, Jessamines, Wood-bines, Honeysuckles, and several other fragrant Vines and Ever-greens, whose aspiring Branches shadow and interweave themselves with the loftiest Timbers, yielding a pleasant Prospect, Shade and Smell, proper Habitations for the Sweet-singing Birds, that melodiously entertain such as travel thro' the Woods of Carolina.

A NEW VOYAGE TO CAROLINA;

CONTAINING THE

Exact Description and *Natural History*

OF THAT

COUNTRY:

Together with the *Present State* thereof.

AND

A JOURNAL

Of a Thousand Miles, Travel'd thro' several
Nations of *INDIANS*.

Giving a particular Account of their Customs,
Manners, &c.

By JOHN LAWSON, Gent. Surveyor-
General of *North-Carolina*.

LONDON:
Printed in the Year 1709.

Title page of John Lawson's *A New Voyage To Carolina*. (Courtesy of the
Caroliniana Library of the University of South Carolina)

Before beginning his natural history, *per se*, he discusses farming and husbandry in the new land, with a thorough grasp of the subject, including the adaptation of English crops, fruits, vegetables, and herbs to the alien soils of Carolina, and the cultivation of crops acquired from the Indians, such as maize, lima beans, cow peas, and ground or Jerusalem artichokes.

When he comes to the wild plants, he apologizes in advance for the incompleteness of his treatment, giving as an excuse the great multitude and variety, listing by name hundreds of plants and adding "abundance more I could name, yet not the hundredth part of what remains, a Catalogue of which is a Work of many Years, and without any other Subject, would swell to a large Volume, and requires the Abilities of a skilful Botanist. . . ." Later on, in the Natural History, he gives us a spirited fifteen pages close-packed with descriptions and special uses of the trees of Carolina.

As there were no reference books on the botany of the New World and his white neighbors were, like himself, strangers in the land, Lawson had to depend on his own observations and on the lore of the Indians. At this time botany and medicine were inextricably related, in the New World as in the Old, and the Indians esteemed most highly those plants considered curative. High on the list were cassena or yaupon, small compact hollies with leaves which he compared to boxwood, "being very like it in Leaf, only dented exactly like Tea, but the Leaf somewhat fatter." He gives detailed instructions as to its preparation for use as a beverage and as a medicine deemed admirable for a variety of ailments. Considered equally versatile was sassafras, a straight, neat, little tree, notable to botanists for the variety in shape of its fragrant leaves, elliptical, mitten-shaped, and three-lobed, but treasured by the Indians and Lawson for its aromatic roots, from which, when pounded, a potion could be brewed to refresh or cure, according to one's need.

Descriptions of the seventy-odd other trees listed commonly include some particular use, frequently medicinal. An infusion of the bark of dogwood was declared "an infallible Remedy against the Worms," the root of the devil's-walking-stick, a cathartic and emetic, "the Bark" of the root of the elm, "a Sovereign Remedy to heal a Cut or green Wound," while elm bark was used for making ropes, and an ointment made from the buds of the tulip tree was a cure for scalds and burns. The tulip tree, largest of the magnolias, impressed him by its "prodigious bigness": "I have been inform'd of a Tulip-Tree, that was ten

Foot Diameter; and another, wherein a lusty Man had his Bed and Houshold Furniture, and liv'd in it, till his Labour got him a more fashionable Mansion."

The berries from another small holly, the inkberry or gallberry, were used to make ink and black dye, those of the aromatic myrtle to make candles incomparable for a lady's chamber, and those from the black gum were added to soup for color and flavor. The wood of the black gum was especially good for the naves of wagon wheels, that of red oak for barrel staves, red cedar for boat bottoms and coffins, white cedar for boat masts, shingles, and wooden buckets. Also of nautical use was the black walnut for boat bottoms, live oak for ribs and shorter members, and pines for tar; but most important of all were the giant cypresses from which whole boats could be fashioned, some of amazing size, such as one, measured by Lawson, thirty-six feet around. Hickory was utilized in making mortars, pestles, turned ware, and cogwheels, holly for trenchers, chestnut for house sills, and mulberry and locust for posts.

Among the interesting comments on the use of trees as food, Lawson notes that the flowers of the redbud or Judas tree make "the best Sallad of any Flower I ever saw," the sweet "Apple" of the pawpaw makes "rare puddings," and the sap of the sugar tree, gathered in gourds by the Indians and boiled, yields a fine sugar.

From the "vegetables" of Carolina, Lawson moves on to discuss the "beasts" which, in his unique taxonomy, meant mammals except bats. Beasts were followed by the "insects," in which classification he placed the cold-blooded land animals, including a subcategory, reptiles, under which were grouped the small insects such as beetles, butterflies, and grasshoppers.

In the lists of the beasts, buffalo, "monsters" weighing more than a ton, claimed priority by sheer bulk and imposing appearance. Lawson noted that "he seldom appears amongst the English Inhabitants . . . I have eaten of their Meat, but do not think it so good as our Beef. . . . It is conjectured, that these Buffelos, mixt in Breed with our tame Cattle, would much better the Breed for Largeness and Milk, which seems very probable."

In common with William Byrd and other colonial chroniclers, Lawson considered bear meat a superior food for flavor, nourishment, and ease of digestion.

I prefer their Flesh before any Beef, Veal, Pork, or Mutton; and they look as well as they eat, their fat being as white as Snow, and the sweetest of any Creature's in the World. If a Man drink a Quart thereof melted, it never will rise in his Stomach. . . . This Creature feeds upon all sorts of wild Fruits. When Herrings run, which is in March, the Flesh of such of those Bears as eat thereof, is nought, all that Season, and eats filthily. . . . At catching of Herrings, they are most expert Fishers. They sit by the Creeksides (which are very narrow) where the Fish run in; and there they take them up, as fast as it's possible they can dip their Paws into the Water.

"The Panther," he says, "is of the Cat's kind; about the height of a very large Greyhound of a reddish Colour, the same as a Lion. He climbs Trees with the greatest Agility imaginable, is very strong limb'd, catching a piece of Meat from any Creature he strikes at. His tail is exceeding long; his Eyes look very fierce and lively. . . ."

Lawson says that "the Wolf of Carolina, is the Dog of the Woods," and that the "Indians had no other Curs, before the Christian came amongst them." He describes them as "neither so large nor fierce as the European Wolf." Not manslayers, "they go in great Droves in the Night, to hunt Deer, which they do as well as the best Pack of Hounds . . . when they hunt in the Night, that there is a great many together, they make the most hideous and frightful Noise, that ever was heard."

The catamount, as he calls it, or mountain cat, can, by his description and his reference to its short tail, be identified as the animal we usually call a bobcat, a creature that "takes most of his Prey by Surprize, getting up the Trees, which they pass by or under, and thence leaping directly upon them." This hunting technique of the bobcat was illustrated in the only engraving, except the map, which appeared in *A New Voyage to Carolina*. A victim deer with the cat on his back and the tree from which he has jumped are the central piece of the rather amateurish page which includes pictures of a buffalo, a raccoon, an opossum, a bear dipping fish, and a coiled rattlesnake. We have nowhere any hint as to the identity of the artist, as keen an observer as he was a maladroit draftsman, but it seems probable that he was Lawson himself.

Evidence of scientific attention to details appears on every page of Lawson's Natural History. Of the beavers he discusses not only their numbers and their skill in building dams and houses but also their favorite foods: the bark of sassafras, ash, and sweet gum. Of the opos-

sum, that "Wonder of all the Land-Animals . . . found no where but
in America," he details its diet, its peculiar genitals, the "false Belly" of
the female, "wherein she carries her Young. . . ." "Minx" he considers
"bold Thieves, and will steal any thing from you in the Night, when
asleep, as I can tell by Experience," a reference to one which ate through
the sail of a canoe to get a goose he had wrapped inside, on a night's
camping, even as the bundle lay under Lawson's head for safekeeping.
The "greatest Destroyers of Rats and Mice, that are in the World," the
mink "is an Enemy of the Tortois, whose Holes in the Sand, where they
hide their Eggs, the Minx finds out, and scratches up and eats."

Moving on to those creatures which he classifies as insects, he again
begins with the bulkiest, the alligator, and follows with the most formidable, the rattlesnake. His one encounter with an alligator has already been quoted. As wilderness traveler and especially as surveyor,
his meetings with rattlesnakes were frequent.

The Rattlesnakes are accounted the peaceablest in the World; for they
never attack any one, or injure them, unless they are trod upon, or
molested. . . . I have myself gone over several of this Sort, and others; yet
it pleased God, I never came to any harm. . . . The Indians are the best
Physicians for the Bite of these and all other venomous Creatures of this
Country. There are four sorts of Snake-Roots already discover'd, which
Knowledge came from the Indians, who have perform'd several great
Cures.

Although there is exaggeration of the blacksnake's enmity toward
the rattlesnake, and misinterpretation of his appearance of flailing as he
throws his constricting coils about his victim, there is, in Lawson's account of this reptile, ample evidence of the man's extraordinary ability
as a naturalist:

The long, black Snake frequents the Land altogether, and is the nimblest
Creature living. His bite has no more Venom, than a Prick with A Pin. He
is the best Mouser that can be; for he leaves not one of that Vermine alive,
where he comes. He also kills the Rattle-Snake, wheresoever he meets him,
by twisting his Head about the Neck of the Rattle-Snake, and whipping
him to Death with this Tail. . . . He is an excellent Egg-Merchant, for he
does not suck the Eggs, but swallows them whole [as all Snakes do].
. . . One of these Snakes, whose Neck is no thicker than a Woman's little
Finger, will swallow a Squirrel; so much does that part stretch, in all these
Creatures.

Illustrations for the Natural History section of John Lawson's *A New Voyage To Carolina*. (Courtesy of the Caroliniana Library of the University of South Carolina)

Before going on to the birds of Carolina, Lawson quaintly explains his omission of the creeping, crawling, and flying multitudes of the insect world thus:

The Reptiles, or smaller Insects, are too numerous to relate here, this Country affording innumerable Quantities thereof; as the Flying-Stags with Horns, Beetles, Butterflies, Grashoppers, Locust, and several hundred uncouth Shapes, which in the Summer-Season are discovered here in Carolina, the Description of which requires a large Volume which is not my Intent at present.

The section of Lawson's Natural History which follows, the "Birds of Carolina," represents a giant step in American ornithology. Nothing previously published on the birds of English America remotely approached it. He comments on well over a hundred different "kinds," many of which he defines as including "several sorts." Although his names comprise a veritable medley of local folk names such as "blue peters" (gallinules) and "summer ducks" (wood ducks), descriptive names such as "divelings" for swifts and "runners" for sandpipers, English names such as "Pheasant" for ruffed grouse or "partridge" for quail, and names apparently improvised such as "East-India Bat" or "Musqueto Hawk" for the nighthawk tribe, it is easy for the modern reader to recognize them, with, too often, the sad realization that many birds commonly observed by John Lawson are now long gone from Carolina and some from the earth forever. Among the definitely extinct are the passenger pigeon and the Carolina parakeet; barely surviving are the ivory-billed woodpecker and the Eskimo curlew, while the golden eagle, the sandhill crane, the ibis, and trumpeter swan are seen no more in Carolina.

As the Eagle is reckon'd the King of Birds, I have begun with him. The first I shall speak of, is the bald Eagle; so call'd, because his Head, to the middle of his Neck, and his Tail, is as white as Snow. . . . They prey on any living thing they can catch. They are heavy of Flight, and cannot get their Food by Swiftness, to help which there is a Fishawk that catches Fishes, and suffers the Eagle to take them from her, although she is long-wing'd and a swift Flyer. . . . The bald Eagle attends the Gunners in Winter, with all the Obsequiousness imaginable, and when he shoots and kills any Fowl, the Eagle surely comes in for his Bird. . . . The Eagle is not bald, until he is one or two years old. . . . The Eagle's Nest is made of Twigs, Sticks and Rubbish. It is big enough to fill a handsome Carts Body, and commonly so full of nasty Bones and Carcasses that it stinks most offensively.

The Fishing-Hawk is the Eagle's Jackal, which most commonly (though not always) takes his Prey for him. . . . He builds his Nest as the Eagles do; that is, in a dead Cypress-Tree, either standing in, or hard by, the Water.

Of the now extinct Carolina parakeet, Lawson says:

The Parrakeetos are of a green Colour, and Orange-Colour'd half way their Head. Of these and the Allegators, there is none found to the Northward of this Province. They visit us first, when Mulberries are ripe, which Fruit they love extremely. They peck the Apples, to eat the Kernels, so that the Fruit rots and perishes. They are mischievous to Orchards. They are often taken alive, and will become familiar and tame in two days. They have their Nests in hollow Trees, in low, swampy Ground. They devour the Birch-Buds in April, and lie hidden when the Weather is frosty and hard.

Lawson, like other bird observers newly arrived in America, finds the mockingbird without a peer.

The Mocking-Bird is about as big as a Throstle in England, but longer; they are of a white, and gray Colour, and are held to be the Choristers of America, as indeed they are. They sing with the greatest Diversity of Notes, that is possible for a Bird to change to. They may be bred up, and will sing with us tame in Cages; yet I never take any of their Nests, altho' they build yearly in my Fruit-Trees, because I have their Company, as much as if tame, as to the Singing Part. They often sit upon our Chimneys in Summer, there being then no Fire in them, and sing the whole Evening and most part of the Night. . . .

For a final example of Lawson's observation and appreciation of American birds, here is his comment on the hummingbird:

The Humming-Bird is the Miracle of all our wing'd Animals; He is feather'd as a Bird, and gets his Living as the Bees, by sucking the Honey from each Flower. In some of the larger sort of Flowers, he will bury himself, by diving to suck the bottom of it, so that he is quite cover'd, and oftentimes Children catch them in those Flowers, and keep them alive for five or six days. They are of different Colours, the Cock differing from the Hen. The Cock is of a green, red, Aurora, and other Colours mixt. He is much less than a Wren, and very Nimble. His Nest is one of the greatest Pieces of Workmanship the whole Tribe of wing'd Animals can shew, it commonly hanging on a single Bryar, most artificially woven, a small Hole being left to go in and out at. The Eggs are the Bigness of Pease.

The final and largest part of John Lawson's trailblazing work is devoted to the highest and most interesting of the creatures of the American wilderness, the American Indian. "An Account of the Indians of North America" remains today the most complete and authoritative source work on the Indians of Carolina. It is an amazingly honest and objective study, unmarred by bigotry on the one hand or sentimental romanticism on the other. With astonishing clarity he recognized both the virtues and vices of the natives, those ways in which they were the equal or even the superior of the English, and those ways in which they fell far short of English standards. He was as generous in charity for their faults as in praise for their good qualities. He was both mystified and distressed by the unhappy results which flowed from their association with the colonists, associations through which they "learned several Vices of the Europeans, but not one Virtue, as I know of."

His account of the natives begins with a strikingly perspicacious preview of a scientific theory which would be proclaimed two hundred years later as a sensational anthropological discovery: that the people found in America by the European settlers were not the people who formerly possessed this land. Upon different and less tangible evidence Lawson was, in effect, suggesting, two centuries ahead of scientific journals, the probable existence of a creature now known as the Folsom man. Among the evidence he cited in support of his thesis was the discovery of timbers of tulip tree and hickory, squared by axes, buried twenty-six feet under ground, a discovery similar to one I myself witnessed of a square-hewn pine log buried under fifteen feet of clay in a supposedly never before inhabited area.

The picture he presents of the Indian, though it avoids the lush sentimentality of the later romantics, is that of a basically superior creature, a "noble savage" living in a wilderness paradise. As Lawson saw the Indians, "were it not for the Feuds amongst themselves, they would enjoy the happiest State (in this World) of all Mankind." The background he limns for these forest children is the full tapestry of nature in the great green wilderness of eastern America. Although basically no more reliant on the products of nature than we who took his earthly paradise and butchered it, his dependence was direct, firsthand, and visible, in contrast to the deviously derived and invisible relationship of modern man. The Indian, in effect, was an integral part of that natural world which, though equally essential to our survival, is seen by us, when seen at all, from a distance, fragmented and alien.

Almost every facet of the Indian's life fitted into that tapestry. Instead of such relatively artificial designations as March, April, and May, his moons were visibly proclaimed by nature, the herring moon when the herring ran up the tidal rivers to spawn, strawberry moon when that luscious wild fruit began to ripen, and dogwood moon at the time when the dogwoods' myriad starlike white sepals bespangled the forest.

Commonly a wild animal of prestige, such as the eagle or the panther, gave a warrior his name. From his punctured earlobes dangled eagle feathers while around his neck hung strings of seashells. A heavy coat of bear grease protected him from chill air and vermin. The venison he barbecued was browsing only a few hours earlier on beechwood buds when pierced by a viburnum shaft, tipped with a shark's tooth and feathered with a hawk's pinion, propelled from a locust bow, strung with sinews drawn from a deer's haunch. His evening repast finished, he crawled into his bark-covered hovel and wrapped himself in bearskin, leaving his tame wolf as guardian of the night against the ever-present threat from the darkness of the surrounding forest, which could be heard as a "frightful Ditty till Day appears."

In many respects Lawson regarded these children of nature as superior people. Physically, few Europeans could equal them.

He admired their happy dispositions and contentment, even in hardship, their lack of covetousness and rivalry for material things, their outstanding courage, loyalty, and generosity. But he reported also the other face of the coin: their weakness for strong drink, their light-fingered and devious ways, their ardent taste for the warpath, their barbarous cruelties to their enemies, their thirst for vengeance for any wrong suffered, allied to a queer sense of justice which sanctioned the murder of an innocent in payment for the crime of an elusive culprit. All in all, however, he was convinced that the Indian had as many virtues to contribute to the Europeans as the latter had to share with him. Consequently he was sharply critical of the way the English were treating the natives and he suggested drastic changes in their attitude.

They are really better to us, than we are to them; they always give us Victuals at their Quarters, and take care we are arm'd against Hunger and Thirst: We do not so by them (generally speaking) but let them walk by our Doors Hungry, and do not often relieve them. We look upon them with Scorn and Disdain, and think them little better than Beasts in Humane Shape, though if well examined, we shall find that, for all our Religion and Education, we possess more Moral Deformities, and Evils than these Savages do, or are acquainted withal.

It is tempting to quote at greater length, for the perception, wisdom, and compassion shown by John Lawson toward a people strange and alien to himself are qualities almost as rare, and certainly as desirable, in our century as in his.

He closes his book with a plea for greater kindness and justice:

> . . . let us cherish their good Deeds, and, with Mildness and Clemency, make them sensible and forewarn them of their ill ones; let our Dealings be just to them in every Respect, and show no ill Example. . . . It is highly necessary . . . to give Encouragement to the ordinary People, and those of a lower Rank, that they might marry with these Indians, and come into Plantations . . . and that the Indians might have Encouragement to send their Children Apprentices to proper Masters, that would be kind to them, and make them Masters of a Trade, whereby they would be drawn to live amongst us, . . . then we should have great Advantages to make daily Conversions amongst them, when they saw that we were kind and just in all our Dealings. Moreover, by the Indians Marrying with the Christians, and coming into Plantations with their English Husbands, or Wives, they would become Christians, and their Idolatry would be quite forgotten. . . .
>
> This seems to be a more reasonable Method of converting the Indians, than to set up our Christian Banner in a Field of Blood, . . . and baptize one hundred with the Sword for one at the Font. Whilst we make way for a Christian Colony through a Field of Blood, and defraud, and make away with those that one day may be wanted in this World, . . . of which we may repent when too late.

⟰ 3

For John Lawson the year 1709, most of which he spent in England, was a busy year, pregnant with consequences. In addition to seeing his book through the press, he was consulted by the Lords Proprietors, that group of noblemen who were partners in the personal ownership of the domain called Carolina, which extended from Florida north to Virginia and from the Atlantic to the "South Seas." From those conferences came his appointment as Surveyor-General of North Carolina, and member of the commission to settle the boundary dispute with Virginia. The title page of his book indicates pride in this appointment, as the author's name is followed by his new professional status, and the book itself is gratefully dedicated to the "True and Absolute Lords-Proprietors."

No doubt at their instigation, he became involved in a plan to settle refugee Swiss and Palatine colonists in Carolina and was introduced to

Baron Christopher de Graffenried, promoter of a Swiss land company, who seems to have been one of the originators of the plan. Probably on Lawson's advice, North Carolina was chosen for the settlement, on land along the Neuse and Trent rivers, purchased from the Proprietors.

Finally, before leaving to return to America, Lawson at last met James Petiver, the botanist-apothecary, to whom he had written offering his services as collector when he first arrived in North Carolina. The meeting seems to have been mutually profitable, for arrangements were made for Lawson to extend his collecting activities for Petiver and his circle, in exchange for their assistance in his great project, of which he had spoken in his book—the preparation of a really comprehensive natural history of Carolina.

With an exciting future in prospect, and home and family awaiting him, Lawson sailed from London in January, 1710, in company with 650 Palatine settlers. It was a terrible voyage of more than three months. The threat of French privateers, reactivated by Queen Anne's War, necessitated a convoy of men-of-war for the first part of the voyage. Progress was slow. Before they had left the last British port, more than forty of the refugees, mostly children, had died. Adverse winds, storms, disease, hunger, and even attack and plunder by a French privateer decimated their ranks. Lawson and the survivors, less than half of those who had set out, were finally landed at the mouth of the James River, two hundred miles short of their destination. Ahead lay wide estuaries to be crossed, a fifty-mile walk around the edge of insect-infested Great Dismal Swamp, a canoe voyage down the Chowan River, down Albemarle and Pamlico sounds, and finally up the Neuse to the delta-shaped neck at its confluence with the Trent. There, in accordance with a plan drawn up by Lawson, the desolate remnant of the settlers built their cabins, naming their town, with what must have been more than a touch of nostalgia, New Bern. In September de Graffenried arrived with about one hundred Swiss settlers. Shortly before this, Lawson had gone back to Virginia for a meeting with the Virginia Boundary Commission to lay plans for the survey of the disputed line between the two colonies. But he was soon back in New Bern, busy surveying, helping to direct the building of the village, and somehow finding time to collect and mount natural history specimens for shipment to Royal Society correspondents.

Before leaving the Neuse settlement to join his family on the Pamlico, he wrote a long letter to Petiver, outlining his ambitious project and expressing the hope that it would lay the "foundation toward a Compleat History of these parts." He promised to send a copy of the careful diary he had been keeping for some months. He explained his plan to make duplicate collections so that he might properly identify and classify his specimens in the light of the superior scientific knowledge of his correspondents. Specifically, he planned to collect and mount "all of plants I can meet withal in Carolina," all the "Beasts" of the region, all birds, "of this place, both land & water fowls from ye Eagle to the Wren, to know if possible the age they arrive to, how & where they build their nests, of what material & form, the colour of their eggs and time of their Incubation & flight, their food, beauty & colour, of wt. medicinall uses if any, if rarily designedd to the Life, this would Illustrate such a history very much, their musical notes & cryes must not be omitted, wch. of them abide with us all ye year & those that go away, and wt. strange birds tempestuous weather winds unusual seasons & other evidence affords us."

The plan went on to include all fishes and how they compare with those of Europe, all insects, with information on their breeding, food, changes, etc., fossils, shells, stones, metals, minerals, and the nature of the soil and land.

It was to be a great work, with no precedent in the New World. He was enthusiastic. He was resolved. "If God prolongs my dayes my Intention is this."

God did not see fit to prolong John Lawson's days. After six months with his family at Bath, much of it spent in collecting and preparing specimens for shipment to England, he was back in Williamsburg in July, 1711, sending off a shipment to Petiver, in the care of Mrs. Hyde, the wife of the governor of North Carolina, and again discussing with the Virginia officials the perennially delayed boundary-line survey. On July 27, William Byrd, the brilliant, egotistical, flamboyant "Black Swan" of Westover, records in his "Secret Diary" a meeting with Lawson at the governor's palace in Williamsburg, where "it was extremely hot so we sat without our capes notwithstanding the ladies."

Two decades later, when the long-delayed survey was finally made, Byrd wrote a bold, spritely, and rather scandalous account of it which has become a classic of sorts, under the title of *The Secret History of the Dividing Line.* The influence of Lawson is obvious, as for instance in Byrd's proposal of Lawson's solution for both the land and Indian problems at one stroke by intermarriage between the natives and the

English. A few years later, to encourage a Swiss settlement on some of his extensive holdings in the backcountry of North Carolina along the Roanoke River, Byrd sent a promotional manuscript to Switzerland for translation and publication. This manuscript, now known as *Byrd's Natural History of Virginia*, is an almost verbatim copy of the latter part of Lawson's book with most of the unpleasant or discouraging details carefully deleted.

September, 1711, found the indefatigable Lawson back with the Swiss at New Bern. To find out how far upstream the Neuse was navigable, he and de Graffenried planned a fifteen-day trip upstream into the interior, intending to go as far as the fall line. Now the cloud of mystery that had concealed John Lawson's origin and early youth, but had lifted somewhat during the few bright years of his life in America, closes in again to obscure all the circumstances of his death. Only this much seems certain: the whole party fell into the hands of Tuscarora Indians. De Graffenried was released; Lawson was executed. To this day, facts and details are debated. Some say that Lawson's surveying activities in Indian territory had made enemies of those he had served as friend and champion. Another account says he suffered death for threatening one of the Indian kings. According to one version, his throat was cut after formal trial and conviction. Another has it that he was subjected to the identical torment he described in the journal of his voyage—pitch-pine splinters driven into the body and lighted to burn "like so many Torches."

Regardless of how he died, at least there was no doubt of his death. Soon afterward his will was filed for probate. By its terms everything was left to his "beloved Hannah Smith" and their children. Items included two homes, large landholdings, and a "hair trunk" containing "several writings." What became of the trunk and what those writings were are more Lawson mysteries.

From this distance it seems strange that the woman he called in his will "my beloved Hannah Smith," the mother of at least one child to whom he gave his name, never became his wife. Why were they never married? Was he fleeing an intolerable marriage in England when he "accidentally met with a Gentleman" who advised him to go to Carolina? We have no answer.

It is puzzling, too, that research has been unable to discover an obituary of John Lawson or any personal record at all of him or his surviving family. In North Carolina he had become one of the colony's

most prominent citizens, founder of its first two towns, surveyor-
general, special agent for settling the boundary-line dispute. In England
he was a part of that ever widening circle of naturalists with the Royal
Society as its focus, and consultant to the Lords Proprietors. At the
time of his death his book, *A New Voyage to Carolina*, containing his
travel journal and his natural history, had become so popular that a
German-language edition was already in preparation, soon to be followed by a new English edition and a plagiarized edition in Switzerland. This book, his will, a few land records, three or four letters to
Petiver, a mention by Petiver in letters to botanical friends, a chance
reference in Byrd's diary, and the petulant report of his death by de
Graffenried are the only records that remain of the enigmatic but
meteoric man who called himself John Lawson.

Yet in spite of the darkness surrounding him his place in the natural
history of America continues to shine with singular brightness. With
his boundless energy, brilliant mind, and keen insight concentrated on
his projected work on the natural history of Carolina, John Lawson,
had he lived to complete it, would no doubt have been one of the great
naturalists of his time. As it was, he laid a substantial foundation for
those who were to follow, whose work he himself anticipated: "As to a
right Knowledge thereof, I say, when another Age is come, the Ingenious then in being may stand upon the Shoulders of those that went
before them, adding their own Experiments to what was delivered
down to them by their Predecessors, and then there will be something
towards a complete Natural History. . . ."

~ Chapter 3

MARK CATESBY

~ 1

America did not have to wait, as John Lawson had foretold, for "another Age" to come before moving forward "towards a complete Natural History." The "Ingenious" man who would "stand upon the Shoulders of those that went before," in this case the sturdy shoulders of Lawson himself, was already waiting in the wings. A bare six months after the tragic death of the gallant Lawson, with all its attendant loss to the cause of natural history, another young Englishman, a very different individual but no less a fellow pilgrim in the same green brotherhood, moved on to the wilderness stage.

Mark Catesby. How shall we ever capture his elusive essence? How shall we ever know him at all? For his vision, like Lawson's, turned ever outward, focused on all the variety and beauty of the wilderness world, which he gave, with pen and brush, as a priceless gift to all mankind. We shall not find this herald and portrait painter of flower and tree, bird and beast of the fields, and even of the myriad creatures of the rivers and the seas, in the meager biographical facts dug from moldering records, or in the few sparse words of dull description carelessly dropped by a chance acquaintance. No. If we are to know him at all, this gentle artist to whose single-hearted devotion we owe so much, we must look for him in the two massive and magnificent volumes of his *Natural History*. There indeed is Mark Catesby, life size; few men have left a prouder monument.

But this achievement, one can safely assume, was not even contemplated, save perhaps as a secret dream, by the young man who landed at Jamestown, Virginia, on April 23, 1712. Scholars, searching for some facts about his life before 1712, though not met with total silence as in the case of John Lawson's early life, have little of interest to report. He was born in 1683, of middle-class parents, in a tiny village about forty miles northeast of London. Possibly through the influence of his association with a neighboring botanical scholar, Samuel Dale, he seems to have felt a vocation for natural history even in his boyhood. As he recalls years later, in one of his rare personal comments: "The early Inclination I had to search after Plants and other Productions in Nature being much supressed by my residing too remote from London, the center of all Science, I was deprived of all Opportunities and Examples to excite me to a stronger Pursuit after those things to which I was naturally bent. . . ." So off to London he went, drawn to the city, as eager young gentlemen from the provinces have always been drawn, by a hunger for knowledge, experience, opportunities, and congenial companions. Just when he went there and what exactly he did there no one knows; but his green fever, far from abating, grew more intense and his ambition more daring, so that, as the above comment continues, "yet my Curiosity was such that not being content with contemplating the Products of our own Country, I soon imbibed a passionate desire of viewing as well the Animal and Vegetable Productions in their Native Countries, which were Strangers to England."

One could not stroll the London streets in the early eighteenth century, or sit in the coffeehouses listening to the gossip, or loiter by the Thames docks, without breathing the heady air of foreign travel, of exotic adventures, and far horizons. And for Catesby the siren lure took the shape of all the green kingdoms of the world. He decided to begin with America. One suspects his choice was partly inspired by a reading of John Lawson's book, *A New Voyage to Carolina*, published in London in 1709 and especially popular among the "curious" gentlemen with whom Catesby mingled in the London coffeehouses. It is even possible that Lawson and Catesby may have met during Lawson's return visit to England for the publication of his book. All that is certain, however, is that Catesby reveals in his writings a familiarity with Lawson's book and often and frankly uses it as a reference. His only personal comment on Lawson is a lament for his death: "I cannot but lament the hard Fate of this inquisitive Traveller, who, tho partial in his favorable Opinions of the Barbarians, died by their bloody Hands for they roasted him alive in Revenge for Injuries they pretended to have received from him."

When he began his book, he emulated Lawson's approach and phrasing in his preface—"Carolina was the best Country I could go to" —with his own version: "Virginia was the Place (I having Relations there) which suited most with my Convenience to go to . . ."

These Virginia relatives were his elder sister, Elizabeth, her husband, Dr. William Cocke, and their family. Against the stubborn opposition of her father, Elizabeth had married young Dr. Cocke soon after his graduation from Cambridge. When Mark joined them in Williamsburg they had already been in Virginia more than ten years, long enough to prove that, in a worldly sense at least, Elizabeth had been wise in her choice. Already Dr. Cocke was the leading physician in the colony, a member of the Governor's Council, and eventually its secretary.

"I arrived the 23rd of April, 1712," Catesby recalled, twenty years later in the preface of his book. Did he also recall, one wonders, the emotions of the young Mark Catesby at that first meeting with "Virginia, the earthly Paradise," in that long-vanished springtime of his youth? Artist-naturalist that he already was at heart, how he must have delighted in the myriad greens of the forest, the riot of rainbow colors in flowering plant and tree, the tantalizing fragrances, music and motion and vivid plumage of the birds, and all the bright intoxication of April in this exotic world.

Looking back, he tells us only, "I thought then so little of prosecuting a Design of the Nature of this Work, that in the seven Years I resided in that Country (I am ashamed to own it) I chiefly gratified my Inclination in observing and admiring the various Productions of those Countries. . . ." Observing and admiring (literally marveling or wondering at)—one can hardly think of a more constructive seedtime for the great work of his maturity.

Though it had been the capital of the Virginia colony only since the abandonment of nearby Jamestown in 1699, the village of Williamsburg, beautifully poised on high land between the York and James rivers, was already almost a century old. Mostly a village of small Georgian houses, each with its formal garden of English or Dutch design, the town had already some impressive buildings suggestive of the role it was to occupy as the political, social, and cultural center of the colony. There were the Christopher Wren building at the center of the College of William and Mary, the grand, newly completed capitol, and the beginnings of the elegant palace of the royal governors. When the general court was in session, twice each year, the town's normal population of around two thousand more than doubled, and there were horse races and balls and festivities of all kinds. And, since the town was actually principally a planters' center, the owners of the large plantations from many miles around not only came frequently to Williamsburg for business or pleasure but often kept a residence there.

It is to one of these planters, William Byrd of Westover, that we owe the only personal comments that we have on young Mark Catesby in Virginia. Almost immediately after Catesby's arrival in the colony there began between these two diverse men a fortuitous association, valuable to the young naturalist's career. William Byrd was then thirty-six years old and a fellow member of the Council with Dr. Cocke, though on the opposite side of the political fence. Heir to great wealth and large colonial holdings, Byrd had been educated in England and had cut quite a swathe in London society before he returned to America in 1705 to receive his princely patrimony. Westover, the fourteen-thousand-acre home plantation with its magnificent setting on the north bank of the James River, some thirty miles upstream from Jamestown, was only one small part of his inheritance, but it was here that he was even then rebuilding the manor house to its present Georgian elegance. Brilliant, vain, flamboyant, ambitious, and frequently absurdly childish, Byrd fancied himself something of a universal genius, a hyperbole no doubt encouraged by his provincial environment where men of his abilities were not common. One of his most useful qualities was his recognition of superiority in others and his tendency to select his associates on this basis, which may explain why, with no visible scientific attainments or any published work, he was elected, in London, at the age of twenty-two, to membership in the august Royal Society, a distinction he valued so much that he had it engraved on his tombstone.

No doubt, as soon as the restless master of Westover heard that the Cockes had a guest fresh from England, one with natural history interests, he must have sent, posthaste, to the doctor's Williamsburg home an invitation to visit Westover. At any rate, before the month was out, Dr. and Mrs. Cocke, their daughter, and brother Mark Catesby arrived by boat at the riverside manor house. As Byrd tells, in his Secret Diary, which lay in undeciphered code for two centuries before its key was discovered:

By twelve o'clock there came the Doctor and his wife and Mr. Catesby and the Doctor's daughter. I received them very courteously and gave them a glass of canary and some cakes to stay their stomachs. . . . About 3 o'clock we went to dinner and I ate some beans and bacon for dinner. In the afternoon the daughter, Mr. Catesby, and I went into the swamp to see the nest of a humming bird and the Doctor following along. However, we found a nest with one young and one egg in it. In the evening we took a walk about the plantation and at night we drank a bottle. I neglected to say my prayers but had good health, good thoughts, and good humour, Thank God almighty.

Two weeks later, although Dr. Cocke had returned to Williamsburg on a horse supplied by his host, the other guests lingered on at West-over. Byrd had a bout of fever and had taken the bark treatment; consequently, when he arose on June 5, he neglected his customary readings of Greek and Hebrew, but not his ritual matins:

I rose at 9 o'clock. . . . I said my prayers and had tea and bread and butter for breakfast. The stonecutter began to work in the library chimney. . . . I ate some boiled mutton for dinner but did not dine with the rest of the company because they would not have the window shut where it rained in. After dinner I found myself better and walked about the garden all evening, and Mr. Catesby directed how I should mend my garden and put it into a better fashion than it is at present. . . .

Yet another week and Catesby is still at Westover. This was the day of leisurely visits and lingering guests and no doubt William Byrd, whose diary entries reveal (for an educated man) a singular poverty of ideas, was hungry for intellectual companionship and eager to share his magnificent library and perhaps not reluctant to impress the young man from England with his own importance in the colony:

June 14th: I rose about 7 o'clock and read two chapters in Hebrew and some Greek in Lucian. I said my prayers and drank some whey for breakfast. . . . About 12 o'clock the boat came for us and about one we went with a fair wind to Swinyards. All the ships there had their ornaments out and we were received by 11 guns by the 'Harrison' . . . We had an abundance of guns all day long so that in all we had about 120 from all the ships. Tom Randolph came in the afternoon and told me all was well everywhere. . . .

Picture the scene in the glorious June weather, on the wide estuary of the majestic James, the square-riggers, gay with flags, standing out against the dark waters and shuddering with the vibration of the great salutes. Surely even the reserved, intent young man from England must have been excited for "then we returned home and were so merry that Mr. Catesby sang. I neglected to say my prayers. . . ."

Mr. Catesby sang, and went away, but in September, after two months, during which we have no inkling of his reactions to the New World or its to him, he was again at Westover and we have again some intimate glimpses from Byrd's ever-unabashed pen:

Sept. 21. In the evening my brother Custis' boy brought me letters from the Doctor to desire me to meet the Governor and come to Pamunkey [Indian] Town with Mr. Catesby. . . .

Sept. 23. . . . We rode to Mr. Goodrich Lightfoot's. . . . We stayed until the Governor and all the company came in by the Man-of-War boat. . . . We went over the [York] River where the Governor received me very kindly. . . . It rained violently all day so that the company could see nothing and the Governor's cook could scarcely get the dinner. However, he did get one about 2 o'clock and I ate some boiled mutton. We were merry but were forced to stay in one of the Indian cabins all day. . . . Abundance of people came to the Indian town to see the Governor but were very wet. There is an Indian called P . . t W . . . l who has now his 20 wives. There was also an Indian who was ill of a bite of a rattlesnake but was on the recovery having taken some snakeroot. About 8 o'clock we ate some blue wing [teal] and then retired to bed. I neglected to say my prayers. . . .

Sept. 25. I rose about 7 o'clock . . . said a short prayer and drank milk tea and ate plum cake for breakfast. Then Mr. Catesby and I took a walk around [Colonel Bassett's] plantation. . . . Mr. Catesby killed two snakes in the pasture. . . .

The visit was almost over. Back at Westover, the diary goes on:

Sept. 27. . . . In the afternoon I found myself a little out of order but did not much regard it. I put several things in order in the library and then I took a walk with Mr. Catesby who was likewise disordered. When I returned I was much worse. However, at night I drank more strong drink than usual. I went to bed and had an ague which was followed by the fever. . . .

Sept. 28. I was pretty well again this morning but did not rise till about 8 o'clock and then went into the river to prevent another fit of the ague and found myself much better after it. . . . Mr. Catesby went in the river with me and had a violent looseness which carried away his fever. . . .

Sept. 29. I rose about 7 o'clock and went again into the river against my ague. I read a chapter in Hebrew and some Greek in Lucian. I said my prayers and ate boiled milk for breakfast. . . . In the afternoon I put several things in order in the library and at night Mr. Catesby came and told me he had seen a bear. I took Tom L-s-n and went with a gun and Mr. Catesby shot him. It was only a cub and he sat in a tree to eat grapes. I was better with this diversion and we were very merry in the evening. . . .

That is the last of our firsthand, intimate glimpses of Mark Catesby. The Secret Diary lapsed at the end of 1712. By 1714 Byrd was in England again, and he did not return to Virginia until shortly before Catesby himself left the colony. Moreover, about the time of Byrd's departure for England, Catesby seized an opportunity to make a trip to Jamaica on a merchantman bound for that Caribbean island. The friendship between the two men was kept alive, however, through a desultory correspondence until Byrd's death in 1744. At times the correspondence was neglected by the engrossed naturalist, and years after the Virginia interlude, when Byrd was again settled at Westover and Catesby at work in London on his natural history, Byrd instructed his London agent to call on "my friend Mr. Cat[es]by, now and then" for letters or commands, adding that his old friend "is such a philosopher that he needs a monitor to put him in mind of his friend."

Unquestionably that friendship was a fruitful one for the young naturalist. William Byrd was a robust and stimulating character with a genuine interest in natural history, although inclined to surprising gullibility. Like John Lawson but with less excuse, since Lawson's time in America was so short, he was inclined to accept Indian lore and superstition as scientific fact, such as that several snakeroots were certain cure for snakebite, that snakes could charm their victims into a willingness to be devoured, and that bear meat was a potent aphrodisiac. Catesby, though more skeptical, never quite brought himself to discard some of these beliefs of his first American mentor. But both he and Byrd also adopted some of Lawson's more forward-looking thinking, notably the belief that interbreeding domestic cattle with the American bison might prove of value to colonial animal husbandry. Also they both warmly supported Lawson's idea that the best way to get Indian souls for Christendom and valid title to Indian lands for colonists was through intermarriage between natives and English.

Except for a few passages in his *Natural History*, little else in the form of tangible report of Mark Catesby's Virginia years has come down to us. Nevertheless they must have been of inestimable value in nourishing his burgeoning interests and abilities as an artist-naturalist, though his great plan had not yet taken definite shape in his mind. Moreover, he must have acquired in those years a thorough familiarity with the natural environment of America and a solid foundation of knowledge of the flora and fauna. He must also have acquired considerable professional skill as a collector, though he himself makes light of his work in this field, saying modestly that it was limited to "sending from thence some dried Specimens of Plants and some of the more Specious of them in Tubs of Earth, at the Request of some curious Friends. . . ." Among the curious was his old friend, Samuel Dale, and a London nurseryman, named Thomas Fairchild, whose shipments helped to bring Catesby's name to the notice of such men as James Petiver, John Lawson's erstwhile correspondent and now England's most active promoter of the study of botany, an informal position to which Peter Collinson would succeed in the middle seventeen-hundreds. Catesby was also coming to the attention of the celebrated botanist, William Sherard, who, a few years later, would play a major role in sending him back to America on a natural history mission.

Accustomed as we are to modern containers, preservatives, and transportation, it is not easy to appreciate the difficulties involved in gathering and shipping these collections. Botanical specimens, to be sent to England alive, had to be brought home from their natural habitat in special saddlebags, then transferred to tubs of suitable earth. Those to be sent as dried specimens had to be kept fresh until they could be pressed, a tedious process involving several steps, then mounted on special sheets of paper, each with its descriptive data. Such creatures as snakes, frogs, and small birds were sent preserved in rum, in large-mouthed jars. Larger specimens were dried in a slow oven and covered with tobacco dust to protect them from vermin. Then to be surmounted was the difficulty of persuading the masters of the sailing ships, infrequent at best, to accept such shipments, involving as they did watering of living specimens, protecting the dried ones from moisture, and keeping thirsty sailors from drinking the spirits from the bottled specimens.

Inevitably such activities were transforming the enthusiastic dilettante into an accomplished naturalist. There were, however, other factors in Virginia assisting that transformation. Williamsburg, at the time of Catesby's visit, was no longer a raw frontier community. Some of its residents were fourth- and fifth-generation Virginians. William and Mary College was now teaching its second generation of students. The Black Swan of Westover was not the only Virginian with sufficient in-

terest in natural history to provide Catesby with the stimulus of congenial companionship. John Custis, Byrd's brother-in-law, was an able
amateur botanist and avid gardener. Dr. Cocke, as a physician, had a
professional interest in botany. Before Catesby left Virginia, it is
probable that John Clayton, famous in botanical circles for his col-
laboration with Gronovius in the production of *Flora Virginica*, may
have arrived in America, and if so, would certainly have been known to
Catesby, since his father, John Clayton, Senior, attorney-general of the
colony, had been among the company with the botanist at Westover.
Wherever and whenever they met, these two young men, both to make
notable contributions to botany, developed a friendship which was kept
alive through a correspondence which lasted until Catesby's death.

Catesby's Virginia apprenticeship was not, however, confined to Williamsburg, Westover, and Pamunkey Town. References to observations
made in widely separated places show he did considerable roaming over
the colony in his collecting activities. In company with others not identified, he even went into the little-known backcountry, as far as the
mountains. In his *Natural History* he describes one of these experiences:

In the year 1714, I travelled from the lower part of the St. James River
in Virginia to that part of the Apalachian Mountains where the Sources of
that River rise. . . . At sixty miles from the Mountains the River, which
fifty miles below was a mile wide, is here contracted to an eighth Part, and
very shallow, being fordable in many Places and so full of Rocks, that by
stepping from one to another it was everywhere passable. Here we killed
plenty of a particular kind of wild Geese; they were very fat by feeding on
fresh Water Snails, which were in great plenty, sticking to the tops and
sides of the Rocks. The low Lands joining the Rivers were vastly rich,
shaded with Trees that naturally dislike a barren soil, such as black Walnut,
Plane [sycamore] and Oaks of vast stature. This low Land stretched along
the River many miles, extending back half a mile, more or less, and was
bounded by a Ridge of steep and lofty Rocks, on the top of which we
climbed and could discern some of the nearer Mountains, and beheld most
delightful Prospects, but the Country being an entire Forest, the Meanders
of the Rivers, with other beauties, were much obscured by the Trees. . . .
Some miles further, the Banks of the River on both sides were formed of
high, perpendicular Rocks, with many lesser ones scattered all over the
River, between which innumerable Torrents of Water were continually
rushing.

At the distance of twelve miles from the Mountains, we left the River
and directed our Course to the nearest of them. . . . Ascending the higher

Grounds we had a large share of the Mountains as well as the River below us, which here divided into narrow, rocky Channels and formed many little Islands.

So soon as we had left the River the Land grew very rugged and hilly, increasing gradually in height all the way. Arriving at the Foot of the first steep Hill we pursued a Bear, but he, climbing the Rocks with much more agility than we, he took his Leave. Proceeding further up we found by many beaten Tracts and Dung of bears that the Mountains were much frequented by them, for the sake of Chestnuts, with which at this Time the Mountains abounded. . . .

Certain Places in Virginia towards the heads of Rivers are very much impregnated with a nitrous Salt, which attracts for many miles numerous heads of Cattle, for the sake of licking the Earth, which at one Place is so wore away into a Cave that a Church, which stands near it, has attained the indecent Name of Licking Hole Church.

With more fanfare the same region was visited two years later by Lieutenant Governor Spotswood's much publicized expedition, made up of some dozen gentlemen, romantically dubbed the Knights of the Golden Horseshoe, who set forth, with an array of servants and a military convoy, to open up the Valley of Virginia for settlement.

⌒〰 2

Meanwhile, back in London, in that tight-knit and enthusiastic fraternity known as the Natural History Circle, the name of Mark Catesby was being heard more and more and with growing respect. Whereas, when he left for Virginia, mention of Catesby's name suggested no more than a convenient possibility for obtaining New World specimens, his name now brought to mind the abilities of an experienced collector and capable naturalist, who was rapidly adding striking artistic skill to his other accomplishments. His reputation had grown not only through the specimens, letters, and paintings sent back from the New World, but through the loyal efforts of his friends to bring his abilities to the attention of the wealthy and influential scientists and friends of science who might aid his career. Among such men, and in fact wherever those interested in natural history gathered, whether at meetings of the Royal Society, at the informal assemblies at the Temple Coffee House, favorite haunt of naturalists, or in private homes and gardens, there had long been dreams and plans for a natural history expedition, financed by suitable patrons, to some place less well known than

Virginia—perhaps to central Africa. It is certain that Catesby's friends would have kept him informed and it seems likely that the lure of some such possibility and his own potential role in the plan influenced his return to London in the autumn of 1719.

His old friend and neighbor, Samuel Dale, in a letter to the botanist, William Sherard, in October of that year wrote:

"Mr. Catesby is come from Virginia. . . . He intends againe to returne, and will take an opportunity to waite upon you with some paintings of Birds, etc. which he hath done. It's [a] pitty some incouragement can't be found for him; he may be very useful for the perfecting of Natural History."

However, it seems to have been the following spring before an actual meeting took place between Mark Catesby and William Sherard, who was to become the leader and organizer among the patrons who were to sponsor his later achievements.

During the two years Catesby spent in England between his American sojourns, plans for an African expedition were discussed and abandoned. Eventually it was settled that Catesby should return to America, this time to South Carolina, then Britain's most southern outpost in continental America. In effect, he was to go as official naturalist for the Royal Society, although his actual sponsors were a group of scientists, wealthy noblemen, and other friends of science. An important sponsor was Governor Francis Nicholson, first royal governor of South Carolina, who left to take his overseas post a short time before Catesby sailed for the colony sometime in February, 1722. Nicholson had been governor of Virginia before Catesby went there. It was he who had supervised the transfer of the capital from Jamestown to Williamsburg, the laying out of which was largely his work.

"I arrived in Carolina," he reported, "23rd of May, 1722, after a pleasant, though not short Passage. In our Voyage we were frequently entertained with Diversions not uncommon in crossing the Atlantic Ocean, such as catching Sharks, striking of Porpoises, Dolphins, Bonetoes, Albecores, and other Fish, which three last we regaled on when Fortune favoured us in catching them; and even the Flesh of Sharks and Porpoises would digest well with the Sailors when long fed on salt Meat."

When the ship was still far out at sea, an exhausted ruddy turnstone alighted in the ship's rigging. Catesby captured it and used it as a model for the first of what would be more than a hundred drawings of New World birds.

Landfall is exciting, even now in the day of the swift steamships, but after months at sea in a square-rigger, for even the dullest traveler it must have been a breathless moment. For Mark Catesby, that May day in 1722, the first glimpse of the Carolina shoreline must have been this and more. He had come of age in his chosen profession. The man now arriving in Charleston was no boyish adventurer, or mere curious traveler, but an accomplished naturalist and artist, emissary of the Royal Society, under the protection of the royal governor himself. He would have been proud and happy, no doubt, full of purpose and anticipation, as he watched the land draw nearer—the brave little fringe of buildings against the green and leafy background, deep green now, for spring is almost over by late May in Carolina and the long, hot summer has begun spreading her wares over field and forest. As the ship dropped anchor in Charleston harbor, did he recall, one wonders, that other landing in Virginia ten years ago, when he and the spring were young together?

He received a warm welcome; hospitality, even then, was indigenous among Charlestonians, especially for a guest in favor with Sir Francis Nicholson. Soon, with the eye and hand that had been trained on the shores of the James, the York, and the Rappahannock, Catesby was hard at work along the Ashley, the Cooper, and the Savannah, observing, collecting, and drawing. As a protégé of the governor, he found a warm reception at the neighboring plantations along the Ashley, where in time he was able to repay hospitality with shipments of lilies, daffodils, narcissus, and other flowers, sent at his behest from England to embellish the plantation gardens.

. . . I unexpectedly found this Country possessed not only with all the Animals and Vegetables of Virginia but abounding with even a greater variety. . . . In these Parts I continued the first year searching after, collecting, and describing the Animals, and Plants.

I then went to the upper, uninhabited parts of the Country and continued at and about Fort Moore [opposite and a little downstream from Augusta], a small Fortress on the banks of the River Savannah, which runs from thence a course of 300 miles down to the Sea, and is about the same distance from its Source in the Mountains.

I was much delighted to see Nature differ in these Parts and to find here abundance of things not to be seen in the lower parts of the Country. This encouraged me to take several Journeys with the Indians higher up the Rivers towards the Mountains, which afforded not only such a succession of new vegetable appearances, but the most delightful Prospects imaginable, besides the diversions of hunting Buffaloes, Bears, Panthers, and other wild Beasts. In the excursions I employed an Indian to carry my Box, in which, besides Paper and Materials for Painting, I put dry Specimens of Plants, Seeds, etc., as I gather'd them. To the Hospitality and Assistance of these Friendly Indians I am much indebted, for I not only subsisted on what they shot, but their First Care was to erect a Bark Hut at the Approach of Rain to keep me and my Cargo from Wet.

In that simple summary, from the preface of his *Natural History*, Mark Catesby gives little inkling of the ordeal and tedium of his Carolina years. As an environment for a serious naturalist, this turbulent frontier colony was in marked contrast to long-settled, stable Virginia. However, in the four decades since the first settlement had been moved to Oyster Point, at the confluence of the Ashley and Cooper, the little capital city of Charleston had made remarkable strides despite what often seemed a diabolical competition between "acts of God" and acts of man to destroy it. Among the acts of God were an earthquake, hurricanes, and devastating epidemics, including a scourge of yellow fever, which killed half of the Colonial Assembly. Vying with these disasters were the constant dangers from their fellow men, notably pirates and Indians. The 1714 Treaty of Utrecht, which ended Queen Anne's War, in effect terminated for the British privateers the open season for hunting French and Spanish shipping, which they had been enjoying for years. Unemployed and no longer entitled to the euphemism of privateers, pirates from their West Indian havens almost strangled the colony. Close on the heels of the pirate ravages came two devastating Indian wars, and finally, to compound the chaos, came the revolution against the Lords Proprietors. Catesby's sponsor, Governor Nicholson, was appointed as a result of the revolution, the first governor under the new royal regime.

In Carolina trouble appeared endemic. A few months after his arrival Catesby reported to Dr. Sherard:

About the middle of September here fell the greatest floud attended with a Hurricane that has been known since this country was settled. Great numbers of Cattle, Horses, Hogs, and some people were drowned. The Deer were found frequently lodged on high trees. The wind was so violent that it tore up by the roots great numbers of Trees, and disrobed most others of their leaves, Cones, and seed; so that, had I been well, the collection would have fallen short of other Years. Perticularly it dispersed all the Laurels, Umbrella and many other things I sent out for, but none to be found.

In addition to the disastrous consequences of the hurricane as a public catastrophe, the storm was a private calamity for one whose livelihood was largely dependent upon gathering botanical specimens and seeds. It coincided with a personal disability referred to above—"had I been well." A few days before the hurricane blew in from the tropics, Catesby was "seized with a swelling," which, twice lanced and treated for some time by a doctor, incapacitated him until well into December.

Even so, the year 1722 may well have been the most significant of his entire American career. Much of the interval between his arrival and illness had been spent as guest at various plantations along the Ashley River. There is reason to believe that in those months he made substantial progress on his great series of drawings depicting birds in association with scientifically appropriate botanical specimens, a trailblazing innovation in ornithological illustration and graphic first lessons in ecology as well.

Next to birds and plants, reptiles received the largest share of Catesby's attention. He describes an involuntary intimacy with a rattlesnake during his first winter in Carolina:

. . . a Negro Woman making my bed, a few minutes after I was out of it, cryed out a Rattle Snake. We, being drinking Tea in the next Room, which was a ground flore, and being Surprised with the vehemence of the wenches bauling, went to see the cause, and found, as the wench had said, a Rattle Snake actually between the Sheets in the very place I lay, vigorous and full of ire, biting at everything that approach't him. Probably It crept in for warmth in the Night, but how long I had the company of [the] charming Bedfellow, I am not able to say.

He tells of another encounter with a rattlesnake in the same neighborhood:

The largest I ever saw was one about eight feet in length weighing between eight and nine pounds. This Monster was gliding into the House of Colonel Blake of Carolina and had certainly taken his Abode there undiscovered had not the domestick Animals alarmed the Family with their repeated Outcries; the Hogs, Dogs, and Poultry united in hatred to him showing the greatest consternation by erecting their Bristles and Feathers, expressing their Wrath and Indignation, surrounded him, but carefully kept their distance; while he regardless of their threats, glided slowly along. . . .

They are . . . never the Aggressors except in what they prey upon; for, unless they are disturbed they will not bite and when provoked they give Warning by shaking their Rattles. They are commonly believed to be the most deadly venomous Serpent of any in these parts of America. I believe they are so as being generally the largest and making a deeper Wound and injecting a greater quantity of Poison.

He discusses the several Indian snakeroots which both Lawson and Byrd, as well as the Indians, believed were infallible cures for rattle-snake bite, but, on the basis of his own observations, he concludes that the most successful remedy the Indians seem to have is to suck the wound, still a recommended field remedy.

The harmless little hognose snake was a particular fascination to Catesby. This creature's survival technique is one of exaggerated mim-icry of the poisonous copperhead, whom it closely resembles in mark-ings and coloration. When threatened it coils menacingly, spreads its head to give the appearance of having poison sacks, hisses, and strikes a little short of its enemy. If the attacker is not frightened away by these maneuvers, the snake rolls over on its back and "dies," so effectively that it can be tied in a knot or hung over a wire fence, and remains im-mobile as long as danger persists. If, however, one turns it over, to test its shamming, it will promptly turn again to its belly-up, "dead" posture.

When Catesby examined a hognose snake preparatory to picturing it with a "martagon," which we know as the lovely Canada lily, he re-mained unconvinced of its innocence. He searched its "mouth for the hollow viper's fangs" and could find only small teeth. But, "it having so much of the characteristic of Vipers, besides its slow motion and sluggishness, [he could not] help suspecting him to be a Viper. . . ."

Ironically, the very persuasiveness of this mimicry, a survival tech-nique, now threatens the hognose snake with extinction, for man, in-stead of being frightened away by the bluff, destroys the mimic, with an assurance that one less "spreading adder" now challenges man's safety on earth.

Of all the earth's creatures, none are more productive of myths and superstitions than snakes. Of the American snakes, excepting the rattle-snake and hognose, perhaps none has inspired more myths than the horn snake or hoop snake. A sharp spine on the tip of its tail, which in struggling with an adversary or victim it uses as a sort of movable thorn, has given rise to a widespread conviction that its tail spine is a deadly venom-filled stinger. Even less justified is the common belief that the hoop snake can form itself into a hoop and speed across the countryside like a free wheel. Calling it the wampum snake, Catesby painted this snake in an attractive composition with the southern red lily. Since both are found in the Ashley River region, it seems likely that he made the sketches for this plate during one of his visits there.

One more snake picture must be mentioned, more for its plant accompaniment than for the snake itself. In an artistic design Catesby pictured the little green snake with the boxwood-like holly, which, he said, the Virginians call yaupon but the South Carolinians call cassena. In his travels up the Savannah he noted artificial plantings of it at Indian villages far in the interior, and an active trade in its leaves carried on between the Indians of the low country, where the plant grows naturally, and those living even beyond the mountains who regularly used as a beverage a tea brewed from the leaves. Quantities of a stronger brew from the same plant were part of their spring purging. He described the green snakes as "easily reclaimed from their wildness, becoming tame and familiar, and are very harmless, so that some People will carry them in their Bosoms."

Although Charleston was headquarters for Mark Catesby during his Carolina years, most of his observing, collecting, and sketching was done in three areas to which he made repeated expeditions. Two of them, the Ashley River region and the sea islands south of the city, were near at hand; to reach the third, far up the Savannah River, he had to make a long and difficult journey, perhaps as much as two hundred miles each way, considering the circuitous routes he had to follow. For those who know these areas and are versed in their particular fauna and flora affinities, it is possible with a fair degree of certainty to name the locale of many of his paintings. The one which seems to have supplied more models than any other is the Ashley River plantation country, where he was so warmly welcomed immediately after his arrival in Carolina.

Since in those times both bald eagles and ospreys were relatively common along the bays and estuaries of the southeast coast, there is good probability that, in Catesby's rather unsuccessful attempt to picture the eagle robbing the fish hawk, he was trying to put on paper an incident he had witnessed over the wide marches bordering the Ashley.

Catesby's Carolina parakeet, feeding on cypress mast. (Courtesy of the Caroliniana Library of the University of South Carolina)

And almost certainly it was in the lofty forests, which once grew in places along the Ashley, that he found his models for his beautifully conceived and delicately done painting of the now extinct parrot of Carolina, feeding on cypress mast. The cypress tree, he reported, also furnished a home for the parakeets, who "delight to make their nests . . ." in its "lofty branches."

These same Ashley River cypresses may have supplied the model for his ivory-billed woodpecker, which he called "the largest white-bill woodpecker." This bird, which is now extremely rare, if not extinct, is described by Catesby as "somewhat larger than a crow" and able, within an hour, with their great beaks, to "raise a bushel of chips."

The Bill is as white as Ivory, three inches long. The Bills of these Birds are much valued by the Canada Indians, who make Coronets of them for their Princes and great Warriers, by fixing them round in a Wreath, with their points outward. The Northern Indians, having none of these Birds in their cold Country, purchase them of the Southern People at the price of two, sometimes three Buckskins a Bill.

There, on the Ashley, he also found his ricebirds (bobolinks) in unwanted hordes, in spite of the vast numbers shot every year for food, esteemed by many, he says, as the most choice of any bird. He reported that in 1724 the entire unharvested crop on a forty-acre rice field on the river was entirely consumed by these birds. There he would have found the wood ibis, which he called a wood pelican and described as being "about the bigness of a goose," and very tasty, although "they feed on fish and other water animals." He regarded the wood ibis as "a stupid bird and void of fear, easily to be shot. They sit in great numbers on tall cypresses and other trees in an erect posture, resting their ponderous bills on their necks for greater ease."

This was the area of the wood duck too. He believed that the wood duck carried its newly hatched young on its back from their nest in the hollow of a tree high above the ground; an erroneous belief, although perhaps easier to believe than the established fact that the newly hatched, down-covered summer ducklings simply jump from their lofty nests.

Another waterfowl then common along the Ashley was the bluewinged teal. Catesby found that "in August these birds come in great plenty to Carolina and continue till the middle of October, at which time the rice is gathered on which they feed. . . . They are given preference to all duck kind for delicacy of taste."

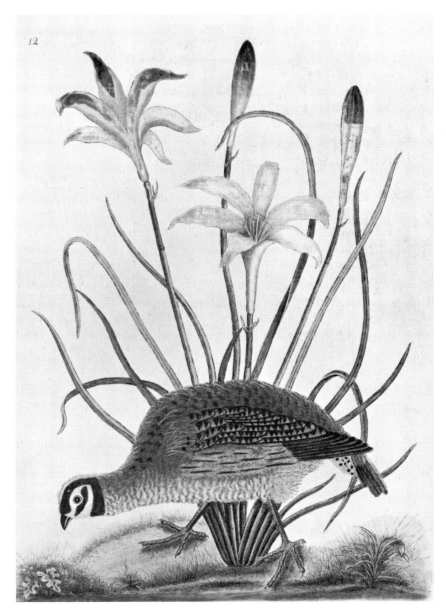

Catesby's quail and Atamasco lily. (Courtesy of the Caroliniana Library of the University of South Carolina)

A very limited coincidence of range in South Carolina makes it at least highly probable that Mark Catesby, while walking along the Ashley River, found his little ground dove and the pellitory tree, which he pictured together. The bark of the pellitory, now better known as Hercules'-club or toothache tree, was then a popular source of an analgesic which the Indians used to kill the pain of an aching tooth.

Since one of the most likely places to see quail amid the delicate white trumpets of the atamasco lilies would be the pine flats extending out northwest and south from the Ashley River, there is at least a good probability that it is there he sketched his "American partridge" with the "Atamasco lilly."

Finally, of the three areas in which he concentrated his work, the Ashley plantation country was the most likely place to find the pitcher plant, the hooded trumpet, and the golden trumpet, which he pictured with frogs as their animal accompaniment. These three strange plants all belong to the *Sarracenia* family, named in honor of Dr. Michel Sarracin of Quebec, who, a few years earlier, had sent back to France a specimen of the pitcher plant. Catesby's drawings of them are of great botanical significance, for as far as we know they are the earliest pictures of any of the numerous species of carnivorous plants of America. These insect-catching plants with widely diverse methods of entrapment belong to four different families, of which three, while very different in appearance, are closely related, while the fourth is, botanically, a complete stranger to them. Two of the four are found only in America, with most of their species confined to the southeastern United States.

The three related families are the *Sarracenias*, which include the pitcher plant and the trumpets, pictured by Catesby, the sundews with their flypaper-like leaves, and the famous Venus's-flytrap which employs the steel-trap principle to capture its victim. All the numerous species included in these families are denizens of bogs, pine flats, or other such acid, nitrogen-deficient sites.

In evolving the insect-catching device with which the *Sarracenias* are equipped, nature employed a mechanism without movable parts, the simple device of the baited fish trap, inviting an easy entrance through a cone, and thence into the trap through a small hole at its apex, a process most creatures are incapable of following in reverse order. In these plants the cone-shaped leaves simulate the cones of the fish trap. Except for the pitcher plant, which has leaves much the size and shape

Catesby's leopard frog and *Sarracenia purpurea,* the pitcher plant. (Courtesy of the Caroliniana Library of the University of South Carolina)

of a demitasse cup, the *Sarracenias* have long, erect leaves, shaped like heralds' trumpets standing on end, each with a cantilevered roof over its mouth, or as in the case of the hooded *Sarracenia,* a hood which "arches over the mouth of the tube in the form of a friar's cowl."

The interior of each cone-shaped leaf is covered with stiff hairs slanting downward, thereby effectively preventing the escape of any unfortunate insect which may have entered the leaf by accident or in search of a sip of the water which fills the lower part of the leaf, water rendered progressively attractive to certain insects through the decaying remains of earlier victims. The *Sarracenia*'s foul-smelling, downward-facing flowers, standing on bare stalks about the height of the leaves (one to three feet), remarkably resemble miniature bridge lamps and the stench of the flowers seems as effective in attracting a miscellany of insects as if they were in truth glowing lamps. Eventually drowning in the leaf's ever present cistern, the insect bodies decompose, releasing their body proteins into the water to become available to the plant to compensate for the nitrogen deficiency of its habitat. There are some ten species of *Sarracenia,* all American and all but two native to the Southeast.

To make the tiny, frying-pan-shaped leaves of the sundews even more lethal to such insects as ants, gnats, and fruit flies, nature increased the effectiveness of their flypaper technique by adding the refinement of movable tentacles, like miniature octopus arms, to grasp and hold a victim mired in the viscous, sticky secretions exuded from the tips of those tentacles. The struggles of the insect activate these tentacles to reach around and grasp the victim, drawing it close to the surface of the leaf, so that, when it dies and decomposes, the leaf can absorb, from the victim's body proteins, the nitrates not available in the acid soil of the bog. Belying their deadly motivation and lethal traps, these tiny plants grow in the form of pretty little rosettes about the size of a silver half dollar and bear on slender stalks delicate little white flowers, the very epitome of "innocence."

The third of the three related insect-eating plants is the Venus's-flytrap, a monotype, a term indicating in this case that it is the only species of its genus and its genus the only one of the family—a very unusual botanical phenomenon. Without doubt, the Venus's-flytrap is one of the most amazing and famous of all the multitude of the earth's plants. That fame arises from its ability to catch with its leaves flies and other small insects, as, like a steel trap, the two lobes of the leaf spring shut on any unwary victim which touches the sensitive hairs, standing on the meat-red surface of the semicircular lobes. As soon as the trap is sprung on the prey, the closed lobes secrete a digestive juice, which processes the insect for utilization by the plant, as in the case of the pitcher plants and sundews. Another unusual feature of the Venus's-flytrap is its extremely restricted range. When Mark Catesby was in tidewater Virginia, he was a good hundred miles north of the plant's northern limits; in Charleston he was seventy-five miles south of the southernmost limits where one might find its delicate anemone-like white flowers rising through the fine grass of the sour, sandy soil of the coastal pine flats.

It seems unlikely that Mark Catesby ever saw the Venus's-flytrap growing in its native habitat. Certainly he did not paint it, nor did he sketch any of that other group of carnivorous plants which, unlike the flytrap, are far removed botanically from the *Sarracenias* which he did portray. This group, with its yellow two-lipped flowers, is related to the snapdragon and ranges over a good part of the world. It includes both bog plants and aquatic plants. An amazing thing about some of the bog species, the *Pinguicula* or butterworts, is that they have evolved an insect-catching technique closely parallel to that of the sundew. Like those of the latter, their sticky leaves act as flypaper, but instead of engulfing the insect with tentacles, the leaves, activated by the insect's struggles, roll up into a sort of jelly roll with the unfortunate insect as filling.

Other genera of the *Pinguicula* family include numerous species of bladderworts, mostly aquatic plants, bearing on their submerged roots bladders equipped with trap doors. These bladders are an intricate combination of trap and primitive stomach. When a small creature, such as a mosquito larva, swims near enough to one of these bladders to touch one of its sensitive trigger hairs, the bladder suddenly changes shape, sucking its prey through the opened trap door, which closes behind the captive, leaving the hapless insect to be digested.

Let us return from this botanical by-path to Mark Catesby as he roams the somber and fecund low country of Carolina in search of specimens for his collections and models for his sketches. Along the tidal stream called Stono and on the lonely and haunting sea islands he wandered, lured on by a seemingly endless variety and abundance of wildlife. On the Stono he was intrigued by some fossils, unearthed by a gang of slaves building a rice-field dike. The discovery was of "four

Teeth of a large Animal, which by the concurring Opinion of all the negroes, Native Africans, that saw them, were the grinders of an Elephant; and in my opinion they could be no other, I having seen some of the like that are brought from Africa." This report of Catesby's being the earliest reference to an American vertebrate fossil, is of milestone significance to paleontologists. His related geological observations show equally remarkable acumen, such as his recognition of the fact that the whole of the Southern coastal plain had once been the bottom of the sea all the way to the fall line. An equally inspired belief of his was that the Indians were Asiatics, who had probably crossed "from the easternmost part of the Old World to America" where, he believed, although without the supporting evidence of subsequent discoveries, "the continent of Asia may be very near, if not contiguous to that of America."

The hammocks along the marshes of the Stono River, the marshes behind the sea islands and their wide, sandy beaches, would have provided Catesby with most of his shore birds and waterfowl. On the sand dunes, along the beach, the artist in him often dominated his sketches as in his beautiful drawing of a lark under a bower of golden sea oats, which, he said, grow "only here on the sandhills of the seashore." Here too he would have found quantities of fragrant wax myrtle, which he used as a "prop" for his kingfisher. He describes the forays of the colonists to the sea islands to gather the berries of the myrtle to make their aromatic candles, the fathers cutting down the fruited trees so that the little children might help with the picking.

The stunted live oaks, cassenas, and bays, whipped and molded by the sea winds into dune-shaped mounds of green, provided the shelter for his lovely blue grosbeak shown with its spray of flowering sweet bay, and for his brilliant painted bunting, called by the Spaniards "mariposa pintada or the painted butterfly," which he sketched with that beauty of the green world, the exquisite *Gordonia*, American cousin of the oriental tea and *Camellia*.

There too he would have seen delicate sandpipers running as on stilts along the wide beaches, and black skimmers in flight, cleaving the sea with their oddly protruding lower beaks. Behind the islands in the grassy marshes Catesby would have found, as one can today, blue herons, bitterns, marsh hens, yellow-crowned herons, and green herons to delight his eye and challenge his brush. Nesting in dwarf sweet

T.32.

Alauda gutture flavo
The Lark

Gramen Myloicephorum Oxyphyllon Carolinianum &c.
Pluk: Almag. p.179.

Catesby's meadowlark and sea oats. (Courtesy of the Caroliniana Library of the University of South Carolina)

myrtle bush, on the edge of the marsh, he could have found models for his beautiful redwing blackbird composition.

Mark Catesby's most extensive journeys away from the Carolina low country were several up the Savannah River, all the way, on at least one occasion, to the Garden of Eden of the Cherokees in the Southern Appalachians, an earthly paradise from which they would be ruthlessly expelled a century later, when gold was discovered in their forests. There, in the foothills of the mountains, Catesby saw the buffalo and found the beautiful *Catalpa bignonioides*, which, like many other natives of the Southern mountains, has its nearest relatives in eastern Asia. He was delighted by the beauty of the catalpa, sometimes called the candle tree, which he probably came upon for the first time in summer, all alight with great erect terminal panicles of white, touched with flecks of gold and purple. He must have waited in the area until autumn, or returned at that season to gather the seeds, long, slim bean pods, sometimes a foot long, for he sent some to his correspondents in England and shared them with his friends in Charleston:

This Tree was unknown to the inhabitanted parts of Carolina till I brought the Seeds from the remoter parts of the country. And though the Inhabitants are little curious in gardening, yet the uncommon beauty of the Tree has induced them to propagate it and it is becoming an Ornament to many of their Gardens. . . .

In his *Natural History*, the leaves, flowers, and seeds of the catalpa are portrayed in company with the brilliant-hued orchard oriole and his demure mate.

On his second expedition to the upper Savannah he encountered an impressive run of spawning sturgeon in the rapids at the fall line, rapids now submerged by Clark Hill Reservoir. Myriads of those mammoth living fossils, some as long as twelve feet, were struggling through the shallow, boulder-studded current, seeking the quiet waters above to drop the two million or more eggs each female carried. It was a simple matter to kill one of the struggling creatures with a blow of an ax, and his party killed sixteen of them in the two days they spent at the cataracts, bringing back two for the garrison down the river at Fort Moore.

There also, in the hills along the upper Savannah, he would have discovered the water ash he sketched, embellished with the exquisite yellow swallowtail butterfly, and the showy *Philadelphus*, for which he made a dramatic luna moth companion, and the red sweet-shrub he paired with the svelte, dainty little waxwing, and the graceful silver-bell tree to accompany the parula warbler. This region is hospitable, too, to the creeping trumpet vine among whose vivid scarlet corollas one often finds the ruby-throated hummingbird. He would have found there, as well, a close relative of the *Gordonia*, the tea, and *Camellia*, the beautiful *Stuartia*, a blossoming spray of which he graced with a little golden-crowned kinglet. The wooded areas, in summer, would have been bright with the gay crimson flowers of the Indian pink, which Catesby pronounced a sovereign cure for worms.

Virgin forests of giant oaks then covered those rich red hills, producing acorns with the incredible profligacy of spawning sturgeon, and to feed on these acorns came fabulous hordes of passenger pigeons. Catesby accompanied his painting of the pigeon with a detailed description and the following comments:

Of these there come in Winter to Virginia and Carolina, from the North, incredible Numbers; in so much that in some Places where they roost, which they do on one another's Backs, they often break down the Limbs of Oak with their weight and leave their Dung some inches thick under the Trees they roost on. Where they light they so effectually clear the Woods of Acorns and other Masts that the Hogs that come after them to the detriment of the Planters fare very poorly. In Virginia I have seen them fly in such continued trains three Days successively; that there was not the least interval in losing sight of them. . . .

In their passage the people of New York and Philadelphia shoot many of them as they fly, from their Balconies and tops of Houses; and in New England there are such numbers that with long Poles they knock them down from their Roosts in the night in great numbers. . . . A Canada Indian . . . told me he had seen them make their Nests in Rocks by the sides of Rivers and Lakes far north of the River St. Lawrence. . . .

There are several other Catesby compositions, including some of his most successful, whose models might have been secured equally well anywhere he went in the South. Such are his summer tanager and sycamore, the tufted titmouse with wild azalea, the cardinal, which he called "the Virginia nightingale," on a hickory branch, and the Baltimore oriole and its hanging nest amid the leaves and tulip-shaped flowers of the tulip tree—the same bird and plant combination used by Audubon a century later in one of his most famous paintings. Both blue jay and bay-leafed smilax, which he painted together in one of his best illustrations, are known everywhere in the region, but few today know that the smilax was an important source of food for the Indians. The great tuberous roots were used to make both a diet drink and a gruel, while the fabulously fast-growing spring shoots, which frequently grow several inches a day, were "boiled by the inhabitants and eaten like asparagus."

Other models he could have found almost anywhere he roamed are the brown thrasher, melodious singer, which he sketched with the chokecherry, the phoebe, perched by Catesby in a mass of yellow jessamine, and the little green lizard, often miscalled chameleon because of his ability to change his usual emerald green to brown and show at will a red balloon at his throat, which Catesby placed among the leaves and seed balls of the sweet gum, then commonly known as the liquid-amber tree.

Just as typical of the region are the "tyrant" flycatcher, better known to us as the kingbird, and the flowering sassafras shown together in the *Natural History*, with an interesting comment on each:

I have seen one of them fix on the Back of an Eagle and persecute him so that he has turned on his Back into various positions in the Air in order to get rid of him, and at last was forced to alight on the top of the next Tree, from where he dared not move till the little Tyrant was tired or thought fit to leave him.

The Virtue of this Tree is well known as the great sweetener of the Blood; I shall therefore only add, that in Virginia a strong Decoction of the Root has been sometimes given with good Success for an intermitting Fever.

However, of all Mark Catesby's lovely paintings, perhaps the hall-mark of the region, the one most characteristic of the part of America Catesby knew best, is his "Mock-Bird" on a spray of flowering white dogwood. Almost everywhere across the South, from the mountains to the sea, the common white dogwood is an all but ubiquitous forest understory, and every year spring rolls northward through the forests of the region on waves of its white sprays, while autumn woods are brightened with its bright red berries and rust-red leaves. On one of Catesby's Virginia rambles he had discovered a rare but recurring botanical sport of this plant, a "peach-coloured dogwood," from which he had rooted cuttings for John Custis and others. Many years later, when Catesby had returned to England from Carolina and was at work on his plates, Custis sent him his pink dogwood as a gift, but it was lost at sea.

Understandably Catesby was enchanted by the mockingbird:

Hernandez calls it the Queen of all singing Birds. The Indians, by way of Eminence or Admiration, call it Concontlatolly, or four hundred Tongues; and we call it (tho' by not so elevated a Name, yet very properly) the Mock-Bird, from its wonderful mocking and imitating the Notes of all Birds from the Hummingbird to the Eagle. . . . They may be said not only to sing but to dance, by gradually raising themselves from the place where they stand, with their Wings extended, and falling with their Heads down to the same Place; then turning round, with their Wings continuing spread, have many pretty antic Gesticulations with their Melody.

When Mark Catesby set out for Carolina in 1722, he had left London under the aegis of a group of devotees of botany—the high fashion of the day. These gentlemen fully expected, in return for their patronage and support, substantial and regular collections of seeds, plants, and mounted botanical specimens. Almost as soon as he arrived in Charleston, however, Catesby became bird-struck and, before long, he had almost abandoned his mission to the green world and joined the more dynamic court of the feathered realm. Shipments lagged. His sponsors grew restive and dissatisfied. As his Carolina months ripened into years and his bird distraction grew with every passing day, he received more and more complaints. To one he desperately replied:

I was sensibly troubled by your last letter of complaints. . . . You say, Sir, several of my Subscribers complain, which surprises me. . . . I wish I could know what you required and by whome. I hope it can't be expected I should send Collections to every of my Subscribers, which is impracticable for me to doe. . . . I should have thought aboundance of my time lost if, at my return to England, I could show no more than the collections I send. Not that anything obstructed my collecting Plants and Seeds, which all gives place to when opportunity offers.

And, in the same letter, an unusually passionate outburst suggests the intensity of his harassment: "I protest before God I never can be more industrious in collecting whatever I could possibly meet with either those few days that I was at Savannah Garrison or Since."

At this time Catesby had already been in Carolina for two years. His stack of bird drawings had gradually grown to a hundred or more. Sightings of new species were getting more and more infrequent. In fact, he believed that there were few birds, either resident or "birds of passage," that had escaped his knowledge "except some water fowl and some that frequent the sea." Soon the feeling that his Carolina mission had been largely fulfilled, and the frustration implied in that letter to his patrons, acting in concert with the impact of a restless fellow spirit, a young Charleston doctor, inspired a plan whereby he and the doctor would voyage overland through two thousand miles of Indian territory to Mexico and down its length, even in the face of the Indian wars then in progress and the chronic hostility of Mexico's Spanish masters to Britons. As Catesby's enthusiasm was unable to inspire any favorable response among his London patrons, the plan had to be abandoned. Disappointed and restless, he sailed for New Providence in the Bahamas, where he spent most of the year 1725, visiting several of the neighboring islands, collecting and painting seashells, an array of exotic fishes, crabs, sea turtles, and some birds and plants. It seems to have been a pleasant interlude, no doubt a time of restoration of mind and body, after nearly three years of travel and hard work and three summers in the depressing, sickly atmosphere of the Carolina low country. It is not surprising that he speaks gratefully of the "most serene air" of the healthful Bahama Islands.

ꙮ 3

The following year he was back in London, that "center of all science." The joys and perils of wilderness life were behind him forever. Ahead lay a Herculean task, the completion of his *Natural History*. His sponsors and others of the natural history circle were warm in praise of the collection of drawings he had brought back with him from Carolina. He was given every encouragement for its publication except the financial aid essential for such an undertaking. However, Catesby's mind and heart were by this time wholly given over to his great project and, inspired by the enthusiastic reception of his paintings, he determined to go ahead. He had fixed upon the dream of a natural history of the American colonies on a scale exceeding anything ever before attempted. The fulfillment of this dream was to consume all his efforts and energies for the next twenty years.

No doubt Catesby was well aware of the daring and ambitious nature of his plan, but he could hardly have realized the magnitude of his undertaking and the difficulties in its accomplishment. He had hoped, at first, to have his drawings put on plates by the expert Parisian engravers, but when he learned the cost entailed, he had to abandon this idea and instead teach himself to be an engraver as he had taught himself to be an artist. In his preface, in his modest, low-keyed style, he explains his approach, beginning with an apology:

As I was not bred a Painter, I hope some faults in Perspective and other niceties may be more reasonably excused: for I humbly conceive that Plants and other things done in a Flat, if in an exact manner, may serve the Purpose of Natural History better in some measure than in a more bold and Painter-like way. In designing the Plants I always did them when fresh and just gathered, and Animals, particularly the Birds, I painted while alive, (except a very few) and gave them their Gestures peculiar to every Kind of Birds, and where it could be admitted I have adapted the Birds to those Plants upon which they fed or have any relation to . . .

And on his newer venture:

At my return from America . . . I had the Satisfaction of having my Labours approved of; and was honoured with the advice of several . . . Gentlemen most skilled in the learning of Nature, who were pleased to think them worth publishing, but that the Expense of Graving would make it too burdensome an Undertaking . . . I altered my design of going to Paris or Amsterdam, where I first proposed to have them done. At length, by the Kind advice and instructions of that inimitable Painter, Mr. Joseph Groupy, I undertook and was initiated in the way of etching them myself, which I have not done in a Graver-like manner, choosing rather to omit their method of Cross-hatching, and to follow the humour of the Feathers which is more laborious.

The illuminating of Natural History is so particularly essential to the perfect understanding of it, that I may aver a clearer idea may be conceived from the Figures of Animals and Plants in their proper colours than from the most exact Description without them. . . .

In the completed volumes, each engraving was supplemented by a descriptive text, on the opposite page, in double columns of French and English. For the French translation, Catesby expressed his obligation "to a very ingenious gentleman, a Doctor of Physic and a Frenchman born, whose modesty will not permit me to mention his name."

Once the format was settled upon and he had developed sufficient skill to etch the copper plates, Catesby devoted himself wholly to the gigantic task of production. So that he could sustain himself financially, he planned to release the work serially, twenty plates, with accompanying texts, at a time. This delivery in sections, at a cost of two guineas, a princely sum in those days, also provided an easy-payment plan for his subscribers, important even for the wealthy, who might have hesitated to obligate themselves to pay five times that sum at once.

Even so, financial difficulties soon threatened the project. Rescue came in the person of Peter Collinson, Quaker merchant and naturalist, who was just beginning to assume his lifelong role as a personal clearing house for the collections, correspondence, and works of the eighteenth-century natural history circle. Collinson became Catesby's good angel, not only lending money without interest to see the *Natural History* through to completion, but encouraging and sustaining the toiling artist with the warmth and enthusiasm of his friendship.

After two years of unremitting work, Catesby had completed the first twenty-plate section, which he was invited to exhibit to the gentlemen of the Royal Society on May 22, 1729, at the first meeting he had ever attended of the august body. Successive presentations followed. The title page of the first volume was printed in 1731, but the final sections were not finished and presented to the society until November 23, 1732.

The title, detailed in the fashion of the day, suggests the scope of the work: *The Natural History of Carolina, Florida, and the Bahama Islands; Containing the Figures of Birds, Beasts, Fishes, Serpents, Insects, and Plants: Particularly, the Forest-Trees, Shrubs, and Other Plants, Not Hitherto Described, or Very Incorrectly Figured by Authors. Together with Their Descriptions in English and French. To Which Are Added Observations on the Air, Soil, and Water; with Remarks upon Agriculture, Grain, Pulse, Roots, Etc. To the Whole is Prefixed a New and Correct Map of the Countries Treated of.* By Mark Catesby. F.R.S.

The dedication to Queen Caroline is worth quoting, for, though its phrasing, a combination of flattery and humble deference, is characteristic of the fashion of the day, the author's pride in his unique achievement shines out:

Madame: As these Volumes contain an Essay towards the Natural History of the Part of your Majesty's Dominions which are particularly honoured by bearing your August Name, Carolina; this and your great Goodness in encouraging all Sorts of Learning, hath emboldened me to implore Your Royal Protection and Favour to my slender Performance. I hope Your Majesty will not think a few Minutes disagreeably spent in casting an Eye on these leaves; which exhibit no contemptible Scene of the glorious Works of the Creator, displayed in the New World; and hitherto lain concealed from the View of Your Majesty, as well as Your Royal Predecessors, though so long possessed of a Country, inferior to none of your Majesty's Dominions.

Wherefore I esteem it a singular Happiness, after several Years Travels and Inquiry in so remote Parts (by generous Encouragement of Several of

Your Majesty's Subjects, Eminent in their Rank and for their being Patrons of Learning) that I am the first that has had an Opportunity of presenting to a Queen of Great Britain a Sample of the hitherto unregarded, though beneficial and beautiful Productions of Your Majesty's Dominions. I am, May it Please Your Majesty, Your Majesty's Most Humble and Most Dutiful Subject, Mark Catesby.

One hopes that good Queen Caroline spent more than a few minutes on the beautiful volume with its colorful birds, strange plants, and stories and descriptions of all the natural wonders of exotic Carolina, and that she expressed her appreciation appropriately, but this is not recorded.

His fellow scientists, at any rate, were well aware of the epoch-making value of this work, a natural history on a new and grand scale, the first illustrated American ornithology, the first introducing the system of presenting birds with paintings of flowers, trees, or shrubs appropriate to their feeding or nesting habits, and, with its companion volume to follow, the first illustrated natural history of America. Mark Catesby had, moreover, laid down the format which would thereafter be imitated in the field of ornithology throughout the world, in America most notably by Alexander Wilson and John James Audubon nearly a century later.

For the weary Catesby the triumphant completion of this first volume was the culmination not only of a long period of travel and study, two voyages across the Atlantic, two to the West Indies, journeys into the wilderness behind the coastal settlements of Virginia and Carolina, with all the incidental hazards, storm, illness, hunger, heat, and cold, but above all of literally years of tedious, almost solitary toil.

To supply a mere hundred copies of this first volume alone had entailed laboriously getting ten thousand engravings from his hundred painstakingly prepared copper plates, then water-coloring by hand every leaf, flower, and bird on each of these ten thousand plates—an incredible accomplishment. But the objective to which he had dedicated himself was not then even half done. There was to be another equally demanding volume, on whose plates he was already at work.

As the paintings he had made in Carolina and the Bahamas began to be exhausted, as he found that he had failed to note the proper colors for a bird sketch or that he lacked a model for a fruit or flower, he turned to his old Virginia friends, Byrd, Custis, and John Clayton. Resourceful Peter Collinson also came again to the rescue by offering exotics from his own garden treasury and by enlisting the help of his American correspondents, especially collector John Bartram of Philadelphia. From Peter's garden came a green lady's-slipper, while a closely related *Orchis*, the yellow lady's-slipper, pictured by Catesby with a black fox squirrel, was sent by Bartram to Collinson and thence to Catesby. From John Bartram directly to Catesby himself came the beautiful scarlet seed head of sumac and the flowers and fruit of the pawpaw, the latter preserved in spirits for the voyage.

Catesby's lifework, whose very nature had from the beginning demanded a large measure of solitary, even isolated, endeavor, was now yielding him a most precious reward, the regard and warm fellowship of congenial spirits. He had succeeded in his profession. He had come of age attuned with the temper of the times. He had achieved eminence in his lifetime. But surely the greatest satisfaction and happiness must have flowed from his role as a functioning part of that delightful and in many ways unique brotherhood, the eighteenth-century natural history circle, whose circumference was elastic enough to stretch to any part of the known world, but whose members, even in that day of slow communications, enjoyed an intimacy and closeness of relationship seldom experienced by any group in our fragmented modern society.

He had, too, the formal recognition of election to membership in the Royal Society, sponsored appropriately by devoted Peter Collinson and his early patron, Sir Hans Sloane.

Work on the second volume, though no less arduous, proceeded in an atmosphere of confidence and mellow security, with the long hours of work lightened by visits and letters and broken by gatherings with scientific friends and associates. At last, eleven years after the completion of the first volume of the *Natural History*, Catesby composed the concluding words for its companion. "I confess," he wrote, "it is now time to conclude this extensive and laborious Work. The whole was done within my House and by my own Hands; for, as my Honour and Credit were alone concerned, I was resolved not to hazard them by committing any part of the work to another Person. Nor can I ever cease to acknowledge the kind dispensation of Providence in making me the happy Instrument of composing a Work of such labour and consequence; the materials for which were collected from the living Subjects themselves in their native Abodes. . . ."

A proud Peter Collinson was soon writing to Linnaeus, the renowned Swedish botanist: "Catesby's noble work is finished."

Simultaneously Mark Catesby arrived at threescore years of age, finished his great work, and reached the pinnacle of his career. It was at about this time that he was described by a friend (the only description of his appearance and manner that has come down to us) as "tall, meagre, hard-favoured, and [with] a sullen look . . . extremely grave or sedate, and of a silent disposition; but when he contracted a friendship, was communicative and affable." The years of lonely and disciplined work may well have made him grave, but we have ample evidence of his capacity to attract and keep friends.

The completed second volume was presented to the Royal Society at its December meeting in 1743. On the program that evening, in symbolic recognition of Catesby's achievement, was the display of a rare genus of West Indian plants, which the Dutch botanist, Gronovius, had named *Catesbaea*, an honor which, in that circle and in that age, was compensation purer and more valued than gold. There were many species of both plants and animals named for Mark Catesby in his lifetime and, after his death, others named in his memory. True, the latter were scientific monuments of lesser stature as they were the names of species, subdivisions, rather than of the larger category of genera. Among them we number *Rana catesbeiana*, better known as the American bullfrog, Catesby's oak, better known as turkey oak, the scrub oak of the South, Catesby's lily, Catesby's clematis, popularly called satincurls, and one of the carnivorous trumpets which he was the first to portray, *Sarracenia catesbaei*.

The beauty and significance of the two volumes of the *Natural History* have tended to obscure Catesby's *Hortus Britanno-Americanus*, which he worked on up until his death, and which was published a few years later. *The Hortus*, a study of American trees and shrubs with special emphasis on their adaptation and cultivation in England, is a delightful book, beautifully illustrated in color with paintings of the plants, including flowers, seeds, and leaves, as in the *Natural History*, and charmingly written in Catesby's quaint, careful, and serious prose style. Though most of the plants included had already been shown in the *Natural History*, the descriptions and the paintings in the *Hortus*, which is a purely botanical work, are far more detailed.

The years following the completion of the second volume of his *Natural History* were busy not only with work on the Appendix, completed three years later, and on the *Hortus*, but on a variety of scientific projects and studies, many of them undertaken especially for the Royal

Society. Of these the one of most interest today is a paper called *Birds of Passage* which contained ideas far in advance of his day. Years before, during his visit to the Bahama Islands, he had spent three nights on a sloop anchored off Andros Island. As he lay on the deck under the gentle tropical sky listening to the ricebirds passing overhead in the darkness, he recalled their dread visitations upon the Ashley River rice plantations and, pondering the meaning of the cyclic appearances and disappearances of bobolinks, robins, waxwings, and juncos from the Virginia and Carolina forests and fields, he conceived an insight into the fascinating but then largely mysterious phenomenon of bird migration. He recognized that the key to the mystery lay in the search for food, and that in summer birds fly north to the great North American and Eurasian land masses to take advantage of the far wider land areas and longer daylight hours there, allowing more food and longer hours for the nurture of fledglings which often require up to their weight in insects every day.

On the other hand, Catesby's explanation of the still far from understood *modus operandi* was naïve; he suggested that birds might find their direction in migration by flying high enough to view their seasonal destinations, to which they would then fly along a declining plane. This speculation, however, is only a little more absurd than some that are still being offered to explain the mysterious "how" of bird migration. At least, in his paper, he dismissed as fiction some of the more popular current superstitions, which even the great Linnaeus still supported, such as that swallows at the approach of winter dove to the bottoms of ponds and hibernated there and that other birds spent the winters dormant in hollow trees and caves.

Later in the same year that he presented this paper to the Royal Society, Mark Catesby married Elizabeth Rowland, the mother of his two half-grown children, Mark and Anne. A little more than two years later he died. The whole of his worldly goods, which passed under his will to his widow and children, was a few finished copies of *The Natural History of Carolina* and the copper plates from which his illustrations were reproduced. The plates went to a bookseller and, fortunately, into the production of two posthumous editions of the *Natural History*. It is chiefly through a few scarce and treasured volumes of these later editions that Americans have an opportunity to make the acquaintance of Mark Catesby, artist and naturalist of British Colonial America.

~~ Chapter 4

JOHN BARTRAM

~~ 1

At his cottage in the London suburban village of Peckham, on December 14, 1737, Peter Collinson, a prosperous London mercer, took quill in hand and started yet another letter to his friend and fellow Quaker, John Bartram of Philadelphia. Although only four days earlier he had sent a letter to Friend John, excitedly telling him of the warm reception the Royal Society had given a reading of a letter from John on cicadas and rattlesnakes, and although a week later he would write yet another, this letter Peter was beginning must have consumed the better part of the long winter evening for it ran to many pages, complimenting John on his "curious" observations on the locust (cicada) and even more on the "sticks" (perforated by the cicada for the deposit of eggs): "It shows how indefatigable thee art after truth and the processes of nature. . . ." Peter had heard of Bartram's house that he had built so skillfully and well on the riverside and he longed to see "both house and builder."

Botany was the chief link that bound him to his correspondent, and he did not fail to give anxious hints for the care of the bays and cypresses he had sent to Bartram, promising more seed and even a hard-to-find cone of the cedar of Lebanon, hardy enough for the Pennsylvania climate. He himself despaired of success with the seed of laurel and shrub honeysuckles sent him by John, "the seed is so small and chaffy." Perhaps some could be sown in a box of mold, as soon as ripe, and so sent, "only leaving some holes for circulations of air." He was grateful for the bulbous roots, which had come "in perfect order," and for the dried specimens, one rather like a columbine, which Collinson called mountain *Ranunculus.*

Behind this long and spirited letter, touching upon a wide miscellany of topics interesting to the curious writer and his correspondent, and signed "thy loving friend, Peter," lay a background of events and circumstances of singular significance in the development of English America's first notable native botanist.

A few years before this time, and not long after the death of James Petiver, Peter Collinson had assumed the role long filled by the learned apothecary, of serving as the active nucleus of the British natural history circle. With his indefatigable quill, his passion for science, especially botany, and his strongly social nature, Collinson, by 1737, had become not only the center of a world-wide correspondence with those of kindred interests but also the clearing house for shipments from abroad for many of the wealthy and prominent similarly infected with the virtual madness of science which was the fashion of the day. His numerous correspondents eventually included botanists such as Linnaeus and Gronovius, high-placed noblemen at home, missionaries in China and consuls in the Middle East, and Americans, such as Benjamin Franklin of Philadelphia, William Byrd and John Clayton of Virginia, and Dr. Alexander Garden of South Carolina. Among all this variety, however, no correspondence was more prized than the one he enjoyed for a great part of both their lives with that sturdy, self-educated farmer-botanist, John Bartram.

Of the transmutation of an almost unlettered Pennsylvania farm boy into the most famous botanist of colonial America there are various accounts, some incredibly romantic; but the actual career of John Bartram, revealed in his own writings and seen through the eyes of contemporaries, is dramatic enough. Scion of a Quaker family, who had emigrated to Pennsylvania in 1682, the year the colony was established, John was born in 1699 near the village of Darby. When he was two years old his mother died and he was given over to the care of his grandparents. His father's proposed remarriage, a few years later, precipitated a dispute with his fellow Quakers of Darby Meeting and, apparently as a consequence of the dispute, his father left Pennsylvania, leaving John with the grandparents, and settled in the Cape Fear region of North Carolina. There, probably in the same Indian uprising which began when John Lawson was killed, John's father was murdered by the Indians and his stepmother and her two young children, a boy and a girl, were carried into captivity, from which they were later ransomed and returned to Philadelphia. One of these same children, John's half brother, William, went south again when he grew up, to make his home on the Cape Fear River near the present Fayetteville.

Meanwhile, back at Darby, John had absorbed the rudimentary instruction in reading, writing, and cyphering provided by the country school, had reached manhood and established himself as a farmer on lands left to him by a bachelor uncle. At twenty-eight he was a widower with two small children, one of whom died young. He married Anne Mendenhall two years later and brought her to live on his newly acquired farm at Kingsessing on the west bank of the Schuylkill River, a few miles below Gray's Ferry on the road to nearby Philadelphia. These were years of struggle and labor, to build with his own hands his stone house, develop his lands, and support a growing family which eventually included ten children.

But always farmer Bartram dreamed of horizons far beyond the furrow's end. In his old age he recalled, in a letter to Collinson, his interest, even as a lad of ten, in the study of botany. Botany and medicine, both embryonic, were inseparable in the early eighteenth century, and as he grew up, perhaps hoping to become a physician, he acquired Latin books, "physic" and botany works, from which he learned enough to minister to his neighbors in times of sickness. As his family grew larger and his farming operations increased, dreams of wider horizons persisted. Natural history, especially botany, became John Bartram's special rainbow, one which he would follow for the rest of his life, seeking and finding treasures at its ever moving end in the American wilderness, from the Great Lakes to southern Florida.

Slowly he began to develop in the grounds around his house, and on the steep slope between the house and the site of his cider mill on the rock outcropping by the river, his own botanical garden with a variety of native trees and shrubs as well as imports from the old country adaptable to the more extreme American climate. He searched up the river, even into the hill country as far as the Blue Mountains, bringing back seeds and plants for his riverside acres. Before long the first botanical garden of English America had gained local fame for its variety and for the all-but-prescient horticultural skill of its master.

During those same years, back in London, merchant Collinson was

RESIDENCE OF JOHN BARTRAM, built with his own hands, 1730.

John Bartram's home, "built with his own hands," overlooking his botanical garden on the Schuylkill River.

also avidly developing his botanical garden, featuring exotics from the distant corners of the earth. His special interest, however, was American plants. To obtain his seeds and plants Collinson tried to bend the resources of his vocation to meet the needs of his avocation, seizing upon every opportunity to entice his business correspondents and foreign agents to send him plants and seeds native to their areas. Even those business associates inclined to be obliging were soon dismayed by the importunities of the insatiable merchant-botanist and eventually became desperate to free themselves from more and more burdensome missions. Among them were two of Collinson's Philadelphia correspondents who knew of industrious farmer Bartram's interest in botany and of the garden he was developing beside the Schuylkill. By a happy chance they saw in Bartram a way to employ other hands than their own in satisfying Collinson's hunger for plants of the region. To free themselves they directed Collinson's attention to Bartram and thereby set in motion the long and fruitful association so full of consequence for the cause of botany in England and in America.

By 1735, the year of the earliest preserved Collinson-Bartram correspondence, the two Quakers, despite the ocean that lay between them, had become warm personal friends and had worked out an informal combination of compensation and barter, satisfactory enough to have launched the American on collecting voyages in search of seeds and plants for the merchant's garden and specimens to be dried and mounted for his herbarium. The letters, which continued with undiminished fervor until Collinson's death in 1768, are a fascinating mirror, reflecting not only much of eighteenth-century life in London and colonial America and the gradual maturing of the science of botany but, on the personal level, the many-faceted natures of two delightful personalities.

The letters are usually long, detailed, lively, and wide-ranging over all the curiosities of the natural world. But plants are the chief topic. The flower-struck Collinson reels off in the earliest surviving letter a dizzying list of "great and small hellebore—pray send a root or two of each," lilies (including spotted Martagons lilies), devil's-bit, or blazing star, and his favorite lady's-slipper, layers of the woody vine with variegated leaves, roots of *Aristolochia*, a "sovereign remedy for sore breasts," wild senna, mountain goat's rue, Solomon's-seal, panax (ginseng), barely pausing for breath to say, "My dear friend, I only mention these plants; but I beg thee not to neglect thy more material affairs to oblige me," before rushing on: "A great many may be put in a box 20 inches or 2 feet square and 15 or 16 inches high; and a foot in earth is enough. This may be put under the captain's bed, or set in the cabin, if it is sent in October or November. Nail a few narrow laths across to keep the cats from scratching it."

But the polite, tentative note—"I only barely mention these plants; not that I expect thee to send them. I don't expect or desire them, but as they happen to be found accidentally . . ."—was only preliminary etiquette, occurring less and less as the relationship deepened into a solid and mutually satisfactory partnership.

No facet of the letters is more fascinating than the revelation of the delicate balance developed and maintained by these two Quaker individualists in their long association. John's hunger for books on natural history had to contend with an irritating condescension from the better educated Londoner, who wrote in 1737:

> I shall take notice of thy request to buy Tournefort. I have enquired and there are so many books or parts, done, as have come to fifty shillings. . . . Now I shall be so friendly as to tell thee, I think this is too much to lay out. Besides, thee has now got *Parkinson* and *Miller*. I would not have thee puzzle thyself with others; for they contain the ancient and modern knowledge of Botany. Remember Solomon's advice in reading of books there is no end.

Back came John's reply, six months later and none the less sturdy for that:

> I take thy advice about books very kindly—although I love reading such dearly; and I believe, if Solomon had loved women less, and books more, he would have been a wiser and happier man than he was.

In the touchy realm of financial compensation, also, the London merchant had met his match in the canny, penny-wise, colonial farmer. Very early in their association the good Peter, commenting on a trip of John's to the Jerseys and Kent County in search of all sorts of pines and firs, white cedar and spruce, for shipment to England, after complimenting John on "thy accurate observation, and perfect knowledge," suggests, "but though thy excursions are attended with difficulties, and great fatigue,—yet, the secret pleasure that accrues—and new discoveries —and the many observations, both informing and entertaining, which tend to enrich thy mind with natural knowledge, and fill it with exalted ideas of the wonderful Hand that made all these things,—must yield thee such a secret pleasure as will fully compensate for and counterbalance all the other . . ."

One can imagine how the suggestion of such spiritual fare in lieu of more substantial payments may have sounded to John, hard at work on his riverside farm, with a rapidly growing family about him. It is worth quoting in full his indignant reply, so revealing of the dignity and independence of his nature:

> In thy letter of December 20th, thee supposes me to spend five or six weeks in collections for you and that ten pounds will defray all my annual expenses; but I assure thee, I spend more than twice that time, annually; and ten pound will not, at a moderate expense, defray my charges abroad— besides my neglect of business at home, in fallowing, harvest, and seed time.
>
> Indeed, I was more than two weeks' time gathering the small acorns of the Willow-leafed Oak, which are very scarce, and falling with the leaves, so that daily I had to rake up leaves and shake the acorns out, before they were devoured by the squirrels and hogs; and I reckoned it good luck if I could gather twenty under one tree and hardly one in twenty bore any. Yet I don't begrudge my labour; but would do anything reasonable to serve you. But by the sequel of thy letter, you are not sensible of the fourth part of the pains I take to oblige you.

Such expressions of frustration from colonial botanists to their English patrons, too remote in every way to appreciate the trials, dangers, and labors of collecting in the wilderness, were inevitable and continuous, as the problem of adequate compensation was never fully resolved. John Bartram, early in his career, faced the matter with characteristic honesty, ending his letter:

> Now my kind and generous friend, I shall return thee my hearty thanks for thy care and pains which thee hath taken, and the good offices thee has done for me; and further, if thee finds any expressions in my letter a little out of the way, thee will not take it in the wrong sense. I assure thee, I bear thee a great deal of good-will; or if thee thinks I am too short and imperfect in explaining any subject, which I give thee any account of, pray let me know and I will satisfy thee according to the best of my knowledge; for I love plain dealing.

Fortunately for Bartram, Peter Collinson was not only an ardent botanist but a most generous patron. Soon after he began his association with Bartram, he had enlisted an imposing group of other patrons to share in the shipments and contribute to the expenses of his Pennsylvania friend's collections. Of all these patrons, many of them among the aristocracy, the favorite was the intelligent and generous Lord Petrie, whose arboretum and greenhouses were exotic wonderlands. His death, of smallpox at age thirty, wrung from Peter Collinson an anguished cry: "I have lost my friend—my brother. The man I loved, and was dearer to me than all men is no more," ending in a despairing "All our schemes are broke." Peter continued to grieve for the glamorous young nobleman, though in later years Lord Petrie's widow and son became his friends and patrons of John Bartram.

However, disagreements over finances and other arrangements never dim for either John Bartram or Peter Collinson the joy in their relationship which overflows into the letters. John declares himself "exceedingly pleased with thy long letters, as thee calls them; but I wish they had been as long again. . . ." And in response to Peter's description already referred to of the warm reception given by the Royal Society to a reading of one of John's letters John bursts out:

> I am almost overjoyed in reading the contents of this letter, wherein thee acknowledges thy satisfaction in my remarks on the Locusts, Caterpillars, Pigeons, and Snakes. I am thankful to thee, and the Royal Society, for taking so much notice of my poor performances. It is a great encouragement for me to continue my observations of natural phenomena.

Though there were much-needed material rewards for John in the partnership, gifts for himself and his family, books and supplies for his botanizing, in addition to the financial subsidies, the intangible satisfactions were incalculable. Through his friendship and association with Peter he had a friend at court and was admitted to the councils of the great, both literally and figuratively. The horizons of his life widened with every year that passed. He had, as it were, at the same time the natural wealth of colonial America all about him and, through Peter, a window on the world of the natural history circles of Europe. Among his most cherished patrons, obtained for him by Peter, was Sir Hans Sloane, president of the Royal Society, who had also assisted Catesby. There would be many others over the years who would receive the benefit of Bartram's shipments for which he would search over an ever widening range. Some would pay in money, some in an exchange of plants, and some, such as the world-renowned men of science, Gronovius and Linnaeus, would return only their thanks and information on the proper classification of specimens sent them.

For Peter Collinson, burning with green fever yet immersed in the web of commerce, the association with the colonial Quaker was not only a way to satisfy his hunger for exotic plants and various curiosities of the natural world but was also a sort of magic carpet to adventure. Through John's eyes and through John's letters he could explore a vast stretch of the eastern United States in all its virgin glory and share with delicious thrills of eagerness and excitement in all the dangers and wonders of his journeys. And more and more, as the business partnership deepened into intimate friendship, Peter became, in spirit, an affectionate and concerned member of the Bartram family and a warm and helpful friend to John's children.

The correspondence was only a few years old when Collinson addressed a letter to "Respected Friend J. Bartram," telling him he had made a shipment of goods pursuant to his request but "as there was no direction either to quality or quantity" he had used his best judgment which he hoped would meet with approbation. Apparently Peter had already begun his avuncular role, for he said, "whatever thou finds is not charged in thy bill of parcels, is presents for thyself, wife, and children. Receive it in love, as it was sent." Aware of John's disappointment in his London friend as a provider of old-country seeds for the Schuylkill garden, Peter added:

I have procured from my knowing friend, Philip Miller, gardener to the Physic garden at Chelsea . . . sixty nine sorts of curious seeds, and some others of my own collecting. This, I hope, will convince thee I do what I can; and if I lived as thou does, always in the country, I should do more; but in my situation it is impossible. Besides, most of the plants thou writes for are not to be found in gardens, but growing spontaneously a many miles off; and a many miles from one another. It is not to be expected I can do as thou does. My inclination is good, but I have affairs of greater consequence to mind. . . .

The cautious merchant quickly followed this letter with another admonishing Bartram to give "nobody a hint how thee or thy wife came by the suit of clothes. There may be some," he said, who "may think they deserve something of that nature."

There is hardly a letter without requests. For his noble friend, Lord Petrie, whose interests now embrace the whole spectrum of natural history, Collinson asks: "any curious insects, beetles, butterflies, etc. . . . Display the butterflies with pins and rub off the down as little as possible. When thee goes abroad, put a little box in thy pocket, and, as thee meets with them, put them in. . . . I want a Terrapin or two. Put them in a box with earth, and they will come safe. They will live a long while without food."

Importunate demands for plants of all kinds are varied with pleas not only for insects and tortoises but for a bewildering variety of specimens, animate and inanimate:

Dear Friend—As thee has given me many instances of thy curious speculative disposition, it has put me on enlarging thy knowledge in nautral enquiries, as the earth is filled with wonders, and everywhere is to be seen the marks and effects of Almighty power. Most things were made for the use and pleasure of mankind; others to raise our admiration and astonishment; as, in particular, what are called fossils—being stones, found all the world over, that have either the impressions, or else the regular form of shells, leaves, fishes, fungi, teeth, sea-eggs, and many other productions. . . . What use the learned make of them is that they are evidences of the Deluge. . . . Pray don't forget, as soon as possible the specimens of Red and White Cedar, and a few white cedar berries.

As Peter became familiar, through the letters, with John's large family, he was eager to enlist the children as helpers: "Friend John," he wrote, "this is only a hint, by the way: Lord Petrie is a great admirer of your foreign water-fowl. If at any time an opportunity offers send him some. Thou will lose nothing by it. But he desired me to tell thee, that he desires thy children will bring him up some Red Birds—cocks and hens—for he has an intention to naturalize them to our climate and I doubt not of success."

Although the multitude of requests, almost stumbling over each other, continued to be largely botanical, they were more and more interspersed with a variety of others. The fable of the rattlesnake's ability to charm its victims was being debated, and "the hearsay of others can't be depended on" so it was hoped that Bartram would make "a nice and exact observation to determine the matter." Land snails and fresh-water shellfish were desired, also butterflies, moths, and "locusts" and mistletoe seeds. And those "fine Lady's Slippers, don't let escape, for they are," Collinson said, his favorite of all plants, and, although he had the yellow one, he much wanted the other sorts. On and on he went, hinting, requesting, desiring, demanding in a never-ending stream, now and then pausing to confess, no doubt with a chuckle at his own weakness, that his "inclination and fondness to natural productions of all kinds is agreeable to the old proverb: *Like the parson's barn—refuses nothing.*"

But Peter was not more eager with demand than John with supply, and the industrious American, happy to be subsidized and appreciated in the field of his own chosen interest, was not only satisfying the "wants" from across the sea but often anticipating them with unusual shipments. "I can't enough admire thy industry and curiosity," wrote Peter, "in descending to so many minute rarities that came in the box by [Captain] Savage; which are things very acceptable, but what commonly escape the observation of most, but such a prying eye as thine . . . It is true, in doing this thou hast very much obliged me; but I suspect thee has entailed on thyself more trouble." And a little later, in the winter of 1737, Peter was showing a proper concern for John's efforts:

It is with pleasure, when we read thy excursions (and wish to bear thee company) but then it is with concern that we reflect on the fatigue thee undergoes, the great risks of thy health in the heats and colds; but above all, the danger of rattlesnakes. This would so curb my ardent desires to see vegetable curiosities, that I should be afraid to venture in your woods, unless on horseback, and so good a guide as thee art by my side.

Naturally, from the beginning, Collinson, as the elder and the better educated, had assumed the role of mentor to the relatively unlettered and certainly provincial colonial. John was an apt learner of great native intelligence and as the years went on he acquired, through correspondence, experience, and study, marked ability and wide recognition as a naturalist. Nevertheless Peter remained his benevolent preceptor, handing down worldly-wise advice to the naïve, as on the occasion of John's expedition into Virginia in 1737, supplied by Peter with letters of introduction to the merchant's Virginia correspondents, he cautioned and instructed John:

As thee designs for Virginia, in the fall, I have sent thee circular letters to all my friends . . . , I have sent my letters open, that thou may make memorandums from some particular contents therein mentioned, and then seal them up. . . .

. . . in Virginia there is Colonel Custis, and Colonel Byrd, are both curious men. Pray take down what I have marked for thee to inquire after, the Umbrella Tree at the first, and the Ginseng at the last.

. . . Then, when thee proceeds home, I know no person will make thee more welcome than Isham Randolph. He lives thirty or forty miles above the falls of James River in Goochland,—and above the other settlements. Now, I take his house to be a very suitable place to make a settlement at,— for to take several days excursions all round, and to return to his house at night. . . . One thing I must desire of thee, and do insist that thee oblige me therein; that thou make up drugget clothes, to go to Virginia in, and not appear to disgrace thyself or me; for though I should not esteem thee the less, come to me in what dress thou will,—yet the Virginians are a very gentle, well-dressed people—and look, perhaps, more at a man's outside than his inside. For these and other reasons, pray go very clean, neat, and hand-somely dressed, to Virginia. Never mind thy clothes: I will send more an-other year.

A few months later the same paternal concern showed itself when Collinson suggested a visit to William Penn's successor:

I can now only tell thee that I have sent a parcel of seeds, in a parcel to your proprietor, Thomas Penn.

Dress thyself neatly in thy best habits, and wait on him for them; for I have in a particular manner recommended thee to him. I have desired him to show thee the Natural History of South Carolina, in eight books, finely coloured to the life; so forget not to ask that favor. First enquire his most leisure time, and then wait on him. . . .

Pray remember, without fail, if thou'll oblige me, to send the Papaw fruit, full ripe, sent in a bottle or little jar of rum, and two or three speci-mens of it in flower, with a description of the colour of the flower; for I want to have it engraved and painted.

The reference to the Natural History of South Carolina is, of course, to the already published sections of Mark Catesby's great work, and the pawpaw fruit and flowers were desired for use in a plate in the series upon which Catesby was then at work.

Despite the ill-concealed tone of superiority in his letters to his Amer-ican friend, equally obvious is his growing respect for Bartram's opin-ions, best illustrated by his readiness to read his letters to the learned company of the Royal Society. One such letter reveals Bartram's an-ticipation of the principles of the unborn science of ecology, the interdependence of life, animal and vegetable. Peter writes in comment:

I have heard frequent accounts of the prodigious flocks of pigeons; by thy remarks on the wonderful provision made by our all-wise Creator, for the support of the creation, are well worth notice. The balance, kept be-tween the vegetable and animal productions, is really a fine thought, and what I never met with before. But it is more remarkable with you than with us; for you have wild animals and mast, in greater plenty than we have.

But the colonial Quaker not only brought to Collinson and his friends information and stimulus for scientific thinking, and an endless variety of natural specimens, but he gave them a chance to share, at a safe distance, in all the exciting and perilous adventures of wilderness living. "Is there any account of the panthers?" asks Peter, early in the correspondence. "Do they attack men or cattle?" And the rattlesnake is an ever recurrent subject of fascination and speculation: "I can't help but being of thy mind," confesses Peter, "with regard to the rattlesnake; for if creatures were bit by him first, I can't imagine they could be able to run away. . . . I wish it may be thy lot, without harm, to meet with this creature, to observe his motions; but I am confirmed of his power over men, in the manner thou mentions, by a very curious friend of mine, and a great philosopher, Colonel Byrd of Virginia,— who says, you must not think me fanciful, when I assure, I have ogled a Rattlesnake so long, till I have perceived a sickness at my stomach."

Peter continued to read John's "curious" letters to the gentlemen of the Royal Society, who were pleased to send thanks and encouragement through Collinson, who added, "Pray make no apology. Thy style is much beyond what one might expect from a man of thy education. The facts are well described and very intelligible." Naturally, however, over so long a span of years, the relationship was not always so mutually gratifying. There were times when feathers were decidedly ruffled. Sometimes Peter showed an irritated impatience at some of his friend's requests, as for a magic lantern, which, Peter said, "is a contrivance to make sport with ignorant people," or for a magnifier for flowers: "Pray make this complaint to J. Logan [a fellow Philadelphian] and try his thoughts."

Sometimes, too, each felt himself unappreciated. Peter complained on one occasion: "What I hinted, as to thy cargo coming when I am so engaged, is not to have the season altered; but to show thee, that, as thee strains a point to serve me, so I strain a point to serve thee . . . what I do, I would do for none but thee: and, yet, by the sequel of thy letter, thee thinks thyself not amply rewarded. . . . Pray let me hear no more of it. If thee canst not afford to go on with this business, tell us so, and it will be at an end." Peter was indignant, too, that Friend John disparaged his gift of lilacs: "I wonder thou should be sorry to see such a bundle of white and blue lilacs. That wonder might have soon ceased, by throwing them away if you had them already. But, as your neighbors of Virginia, in particular Colonel Custis at Williamsburgh, who has undoubtedly the best collection in that country, desired some, I thought you might want them, for I was never over to see . . ."

"I was never over to see . . ." But America came to him, month after month, year after year, in boxes, and bundles, and bottles, and crates, aboard the sailing ships, and subject to vicissitudes of wind and wave and the good will or indifference of captain and crew. With what eagerness Friend Peter would hasten from his counting house at word of the landing of some long-awaited vessel, sometimes to face catastrophe:

I dreaded to go aboard to see the disaster, and so much labour and pains thrown away by such a swarm of pestilent beetles. As we say by a fine old woman, "There's the ruin of a fine face," so I may say, "There's the ruin of fine flies," and such as I never saw before. Pray next time divide the precious from the vile; I will send thee boxes enough. Keep the butterflies, or dayflies, by themselves, the moths by themselves, and these devouring beetles by themselves, . . . As thee intends to repair that loss, which is very obliging, I only give this hint, that I prefer butterflies and moths before beetles. . . .

But this disappointment gave way to delight a few months later, as Peter hastened to write:

I shall now tell thee something which very much pleased me and will surprise thee. The box of turtle eggs (which was an ingenious thought of thine to send) on the day I brought it from on board ship, being the 20th of October, I took off the lid, having a mind to see the eggs, and on peeping about I saw a little head, and while I was looking I saw the ground move in a place or two more. In short, in the space of three or four hours, eight tortoises were hatched. It was well worth observing, how artfully they disengaged themselves from the shell, and then, with their fore-feet scratched their eyes open. They have many visiters, such a thing never happening, I dare say, in England before. . . .

Nor can it ever happen quite that way again. For these tiny turtles pushing through their shells to breathe the English air, or the myriad young plants burgeoning from American seeds sent by John, were not any younger and fresher than the science of natural history was in this fourth decade of the eighteenth century, when any man might pioneer in the natural world, had he only a seeing eye and a curious mind. John Bartram, carefully and lovingly gathering and packing his specimens, animal or vegetable, in his snug Pennsylvania farmhouse, and Peter Collinson, and his learned and noble friends, were, alike, learners and disciples of the same new science.

⁓ 2

As John Bartram approached twoscore years, he was definitely regarded more correctly as a naturalist than as a farmer. Almost every autumn called for collecting expeditions, farther and farther afield. The fall of 1738 found him on a long collecting journey southward into Virginia and westward beyond the Blue Ridge into the Shenandoah Valley. This eleven-hundred-mile trip was a daring undertaking for a lone man on horseback. Such a journey, much of it in a wilderness where roads were few and settlements far apart, called for ardor of purpose and intrepidity. His route was over to Chesapeake Bay and down its western shore in Maryland. There Collinson's friends, although, according to him, not "Curious in our branch of knowledge" and therefore "not worth thy while to go out of thy way to see," entertained him kindly, despite their lack of that common bond of interest. He crossed the Potomac and traveled down the neck between the York and the Rappahannock where, armed with Collinson's letter of introduction, he called at the plantation of botanist John Clayton, who, to his great disappointment, was away, so that they could not, in Collinson's phrase, "open their budgets and compare notes."

He went on to the Williamsburg home of Colonel Custis, to whom he carried a revealing letter of introduction from Peter Collinson:

> Don't be surprised if a down right plain Country Man—perhaps he may be a Quaker too Into the Bargain & you know they are said to be a odd sort of a People but this makes mee call to mind an old proverbe the Devil is not so Black as painted. Now if such a Medley Composition should come alltogether, Don't be startled. That you may not Mistake the Man He will bring a Credential from Mee, I so much persuaded my self of such an interest in your Friendship you'l not Look att the Man but his Mind for my sake. His conversation I dare say you'l find compensate for his appearance—He is well Versed in Nature and Can give a good Account of Her Works. He Comes to Visit your parts in serch of Curiosities. In the vegetible kingdom perhaps you'l find him more knowing in that Science than any you Have Mett With.

He is Imployed by a Sett of Noble Men (by my Recommendation) to Collect seeds & specimens of Rare plants, and he has been very successful in this affair, which proceeds from His thorough knowledge in these Matters. Be so kind to give him a Little Entertainm't & Recommend Him to a Friend or Two of yours in the Country, for He does not Value rideing 50 or 100 Miles to see a New plant. Pray Direct Him to the Umbrella Tree, this plant or Tree will make him think his Journey worth Comeing. . . . His name is John Bartram.

John Custis made the traveler welcome, and Bartram, fascinated by the colonel's garden, spent there a full day of rest from journeying, the only one of his entire trip. From Williamsburg he traveled up the north bank of the James River to enjoy William Byrd's hospitality at Westover. There the two discussed plant sexuality, a subject just then of exciting interest, not only because of the significant part played by floral sexual organs, stamens and pistils, in the new plant classification system of Linnaeus, but also because of the intriguing possibilities of hybridization through crossbreeding. At home, in his garden, Bartram already had under way ingenious experiments in this area of botany. The following spring, in a letter to Byrd, he reported that he had made "several successful experiments of joining several species of the same genus" and had obtained "curious mixed colours in flowers never known before." He hoped "these practical observations to open the gate to a very large field of experimental knowledge."

Leaving Westover, he continued on upriver to the mountains, stopping en route at Dungeness, Isham Randolph's place on the James in the red hill country of Piedmont Virginia, then across the mountains into what was to become Bartram's favorite of all botanizing areas: "that spacious vale of six hundred miles in length . . . in which I have gathered the finest of my autumnal flowers" where "it is like as if Flora sported in solitary retirement." His homeward route was northward down the Shenandoah River to its confluence with the Potomac, wild Indian frontier country where troubles with the natives were common. Years later, recalling his travels in that region, he told of "walking in a path with an Indian guide, hired for two dollars, an Indian man met me and pulled off my hat in a great passion, and chawed it all round . . . I suppose to show me that they would eat me if I came in that country again." Nevertheless, he made it safely across Maryland and southern Pennsylvania to his stone house overlooking the river, "thankful to Divine Providence, whose powerful regard is to all his creation."

This long and successful journey was only the first of many ambitious and daring expeditions as John grew in confidence and experience as explorer and scientist, while the horizons of his life steadily expanded. Life in the stone farmhouse beside the river was a lively and busy affair, full of affection and warmth, presided over by Anne, of whom John said "all her riches consisted in her good temper and great knowledge of housewifery." By 1748 nine children had been born to John and Anne, among them a boy, William, of special significance in the realms of natural history and of letters, for he too was destined to be smitten with green rapture, but, unlike his father, he would find the artistry to express his rapture with pen and brush.

There was plenty of room for the large family of children to overflow into the out of doors, where the garden on the Schuylkill was steadily growing in size, variety, and fame. It was rapidly becoming a veritable mecca for the "curious." With this appropriate setting, John Bartram was gradually taking center stage in the colonial natural history coterie which, from its beginning, had had its nucleus in Philadelphia but now had come to embrace satellite groups from Connecticut to Charleston. Visits to his garden by eminent naturalists were matched by his own visits in the homes of fellow naturalists such as Jared Eliot of Connecticut, Cadwallader Colden on the Hudson, Dr. John Mitchell and others of the Virginia group, and Dr. Alexander Garden of Charleston. These friendships, plus his increasing fame abroad and his continuous collecting activities, doubled and redoubled his correspondence—at the price of long evening hours by candlelight.

Time had to be found, too, for studying the cherished volumes of his steadily growing library of scientific works, many of them sent by their authors as gifts to John in return for specimens. Thus he acquired Mark Catesby's *Natural History of Carolina,* an especially prized gift, which, more than a half-century later, would be one of the critical inspirations leading Alexander Wilson to venture on his own great work on American ornithology. In the same way, copies of Linnaeus' *Characteres Plantarum* and of the *Flora Virginica* of his friend John Clayton and his Dutch correspondent, Gronovius, were added to his bookshelf. Lord Petrie sent him Miller's *Gardener's Dictionary* and the works of the French botanist, Tournefort, and others of his patrons sent gifts of books from time to time. The faithful Peter, reluctant in the first years of their relationship to send to his farmer friend as many volumes as John's avid mind hungered for, had long since capitulated, and it is an indication of the subtle but very real evolution of John's status from simple collector to respected naturalist that Peter soon became as eager to send any significant works across the sea, for John's attention and comment, as his colonial friend was to receive them.

Just to contemplate the wholeness and abundance of John Bartram's day-to-day existence during these middle years is to feel nourished and warmed by its richness, the robust circle of vital life of which he was the center. All that he loved and enjoyed, however—family, garden, farm, library, friends far and near—could not keep him rooted in home soil for long, could not still the restless urge toward a far horizon. For, though he was the most domesticated and the most firmly anchored in family life of any of our group of naturalists, he too had been touched with wilderness fever, whose intermittent pangs could only be assuaged by long weeks on wilderness trails.

Beginning with the long trip to Virginia, the frequency and range of his travels grew. Among the more extensive were another voyage to both the tidewater and the mountains of Virginia, one to the Mohawk River region of New York, and several to the Catskills, where, according to Bartram, "There is the greatest variety of uncommon trees and shrubs that I ever saw in such a compass of ground." But his most notable wilderness expedition of that period was the one he took to Lake Ontario in the summer of 1743. Bartram, who had long wished to collect specimens in this northern area, had an opportunity to accompany an expedition, commissioned by the Virginia authorities, to formulate plans for peace negotiations with the Iroquois chieftains, and led by Conrad Weiser, experienced frontier diplomat, versed in the Iroquois language. Their projected route lay generally up the Schuylkill to its headwaters, thence up to the Susquehanna and then down the Oswego to Lake Ontario.

It was a hot summer day when Bartram and some of the company set out on horseback for Weiser's cabin on the farther side of the Blue Mountains. En route their trail ascended Flying Hills, which, he said, was "so called from the great number of wild turkeys that used to fly from them to the plains." (From now on, with increasing frequency, Bartram takes note of the diminishing wildlife and timber resources of the colonies.) A week later the group, which now included Weiser and their cartographer, was deep in unmapped Indian country. The names this map maker gave to the nameless terrain they crossed is a commentary on the hardships and anxieties of the journey. Beyond the Blue Mountains, their way lay across St. Andrews Wilderness, over the Impenetrable Mountains, only to face others, the Endless Mountains, and then across the Dismal Vale.

Bartram told of having to pass through "a great white pine and spruce swamp full of roots and an abundance of old trees lying on the ground, or leaning against live ones. They stood so thick that we concluded it almost impossible to shoot a man at 100 yards distance, let him stand never so fair." There were accounts of drunken Indians, their flea-ridden huts and half-starved dogs. But there were compensations; streams in which to swim in water "so clear one might have seen a pin on the bottom," "licking ponds," which attracted deer and elk from many miles around, a hillside "where grew an abundance of goose-berries" and "the trees were crowded with wild pigeons." Another hill-side offered "an abundance of ginseng," a particularly exciting discovery in view of the fact that at that time Friend Collinson was trying to arrange for export of the roots to China where a closely related species had become greatly valued. However, his most gratifying discovery was a giant magnolia which he believed to be a new variety. Later it developed that this was the mountain magnolia known today as the cucumber tree, specimens of which had been sent earlier to Collinson from Virginia.

The expedition was successful in its diplomatic mission, for satisfactory arrangements were made for a formal conference between Iroquois chieftains and Virginia officials, at which an acceptable peace treaty was signed. The experience, however, seems only to have deepened John Bartram's antipathy to the red man against whom he was already prejudiced, not only because of his father's massacre by Indians, but because the ominous and ever-present possibility of Indian violence threatened to limit or even prohibit his explorations. Their uncouth life, as he saw them in their villages, added dislike to suspicion in his mind.

Such lack of charity toward the Indians seems a strange paradox in John's character if one accepts the popular description of him as a simple and pious Quaker farmer. In truth, however, Bartram, as he gradually reveals himself in these middle years of his life, was a complex and many-faceted personality, deeply thoughtful, devoutly religious but iconoclastic, competent and practical yet avid for learning, and, withal, intensely independent in nature, faithful to his own sturdy morality. Days and weeks of travel alone on his longer expeditions, lonely nights with only his horse, his campfire, and the sounds, often menacing, of dark forests beyond the fire's glimmering light, were, of necessity, for a man of his questioning mind, times of introspection and speculation.

Here and there in his letters to his friend, Peter, one has glimpses of such thoughts. When Collison sent him a copy of Barclay's *Apology*, he makes no effort to conceal his distaste for such aspects of religion:

[The] *Apology* I shall take care of for thy sake. It answers thy advice, much better than if thee had sent me one of Natural History, or Botany, which I might have spent ten times the hours in reading of, while I might have laboured for the maintenance of my family. Indeed, I have little respect to *apologies* and disputes about the ceremonial parts of religion, which often introduces animosities, confusion, and disorders of the mind—and sometimes body too; but, Dear Peter, let us worship the one Almighty Power, in sincerety of heart, with resignation to His divine will,—doing to others as we would have them do to us, if we were in their circumstances. Living in love and innocency, we may die in hope.

He was equally impatient with everything smacking of "astrology, magic and mystic divinity," with which, he told Peter, he was "apt to be troublesome, by enquiring into the foundation and reasonableness of these notions. . . ."

But the reasoned conviction which brought him into conflict with his fellow Quakers of the Darby Meeting was his belief in one "Almighty Power" with a consequent denial of the Trinity and a rejection of the divinity of Jesus. The brethren, increasingly dismayed by his steadfast harboring of such a "disorderly belief," formally expelled him from the meeting. To their consternation the unshaken naturalist paid not one whit of attention to their edict, continuing regularly, Sunday after Sunday, to occupy his accustomed place in the meeting house. To proclaim his faith in the integrity of the individual conscience, and his declaration of independence from restrictive religious tradition, he chiseled in stone above his greenhouse door this couplet of Alexander Pope's:

> Slave to no sect, who takes no private road,
> But looks through Nature up to Nature's God.

As a lasting testament of his faith, he carved into a stone panel, on the outside wall of his study window, for all to see, the words:

It is God alone, Almighty Lord,
The Holy One by Me Ador'd
John Bartram, 1770

In one of his letters to Collinson he describes his own kind of pantheism: "My head runs all upon the works of God in Nature. It is through that telescope I see God in his glory."

During all the busy years of his maturity, this healthy spiritual vitality and integrity was matched and balanced by steady intellectual growth and practical achievements. The result could not fail to be a personality and character both impressive and magnetic, as is revealed in comments of many of his contemporaries. One of these was a young Swedish botanist, Peter Kalm, who arrived in Philadelphia in the late summer of 1748, armed with letters of introduction from Peter Collinson.

Three days after his ship cast anchor in the Delaware, Kalm journeyed down to Kingsessing to see John Bartram and his famous garden. In his *Travels*, a report of his American visit, published after his return to Europe, Kalm describes John:

He has acquired a great knowledge of natural philosophy and history, and seems to be born with a peculiar genius for those sciences. In his youth he had no opportunity of going to school, but by his own diligence and indefatigable application he got, without instruction, so far in Latin as to understand all books in that language and even those which were filled with botanical terms. He has in several successive years made frequent excursions into different distant parts of North America with an intention of gathering all sorts of plants he has planted in his own botanical garden. . . . We owe to him the knowledge of many rare plants which he first found and were never known before. He has shown great judgment and an attention which lets nothing escape unnoticed. Yet with all these qualities he is to be blamed for his negligence, for he did not care to write down his numerous and useful observations. . . . I have often been at a loss to think of the sources whence he obtained many things which came to his knowledge.

Peter Kalm was a former pupil of the famous Dr. Linnaeus of the University of Upsala and one of that teacher's favorite pupils, a position the master proclaimed by giving the young botanist's name to one of America's most beautiful groups, the mountain laurels, which thenceforth became officially known as *Kalmias*. Kalm was one of a large and international group of students who, having studied under the magnetic Dr. Linnaeus, were so inspired by him that they went forth from the classroom, like the Knights of King Arthur's Round Table in quest of the Holy Grail, scattering to the four corners of the earth in search of nature's sacred treasures. Many of these dedicated and eager students were swallowed by the jungles of Africa and South America and never heard from again; others died of fevers in Asia and the Indies. Peter Kalm, more fortunate in the corner of the world in which he chose to botanize, survived to return home and live a long and fruitful life.

Mention of Peter Kalm, *Kalmia*, and Carl Linnaeus, together with several previous references to the latter, suggests a brief look at the origins of the plant nomenclature John Bartram had mastered in these busy middle years. Today we call it the Linnaean system and not very accurately credit Carl Linnaeus with inventing it. Although the binomial nomenclature, by which, in simple terms, a plant is known by a combination of two names, a generic or family name first, followed by a specific or trivial name second, had long been proposed and used to a limited extent, it was Linnaeus who made this practice universal. The Latinizing of the scientific names offered obvious advantages, as the classical terminology served as a sort of Esperanto for naturalists, whereby an oxeye daisy, for instance, though it may have as many common names as there are languages in its wide range, will be readily identified in Chicago, Moscow, or Shanghai as *Chrysanthemum leucanthemum*. Furthermore, such a naming system tended to correct the false impression created by misleading common names and false labels such as that of the dogtooth violet, which is not a violet but a lily, the atamasco lily, which is not a lily but an amaryllis, and the Spanish moss, which has no kinship to moss but is closely related to the pineapple.

The importance of some stable form of nomenclature might have been particularly appreciated by Linnaeus, for the Swedes, along with other Scandinavians, had lagged behind most European countries in the adoption of a system of permanent family names for themselves. Carl Linnaeus' father was Nils Ingemarsson. The latter was not a family name but simply a statement that Nils was the son of Ingemars. Thus there was the confusing situation of a different surname for each generation. It was in the lifetime of Nils that the Swedes recognized the value of permanent surnames and families selected names to suit themselves. With prophetic appropriateness, Nils, a passionate lover of flowers and trees, selected the name of a native tree, the linden (Linn in Swedish), as his family surname. In later years his famous son, Carl,

Latinized his name as he was wont to do that of any plant or bird and bcame Carolus Linnaeus.

The life story of Linnaeus, his childhood in eighteenth-century rural Sweden, his adventurous youth as plant explorer, his distinguished career as leader and mentor for naturalists all over the Western world, is one of the great sagas of natural history, complete with youthful struggles and despair, romantic love, and final triumph of virtue and industry. All the elements of his life story combine in a relationship as harmonious and satisfying and as seemingly guided by destiny as the relationship of flower and seed and root and nourishing soil in the plant world. Without entering into the controversial question of the interrelationship of history and its leaders, one may safely say of Linnaeus that he was the right man in the right place at the right time. Born in rural Sweden in 1707, he came to the study of botany through that of medicine, the only practical approach in the early eighteenth century, but before he died in 1778 he saw his University of Upsala become a mecca for aspiring botanists and himself almost a dictator in the new science of modern botany.

Species and genera are the foundation levels of the classification pyramid. The classification system, which modern taxonomists use, still rests on that foundation. But since Linnaeus' day they have been extensively rearranged to reflect relationships agreeable to the laws of evolution, so that today's classification system represents in outline the biological family tree of life all the way back to the single primitive cell from whence it sprang. As species are grouped into genera, genera are arranged into families, which in turn are arranged into orders from which classes are built, and classes are subdivisions of phyla, and the phyla are subdivisions of the kingdoms, animal and vegetable.

Linnaeus made substantial contributions to this system of classification, but he did not invent it. His most notable contribution was his demonstration of the utility of the forms and numbers of the sexual parts of flowers, the stamens and pistils, in classification. It was, however, his industry and contagious enthusiasm, more than anything else, that enabled him to induce the scientific world to adopt the binomial system which Magnol, Tournefort, and others had in turn futilely proposed. And it was those same qualities which helped him to become the great coiner of scientific names of all time. If Peter Collinson was the clearing house for the eighteenth-century international natural history circle, Linnaeus was director of its mint.

Even in this brief brush with the Linnaean system it is essential to mention how species have gotten their names. Usually the first name, the name of the genus, honors a person, most often a botanist. Thus we have "family" or generic names such as *Kalmia, Bartramia, Catesbaea, Mitchella* (the partridgeberry, for John Mitchell), *Claytonia* (the spring beauty, for John Clayton), *Gardenia* (for Alexander Garden), and *Magnolia* (for the French botanist, Pierre Magnol). The name of any particular species is that of the genus followed by a modifying term which especially distinguishes that individual species from its generic brothers. For example, the famous southern magnolia is most noted for its great flowers so we have *Magnolia grandiflora*. Likewise, *Magnolia virginiana* describes the sweet bay by its locality, and *Magnolia macrophylla* proclaims in Latin the big leaves of the big-leaf magnolia.

For John Bartram the waves of new names emanating from Upsala in mid-century brought in turn pleasure and distress. For John Bartram, naturalist, whom Linnaeus himself recognized as "the best natural botanist in the world," the scientific systematics upon which all those new and altered names were based represented a beautiful and logical structure, appealing enough to justify all the trouble and brain-weariness involved in mastering them. But for John Bartram, gardener, it was distressing and difficult to give new and fashionable Linnaean names to old green friends whom he had long thought of in other terms. The new system, however, represented progress, and John Bartram was never one to tolerate, much less to harbor, a fettered mind.

For the gardens and drawing rooms of botany's devotees from Colden's home at Newburgh, New York, to Dr. Alexander Garden's town house in Charleston, the new system provided an exciting new subject of discussion, debate, and mutual instruction. When Bartram's excursions took him to the Catskills or up the Hudson in search of trees, Dr. Colden's door was always open to him. And he was certain of finding kindred spirits under the doctor's roof. The doctor himself was one of the most learned of the colonial naturalists and one who early embraced the Linnaean system, while his daughter, Jane, was not only a talented botanical artist but a scientific botanist as well. She was reputed to have been the first American woman to master the new cla ification.

On one occasion in 1755 when Bartram called at Colden s, it happened that Dr. Alexander Garden was also a guest there. Thus began a rich friendship, correspondence and visits to each other which continued until the outbreak of the American Revolution, when Garden, a staunch Loyalist, returned to England, leaving behind his son and name-sake to become a leader in the Rebel cause. Dr. Garden, already an ardent admirer of Linnaeus, became, as a consequence of this visit to Newburgh, a correspondent and Carolina collector for the professor at Upsala. "Here by good fortune," he wrote to the Swedish luminary, "I first met with John Bartram, returning from the Blue Mountains. . . . How happy I should be to pass my life with men so distinguished by genius, acuteness, and liberality, as well as by eminent botanical learning and experience! . . . Whilst I was passing my time most delightfully with these gentlemen, they were both so obliging as to show me your letters to them; which has induced me, sir, to take the liberty of writing to you in order to begin a correspondence, for which I have long wished. . . ." So the club grew; the circle widened; so sincere and intense was their ardor for the world of nature, so generous and fruitful were their friendships with each other, that even today the fragrance of their green fraternity lingers on, refreshingly, in our harried twentieth century.

For two years Bartram's fourth son, Billy, had been accompanying his father on those trips into the Catskills. In a letter to Collinson, in the summer of 1753, John had written of plans "to journey to Dr. Colden's, and the mountains. I plan to set out with my little botanist, the first of September, which is ten days sooner than usual, hoping to gather the Balm of Gilead [balsam poplar] and *Larix* [larch]." Now fifteen years old and already evoking his father's pride for his skill in drawing, Billy was taken on longer trips, one far into New England, where they visited Rev. Jared Eliot at his Connecticut home. As Eliot was more agriculturist than botanist, the letters between them were chiefly concerned with such horticultural subjects as ditching, manuring with marsh humus, and the alarming rate of destruction of the forests, which for Bartram, even then, presaged "our approaching distress on account of our want of timber for fencing." But the Connecticut minister was botanist enough to be sent by Bartram, courtesy of "our friend Franklin," indigo seed, packed in a section of hollow cane, and a collection of Billy's botanical drawings.

The reference to Franklin is, of course, to Benjamin Franklin. From 1743, when he was instrumental in the founding of the American Philosophical Society, with John Bartram and Cadwallader Colden as fellow founders, Dr. Franklin was, for thirty years, an integral part of the international natural history circle. Through his position of postmaster general for the colonies he was often able to be of material assistance in the form of free postage—in those times a substantial consideration. Between Benjamin Franklin and John Bartram there was an especially close bond. For surcease from care and for congenial company, Bartram's garden was a favorite haunt of the worldly philosopher. One of the first of his newly invented stoves, a gift from its inventor, still stands in the Bartram home. As the young William Bartram approached manhood, Franklin, as an intimate friend of the family, joined with Peter Collinson in counseling with John on the matter of a career for this talented son.

Meanwhile, the newly established friendship with the versatile Dr. Garden was proving particularly timely for Bartram who interests were constantly ranging beyond the special concerns of his various friends and correspondents. Collinson, absorbed in botany and collecting, gave little encouragement to John's theory, basically sound, that limestone was hardened sea mud and that marble was but another form of limestone. Gronovius had shown little interest in Bartram's belief that submerged mountains might be found beneath the sea and that by soundings to locate them new fishing grounds might be found. Bartram's conviction that vast areas of the American east coast had once been the bottom of the sea flew in the teeth of the popular belief in a literal interpretation of the Deluge. It was to Dr. Garden, soon after they met, that he penned one of his most prescient ideas, presaging our modern geological surveys: "that the whole country be mapped and earth borings systematically made to discover the resources which might otherwise lie forever concealed beneath the surface."

The friendship with Dr. Garden had also a timely practical value. The French and Indian War, by making the border country to the west too hazardous for botanizing expeditions, was forcing Bartram, in spite of his longing to explore the Ohio and the Mississippi country, to satisfy himself with travels in the more settled parts of the Northern colonies. Now Dr. Garden's hospitality and encouragement offered an alluring alternative. Although the way was long and the hazards great, John Bartram, albeit more than sixty years old, could not resist the green and romantic lure of country long familiar to him through Catesby's paintings, and in 1760 he set out alone for South Carolina, on the first of several voyages to this area.

The journals describing these first travels to Carolina, sent to Peter Collinson, have been lost, as well as the journal of the expedition westward as far as the present Pittsburgh, which he undertook in 1761. One would like especially to be able to read the day-by-day account of the two thousand miles of wilderness trail which John Bartram traversed, alone on horseback, in the fall of 1762. After visiting his son Billy, who was then with his uncle in the Cape Fear region, John traveled down into South Carolina, and, after a side trip down the Sand Hills to Georgia, he rode up the Wateree-Catawba River to the mountains, crossed them to the Holston River and the land of the Cherokees, in what is now eastern Tennessee, then, turning northward, followed New River to the Shenandoah Valley and his old familiar route homeward from the "Vale."

It seems an incredible journey for a lone, sixty-three-year-old horseman, but John's letter to his son at Cape Fear, reporting on his safe arrival home, was exuberant. "I had the most prosperous journey that ever I was favoured with," he wrote. "Everything succeeded beyond my expectation; and my guardian angel seemed to direct my steps, to discover the greatest curiosities."

And to Peter Collinson he must have written a similar report, for Peter replied: "I am greatly rejoiced to read . . . of thy safe return from thy delightful journey from the terrestrial Paradise, for such it must be, that could raise such ecstasies of joy at viewing those charming scenes, enriched with such elegant productions. I long to see a sketch of thy Journal."

⟨⟩ 3

As the years of his sixties mounted and he began to feel the physical limitations of age, the stubborn perversity of John Bartram's spirit asserted itself in an even more intense fascination with far horizons. For years he had dreamed of an expedition down the Ohio and Mississippi, but, when the war and the "barbarous Indians" prevented this and his attention was shunted southward to Carolina and Georgia, the unexplored regions behind these provinces began to beckon the naturalist with irresistible force. With every passing year his impatience grew apace to see the wonderful productions of nature in those distant parts before his traveling days were ended.

For a decade now, while his time was running short, imperial struggles emanating from Europe had kept John from exploring the lands of his dreams, though he cared not a whit who owned them as long as nature ruled there. He wrote Collinson of his longing "to search not only at Pensacola, but the coast of Florida, Alabama, Georgia, and the banks of the Mississippi," and it made "no difference to him who got it" under the treaty just then concluded, if only he could travel safely there. (Fortunately, England had gotten it, all of Florida which then ran along the Gulf coast all the way to Louisiana.) Could not Collinson find some wealthy sponsors to permit him to undertake such an expedition? With fervor, Bartram wrote to him in another letter: "There is no end of the wonders of nature. The more I see the more I covet to see; not to gratify a trifling curiosity, but to raise my mind in sublime contemplation on the unlimited power and wisdom of the Great Creator of all things."

Repeated appeals went off to his "good old friend" Collinson. Hadn't he wealthy and noble friends, who were also "men of curiosity," who could be prevailed upon to enable Bartram "to travel a year or two through our King's new acquisitions to make a thorough natural and vegetable search. . . ?" Though few men have made less concession to advancing age, John was not unaware of his sixty-five years. He wrote that he must have someone to accompany him, and that he must not be hurried in his work, and that he must have carriage to transport his discoveries: "I am too old to go alone, and I think my son William will be a fit person to accompany me, as he by this time, I believe, can draw well." So little time left, so much to see and learn—one senses the urgency in his letters, "I can't expect to be able to perform such a task many years hence. I must yield to the infirmities of age or death."

His pleas stirred his old but still vital friend, enthusiastic and resourceful as ever in spite of his seventy years. Enlisting the help of others of the Circle, including Benjamin Franklin, newly returned to London, Collinson, in seeking a sponsor for his American friend, reached for the top. He petitioned the crown to sponsor John Bartram's proposed explorations into its newly acquired southern provinces.

By April, 1765, a jubilant Peter was dispatching by a succession of ships letters proclaiming success at court. In the first he wrote: "I have the pleasure to inform my good friend that my repeated solicitations have not been in vain; for this day I received certain intelligence from our gracious King, that he had appointed thee his botanist, with a salary of fifty pounds a years; . . ." But in a follow-up letter by another ship, in case the first failed of delivery, he confessed that the King's interest in the matter was exhausted after the appointment was made. Peter added: "John, thou knows nothing what it is to solicit at court any favour; nay, though it is for their own interest, they are so taken up with public affairs, little things slip through their fingers. For all I can do, I cannot get thee letters of recommendation to any of the Governors. All I can at present do, is, our good friend Ellis, who is appointed to an office in the Floridas, has writ to the Governors in thy favour."

Peter need not have been so distressed by his failure to get royal recommendations for his friend. By now, in any colonial capital the botanist visited, doors were likely to be opened to plain, unpolished, honest John Bartram. And so it was in Charleston to which he set sail soon after receiving Peter's glorious intelligence. There he was entertained by Dr. Garden and Thomas Lamboll, both Collinson correspondents, and he writes of pleasant visits with Henry Laurens and William Moultrie, whose names are well known in American Revolutionary history.

In spite of Dr. Garden's friendship for John Bartram and his often expressed admiration for his ability as a naturalist, the Charleston doctor expressed dismay, in a letter to John Ellis of London, at the news of John's royal commission: "He tells me that he is appointed King's Botanist in America," he wrote. "Is it really so? Surely John is a worthy man, but yet to give the title of King's Botanist to a man who can scarcely spell, much less make out the characters of any one genus of plants, appears rather hyperbolical. Pray, how is this matter? . . ."

Before leaving Philadelphia, John wrote to his son, Billy, to offer him the opportunity to accompany him on the Florida venture, and, apparently sure of Billy's response, he set out, a few days after landing in Charleston, for his brother William's home on Cape Fear, near which Billy had a trading post. It is easy to imagine the joy with which Billy must have welcomed the change from the uncongenial role of merchant to that of naturalist and artist once more. While Billy was closing his languishing country store and making final arrangements for the journey, his uncle William was showing John what the neighborhood had to offer a naturalist: Lake Waccamaw, rich in botanical offerings, and wide areas of low pine barrens, abounding with tall trumpets and Venus's-flytraps. He had first seen these astonishing carnivorous plants five years before, on his first Carolina visit. At that time he had devised his own name for the Venus's-flytrap, calling it his "tipitiwitchet." He had carried live plants back to his garden and sent both Collinson and Linnaeus into botanical raptures with specimens of the remarkable steel-trap leaves.

Another day was spent inspecting the numerous petrified tree trunks protruding from the bank of the Cape Fear River, some of which Bartram was able to determine were living hundreds of thousands of years before. One of their most interesting excursions took them across the river to Singletary's Lake, in the midst of that multitude of north-west–southeast-oriented elliptical lakes, which are known today as Bladen Lakes. One of the lakes, probably Singletary's or Jones's or White Lake, featured a magnificent display of American lotus, *Nelumbo lutea*, a prized discovery since the seeds of this very close relative of the sacred lotus of Egypt and the Orient were avidly sought by the natural history circle abroad.

Those lakes of Bladen County, North Carolina, are the most striking examples of Carolina bays, geological formations which rank among the world's most intriguing geological mysteries. Tens of thousands, perhaps even hundreds of thousands, of them may be observed in the Carolinas and in eastern Georgia, mostly in the flat lands of the coastal plain, but sometimes spilling over into the sandhills beyond. Some appear as perfectly elliptical, shallow lakes, others as elliptical swamps filled with bay trees, hence the name by which they are commonly known. Still others have been all but filled by time and now appear in cultivated fields only as dark ovals. Some are small, no larger than an ordinary house; others are several miles in length. Often they are aligned as though marching in formation. Sometimes they intersect, one biting a clear segment from the other. The only significant variations from these specifications appear in southern South Carolina and Georgia where they tend to be more egg-shaped than oval and their orientation is more southerly than that of those elsewhere.

For forty years, ever since aviation and aerial photography revealed their fantastic numbers and amazing general uniformity, geologists have debated the origin of the Carolina bays. Of the several theories which have been postulated to explain their origin the only one which approaches a satisfactory explanation is the comet theory. According to this theory, in recent geological times, when the coastal plain was sodden and soft, a great swarm of molten meteors streaked in from the northwest, striking the ground at a low angle. The explosions resulting from the contact of the molten star matter, striking the water-sodden earth, consumed the bulk of the meteor material and deposited the displaced sand around the edges of the explosion area, especially around its southeast edge, forming that characteristic feature of bays.

Be that as it may, the Bartrams, as they traveled through the South-east in the months to follow, would be circling around or slogging through many a swamp and many a savanna without noting the similarities that mark them as Carolina bays, cut from the same cloth or scooped by the same meteor explosion as Singletary's and Jones's Lakes near brother William's Cape Fear home, where the great yellow lotus blossomed in 1765.

In early August the Bartrams, John, brother William, and Billy, set out downriver toward Brunswick, the colonial capital, now extinct, aiming to pay their respects to the royal governor before John and Billy began their journey to Florida on the King's mission. There had just been a change of governors; Arthur Dobbs, Bartram's friend and botanical correspondent, who is said to have sent the first Venus's-fly-traps to England, had been succeeded in the governor's house by William Tryon, who was destined to face long and bloody struggles with the Regulators in the Carolina backcountry just prior to the American Revolution. Governor Tryon received them "very kindly."

After parting with brother William, John and Billy took the shore trail to Charleston, via Little River and Long Bay. As usual, John put in his journal careful notations, briefly listed, of plants, soils, fossils, animals, and all other natural productions observed along the way, but few personal comments. It is easy to imagine, however, with what glad hearts and hopeful spirits father and son rode together southward along the lonely Carolina coast; John, proud in his new distinction as royal emmisary, happy once more in the companionship of his nature-loving son, and Billy, again reprieved from a hated trade and blissful in the freedom of the open trail. It was the beginning of a great adventure for both men and nothing to sadden their hearts with warning that this was to be their last journey together. The journal strikes what is for John a merry note, recounting their ride along the shores of Long Bay: "its very pleasant rideing on hard sand close to ye roling waves Just washing ye horses feet."

In Charleston a rainy but busy two weeks were spent in preparations for the Florida undertaking. Their chests were put aboard a boat leaving for St. Augustine, instructions and letters were obtained from Indian Commissioner John Stuart, in case they decided to follow Mark Catesby's collecting trail up the Savannah into Cherokee country. August was almost gone before they set out for Savannah. Although their path to that town lay through a long settled section, it offered hardships enough to test their mettle as well as their Quaker faith in the brotherhood of man. The journal notes, as entries for part of this travel from Charleston to Savannah:

. . . dined at Coopers at ye first bridge; then over rantols bridge; after which we mist our right road & took ye left which lead us much too near ye salts and sometimes over much tolerable piney soil until toward night, when wee began to looke for A house, one of which we rode to, haveing ye appearance of A gentlemans house; but he would not lett us stay upon any terms but directed us to ye next plantation, he said was about A mile off but we found it above two mile. but he would not let us stay tho it was then Just dark. he directed us to ye next neibour, he said was not above half. A mile off. he ordered his negro to put us in ye way. he lead us A great way round A deep branch then over a broked dam, but ye water was so deep that thay allmost swam & our feet & legs was wet. when we came to ye house, which made A good appearance, but ye master was as ill natured as ye other, he tould us that he could not entertain us for he entertained no travellers. we tould him that we had traveled A great way & was very weary & our horses was quite tired & could go no further & must lay us down in ye field. after A good while he consented that we should stay but must ly in a little ould hut little better than A hog sty, being ye worst out house he had & much worse than any of his negro houses, many of which was at several distances about ye mantion house. we was at last admided into ye porch while ye little ould corn house was cleaned by pushing ye ould mouldy corn in A heap on one side to make room for An ould bed to be laid on ye floor for us to rest upon, when ye gentleman told us our room was ready for us and that we might go there as soon as we pleased. so we went directly about 100 yards from ye dwelling hous. we found A candle set in an ould bottle for A candlestick & some hommony & two horn spoons to eat it with. we pulled of our wett cloath & hung them up to dry & lay down amongst ye ratts, weevils, grubs, & muschatoes to refresh ourselves after A tedious ride of near 35 ? miles.

Such a long entry devoted to his personal experiences is very unusual in John's journals; it was, however, most unusual for him to be refused hospitality or to be treated with such suspicion and unkindness, and one suspects that perhaps his detailed report reveals a just indignation, denied by his Quaker ethics a more direct outlet. Though he and William were received with more cordiality on the following night, they observed in the next village "two negroes jibited alive for poisoning thair Master," a far more somber footnote of man's cruelty.

But man, the most terrible of nature's productions, was, after all, only a small part of the landscape in the Bartrams' green safari. Everywhere they went nature spread her wonders, theirs for the seeing: here is the pretty blazing star and a new genus very like *Kalmia, Sabbatia,* bog bachelor's button, cannas, and white fringed orchis. Here is horse balm, the aromatic mint named *Collinsonia* in honor of their dear old London friend. Day after day they ride along lanes shadowed by great trees: "I believe no roads is finer to travail than ye carolinas," says John, "mostly shaded with lofty pines, oaks, tupelo, or liquidamber."

Nature, however, in spite of the soft look of the southern landscape, was not so amiable. "This morning we was so pestered with A monstrous sised musketo thay found us sufficient employment to beat them of. yet there is scarsly A spot on our hand so big as A wheat corn but where our skin is pierced."

They were approaching the Savannah River. To cross it they engaged a flat-bottom boat which landed them on the Georgia side ten miles downstream. En route alligators slipped into the water at their approach. Through mosquitoes "as thick as bees in A swarm" and over roads through swamps so deep they several times had to swim their horses, they approached Savannah town where they were welcomed by leading citizen James Habersham and Governor James Wright, who "received us very kindly."

This river that flowed by Savannah and shared its name had been well known to John Bartram for thirty years now, through the paintings and descriptions of Mark Catesby in his *Natural History of Carolina.* Often in its pages he had studied the trees, flowers, and birds Catesby had found there. To see them now alive and growing, to gather ones never found in other places, and to wait a little longer for summer's heat to wane before going on to Florida, Bartram and his son set out for Fort Moore, Augusta, and the falls where Catesby had hunted buffalo and seen giant sturgeon slaughtered. It was not the season for sturgeon, and if there still were buffalo John makes no mention of them. Two weeks later they were back in Savannah dining with Governor Wright and laying out their route for St. Augustine.

No road connected Savannah and St. Augustine in 1765. Except for its two towns on the river and a few outposts along the coast, Georgia, newest of the colonies, was still geography, wilderness, and a few scattered Indian villages, mostly in the hill country. Thus the Bartrams' route southward over the low pine flats was still a wilderness trail most of the way. There was a road of sorts as far as Fort Barrington on the

Altamaha River. In places it passed through pines so tall that the lowest branches were ninety feet above the ground. But as it neared the river it was so ill defined that the travelers missed their way. From this mischance came one of the highlights of American botanical history. Where the Bartrams camped that night, miles below the fort they had aimed for, they found "severall very curious shrubs, one bearing beautiful good fruite." This is the simple record of the discovery of two of our rarest and most beautiful shrubs, the *Franklinia* and the *Pinckneya*. There where mischance led them is the only place the *Franklinia*, which John Bartram named for his friend Benjamin, has ever been found growing in the wild.

The rest of the way to St. Augustine was unbroken wilderness with nature their only host: "Dined by a swamp on bread and a pomegranate" . . . "Lodged under a pine tree" . . . "Lodged in ye woods under a pine and palmetoes, and near a pond and musketoes." So it was all the way down, across the St. Johns River at Cow Ford, where Jacksonville would later be built, and on down to St. Augustine where they were hospitably received by Governor Grant.

No sooner had they secured lodgings in St. Augustine than John Bartram came down with a virulent attack of malaria, a victim of one of the multitude of mosquitoes of which he had complained along the way, the vicious little ones of Charleston with their long-lasting bites, the swarms of big hungry ones near Savannah, whose bites did not last, or the clouds about their camp in southern Georgia. His journal confessed that he had suffered more from mosquitoes in Jersey and in "our lower counties" than in all the Southern journey, but obviously the Jersey and Pennsylvania mosquitoes did not carry the dangerous enemy that now laid John low for nearly two months. On the days between his bouts with chills and fever he managed to do a little botanizing in the neighborhood, and on one occasion, despite an attack in progress, he could not resist accompanying Governor Grant and Superintendent Stuart to the Indian congress at Picolata, a fort on the St. Johns twenty miles west of St. Augustine. Although so ill that he was unable to stand during the pageantry, he nevertheless later recorded one of the most valued accounts of such affairs. The occasion was the negotiation of a treaty between the English and the Lower Creeks. Some fifty elaborately decorated chieftains, representing the Indians, strove to excel in pageantry the elegantly attired English. A great show of parading, singing, dancing, and handshaking all around, all done with the utmost

William Bartram's drawing of *Franklinia alatamaha*. (Courtesy of the British Museum, Natural History)

panoply and display, brought the affair to its climax, the signing of the treaty, the presentation of great silver medals strung on gay colored ribbons to each chief, and the smoking of the peace pipes "decorated all round with eagles' feathers."

It was almost Christmas before John was well enough to resume his travels. To search for the head of the river St. Johns, the governor had provided a guide to conduct them and to hunt venison for them and a Negro to row and cook for the party, "the Governor bearing our expences." They crossed again over to the river, to Fort Picolata, and set out upstream in a bateau, with the intention of traveling up the river to its source. Although they fell far short of that objective, reaching only a little beyond the location of Orlando, they traveled energetically for two months to explore even that three or four hundred miles.

However, the expedition was deeply rewarding for both of the Bartrams personally. For the older man it was the climax of his career. Never had he been so rapt in and wrapped about by his beloved verdant world as he was now, day after day, along the wide, quiet waters of the St. Johns, which, to the right and left, doubled with its reflections the bordering tropical lushness. For the younger man it was an absorbing fascination which gripped him as relentlessly as any of the mammoth grape vines entwined the supporting trees along the banks. He would have to stay; if torn away, he would have to return; the tendrils reached to his heart and held him fast.

Adverse winds slowed their progress, but that mattered little. There was so much to see. Wrote John: " 'Tis diverting to observe the monstrous grape-vines, 8 inches in diameter, running up the oaks 6 foot in diameter, swamp-magnolia 70 foot high strait, and a foot diameter, the great magnolia very large, liquid amber, white swamp and live oaks. chinquapines and cluster-cherry all of an uncommon size, mixed with orange-trees, either full of fruit or scattered on the ground, where the sun can hardly shine for the green leaves at Christmas. . . ." Elsewhere he comments on a large snail-shell ridge, on the abundance of turkeys and alligators, on an Indian tumulus twenty yards in diameter.

The great springs were a special fascination. He describes the sulphurous spring now known as Funk's spring:

We came down a steep hill 20 foot high and about 4 or 500 yards from the river, under the foot of which issued out a large fountain (big enough to turn a mill) of warm clear water of a very offensive taste, and smelt like bilge-water, or the washings of a gun-barrel; the sediment that adhered to the trees fallen therein, looked of a pale white or bluish cast, like milk and water mixed: . . .

At Blue Springs, although the water was warm and very clear but tasted just as loathsome, there were added attractions:

. . . multitudes of fish resort to its head, as very large garr, cats, and several other sorts, ye alligators very numerous either on the shore or swimming on the surface of the water, and some on the bottom, so tame, or rather bold, as to allow us to row very near to them.

Beyond the last trading post, in the region of Lake Jessup and Lake Harney, wild animals were more plentiful. It was at their camp on the shore of Harney that for the first time in Florida they heard the howling of wolves. Here, too, they saw the wood rats' nest four feet high and five feet in diameter, built all of sticks in piled confusion, from which a mother rat ran out with a young one clinging to her tail. Game in this area was abundant and varied. "Our hunter," Bartram reported, "killed a large he-bear supposed to weigh 400 pounds, was 7 foot long. . . ." Though it was an old bear, they found the meat "mild and Sweet," and that opinion of the gustatory excellence of bear meat was in no way a product of hunger "for we had a fat young buck and three turkeys fresh shot at the same time. . . ."

As they were now facing the return trip downstream where game was less plentiful, they tarried at their lakeside camp to preserve their bounty, through a day of intense discomfort:

This morning was very warm and a little showery; the muskatoes were troublesome last night, and this morning the flies blowed our meat before 10 o'clock; the ticks creeping and lizards running about our tent; we staid here all day to barbecue our meat to serve us down the river, which would soon spoil if not preserved either by fire or salt, and of which last we had only enough to season our victuals with it. . . .

The return journey downstream had a golden, leisurely quality with time for discoveries and experiences delightful for the curious Bartrams. They noted the multitude of ducks all over the river while the geese could only be found in the grassy savannas, well back from it. There was leisure enough to cut down the tall palmettos for the single, cabbage-like, succulent bud, to be boiled in bear's grease for a wilderness delicacy. There was time to walk through the wild orange groves sometimes so thick that one could hardly push one's way between the trees, and time to wonder that some bore sour fruit and some sweet, to marvel that this oriental exotic, in the two centuries since its introduction by the Spaniards, could have crowded the native flora from many wide areas deep into the uninhabited wilderness. There was leisure enough for finding bee trees, to steal their store of concentrated nectar to sweeten the sour oranges to taste. If John Bartram was aware that the bees that stored the honey were themselves exotics, with an even briefer time in America since their introduction into New England, he did not comment on this or on the fact that the bees had proved even more aggressive and adaptable than the orange in making the New World their own.

These were days so fine they could arouse a touch of the poet even in John Bartram. The joy in his heart shone through in parts of the diary as when he began a day's entry with "Fine warm morning, birds singing, fish jumping, and turkies gobbling. . . ." For Billy, always the poet and artist, they were days of romancing with nature, dreaming and sketching the myriad facets of his love. But he also had his father's botanical eye. Many of the new discoveries they made in Florida were his, notably the beautiful, heavily aromatic star anise which was always to be one of Billy's most loved Southern plants. John says of its discovery: "Here my son found a sweet, lovely tree, with leaves like the sweet bay, which smelled like sassafras, and produced a very strange kind of seed-pod, . . . some of them grew near 20 foot high, a charming bright evergreen aromatic."

Along the way there was time for John's farmer eye to calculate the farm potential of swamp, savanna, and bluff as they drifted by. From time to time he must go ashore to sample the earth. Here was a swamp which would make a good field. This bluff would produce good corn. With industry a man might make a fine plantation here.

There was leisure, too, for Billy to think. How could he leave this voluptuous mistress and the ecstasy of her gentle green caress? He could not bear the thought of exchanging her clean fragrance for the revolting redolence of bolts of cloth, new-tanned leather, and vinegar. Perhaps from these lands along the river might come his reprieve from the conventional world of business he found so alien to his nature.

After their return to St. Augustine, John Bartram's journal records repeated expeditions from the town to the river in the neighborhood of Fort Picolata, but there is no hint of their purpose. It is not until June,

1766, that John, back at home on the Schuylkill, unburdens himself to Peter: "I am now returned to my family; all of whom I found in good health. God Almighty be praised for his favours. I am at present tolerable well, but can hardly get over the dreadful seasickness and the southward fever." Then, with perhaps a too careful casualness, he continues: "I have left my son Billy in Florida. Nothing will do with him now, but he will be a planter upon St. John's River, about twenty-four miles from St. Augustine, and six from the Fort at Picolata. This frolic of his and our maintenance, hath drove me to great straits; so I was forced to draw upon thee, at St. Augustine, and twice at Charleston."

There is only a hint here of the distress of mind and spirit which John must have suffered during those last weeks in Florida, faced with William's determination to remain behind in the dangerous Florida wilderness, beautiful and terrible, especially in the approaching season of sultry and fever-ridden summer.

He had not neglected his mission, however: "I have brought home with me, a fine collection of strange Florida Plants; which, perhaps, I may send sometime this summer, some for the King and some for thyself . . . the collecting of which hath cost thy friend many score pounds, pains, and sickness, which held me constantly near or quite two months; . . ."

At this writing John Bartram had more than ten years left to live. Although these were years of recognition and relative ease, the good fortune that had seemed his unfailing star, guiding him through so many years and through so many hazards, was no longer his constant companion. The gratification of having his *Account of East Florida* published in London, his election to membership in the Royal Academy of Stockholm, an award of a gold medal by the Edinburgh Society, and the esteem and honor widely accorded him could not lessen the grief and loss he suffered in 1768 in the death of Peter Collinson. And although the garden on the Schuylkill had become a mecca for the curious of the day, including many whose names are still well known, this satisfaction could not still John's constant, gnawing concern for Billy, child of his heart, who had helped to collect so many of the plants in the garden and preserved their blooms in his paintings. For Billy, his most talented child, the one to whom he had given most attention and for whom he had such high hopes, seemed utterly unable to cope with the workaday world, seemed lost in an endless miasma of failures.

The outbreak of the war in 1775 dropped a black curtain between

John and all those across the sea whose kindred interest and friendship had, for so many years, brightened his life. War itself was no new shadow; the imperial struggles of Europe with their bloody overflow into the colonies had been an accustomed evil in his life. But this war posed a new and altogether intolerable question—an agonizing choice. John Bartram was a sturdy individualist, rooted firmly in native soil, American to the bone. But was he not too an Englishman? Was he not the King's Botanist? Were not his lifelong and most devoted friends in England? He was, furthermore, a Quaker, pledged to peace, not war, a naturalist, tuned to life, not death.

There was a burst of sunlight through his glowering sunset sky. In the January before John Bartram's death in September, 1777, Billy, who had disappeared into the Southern wilderness some time before and had not been heard from in years, came home to Kingsessing. And Billy did not come home empty-handed, but rich in experiences, with diaries of botanical lore and saddlebags full of seed to share with his father, and tales of adventure and discovery that the old traveler-botanist knew how to appreciate. It is probable that Billy was still an enigma to his father, for John, who understood so much, was never able to understand his artistic son—the obverse side of the Bartram coin. Now, however, William had proved his competence, and the father's heart could rejoice with gratitude and relief.

Nevertheless, even the comforting presence of William could not drive off the shadows as the intolerable war grew larger and more ominous. As the British armies approached the Continental capital of Philadelphia, John was in constant dread lest his garden, the cherished collection and labor of a lifetime, would be wantonly overrun and destroyed by the soldiers. He had never desired old age, his restless nature fearing any invalidism. Luckily he remained active and independent until his death, which came after a very brief illness, on September 22, just four days before British troops marched into the capital after the American defeat at Brandywine. His last words, as reported by his son, William, were characteristic of John Bartram, honest and plain dealing to the end: "I want to die."

~ Chapter 5

WILLIAM BARTRAM

~ 1

In the late summer of 1766, a few months after John Bartram had returned alone from his Florida expedition, a ship from Charleston arrived with a distressing letter for the old botanist. The letter was from his friend, Henry Laurens, whose talents and fate would later conspire to write his name large in the annals of the Revolutionary period, but who, at this time, was simply a wealthy and respected merchant-planter of Charleston, with an active interest in botany. In addition to his extensive plantation holdings in Carolina, he had recently acquired sites on the St. Johns River in Florida, and it was an inspection trip to these latter holdings that brought about his letter to his botanical friend in Pennsylvania. On his voyage up the river and again on his way back three weeks later, Laurens had stopped by to see Billy Bartram, who was attempting to establish a farm on the riverside, "on a low sheet of sandy pine barren," adjacent to a dismal swamp.

The letter from Laurens more than confirmed the misgivings John Bartram had felt since saying good-by to Billy in Florida in the spring of this same year. At that time John, weakened by fever, weary of traveling, and longing to return home, had finally given his reluctant cooperation to his son's ill-conceived venture. Now the worried father could not have been surprised to read in his friend's letter that Billy's "frolic," as John had called it in a letter to Peter, was about to become Billy's tragedy.

"You may be sure," wrote Laurens, "I did not carelessly pass by your son's habitation. . . . I hope you will not think me quite impertinent if I detain you to say a word or two touching the particular situation and circumstance of that poor young man. . . ." His word or two turned into page after page of lament for the poor young man, as he described with indignation Billy's distressing situation, the sorry site he had chosen for his home, its loneliness, the inferiority of the soil, the inadequacy of his shelter. Laurens reported that the small plantings Billy had made were showing poor growth, that little progress was being made in clearing the swamp for rice "for want of strong hands," that only two among the six Negroes John had given him could handle an ax tolerably well, that the young man was completely alone except for the six slaves, "six negroes, rather plagues than aids to him, of whom one is so insolent as to threaten his life, one a useless expense, one a helpless child in arms."

As for Billy's home, the letter continues grimly: "The house, or rather hovel, that he lives in, is extremely confined, and not proof against the weather. He has not proper assistance to make a better, and from its situation it is very hot, the only disagreeably hot place I found in East Florida. . . . His provision of grain, flesh, and spirits, is scanty, even to penury, the latter article very much so. His own health is very imperfect. . . ."

This detailed and eloquent letter from Henry Laurens to John Bartram seems especially significant, not only for the vivid description of Billy's desolate predicament, nor for its immediate importance in Billy's rescue, but for what it suggests of the unusual and magnetic personality of the "poor young man" on whose behalf it was written. For William was not at this time, strictly speaking, a very young man, whose youth alone would have made a valid claim for protection. He was already twenty-seven, well educated, widely traveled, and experienced in various trades. The passionate fervor with which the stable, intelligent, and busy man of affairs, Henry Laurens, championed his cause is forceful evidence of Laurens' recognition of the special quality of the youthful artist, a young man whom the world could ill afford to lose, rotting away in an isolated, miasmic wilderness.

One can only imagine the emotion with which John Bartram read the depressing and forlorn account and particularly the urgent paragraph:

Possibly, sir, your son, though a worthy, ingenious man, may not have resolution, or not that sort of resolution, that is necessary to encounter the difficulties incident to, and unavoidable in his present state of life. You and I, probably, could surmount all those hardships without much chagrin. I believe that I could. But, at the same time, I protest that I should think it less grievous to disinherit my own son, and turn him into the wide world, if he was of a tender and delicate frame of body and intellects, as yours seems to be, than to restrict him in my favour, just in the state that your son is reduced to. . . . In fact, according to my ideas, no colouring can do justice to the forlorn state of poor Billy Bartram. A gentle, mild young man, no wife, no friend, no companion, no neighbor . . . totally void of all the comforts of life except an inimitable degree of patience, for which he deserves a thousand times better fate. . . .

Long before John Bartram finished reading this letter, his heart must have been wrung with grief, and Billy's enclosed letter, at whose contents we can only guess, was hardly needed to bring the anguished and bewildered father once more to the rescue of his son, so gifted, so loved, so apparently doomed to failure.

But was this latest failure, like each of those which had preceded it and each of those which were to come, really a failure? By the standards of the marketplace no other term is accurate. There are, however, different and more profound standards. Is the failure of a square peg to fit snugly into a round hole necessarily a failure on the part of the peg? Is the shape of the hole or the shape of the peg at fault? This metaphor, at any rate, seems appropriate for the years of Billy's young manhood during which his father, with his forceful and relatively inflexible personality, Peter Collinson, steeped in the world of trade, and practical, worldly Benjamin Franklin all conspired, with well-meaning but blind insistence, to set Billy up in one business after another—nothing but a series of round holes into which, whenever the pressure of family and friends became too great, Billy would endeavor to fit the square peg of his artist nature.

The pressure to get Billy settled advantageously in life was intensified through the early recognition of his talents, by his father and his father's friends, Billy's mentors and advisers. He was still barely entered upon his teens when his father began to delight Peter Collinson and his group in London with samples of the boy's drawings, showing an amazingly accurate eye for nature and striking artistic gifts.

The proud father, well aware of the handicaps of his own lack of formal teaching in childhood, saw to it that this promising son had a privileged education at the Old College in Philadelphia, and he wrote to Peter in 1755: "I design to set Billy to draw all our turtles, with remarks, as he has time, which is only on Seventh days, in the afternoon, and First day mornings; for he is constantly kept to school, to learn Latin and French. . . ."

John, however, was a practical man whose nature and experience in life made him intensely conscious of the need for economic security. Industrious, steady application in some stable occupation to John Bartram was not only a virtue but a necessity. He, who recognized in the plants he loved the separate needs of each species in soil, environmental conditions, nurture and, above all, time to grow, lacked the rarer perception to recognize in the son he loved the separate and special need of the artist for long fallow periods, for slow, dreamy seasons of dormant, imperceptible maturation. With the all too common blindness of the human parent he could not resist trying to shape and prune and force into patterned maturity the tender, unready, and resistant young shoot.

When Billy turned sixteen, John had written to his friend Collinson:

It is now time to propose some way for him to get his living by. I don't want him to be what is commonly called a gentleman. I want to put him to some business by which he may, with care and industry, get a temperate, reasonable living. I am afraid botany and drawing will not afford him one. I have designed several years to put him to a doctor, to learn physic and surgery; but that will take him from his drawing, which he takes particular delight in. Pray, my dear Peter, let me have thy opinion about it.

And a few months later, in another letter: "I am pleased that Billy gives you such satisfaction in his drawing. I wish he could get a handsome livelihood by it. Botany and drawing are his darling delight; am afraid he can't settle to any business else."

John considered the possibility of surveying as a business for his son but dismissed it because the field was already overfilled. Collinson proposed that Billy be a printer like Friend Benjamin. Bartram objected that Franklin was the only printer he ever knew to make a decent living from it. Franklin suggested engraving. So, over the years, sometimes it seems almost losing sight of the subject of their discussions, these able and practical men busied themselves with patterns for the precious fabric of Billy's life, while the dreamy boy was shifted, willy-nilly, from one false start to another in the alien world of business, for which he had neither taste, talent, nor tolerance.

Through all the talk, in long periods between the short and abortive job ventures, William continued to sketch with absorbed devotion the only world he understood or cared to understand. Drawings and paintings—not just of turtles, but of rare birds, seashells, plants of all kinds, lizards, every aspect of the natural world—poured across the sea, into Peter Collinson's counting house and from there into the town and country houses of the natural history circle of London, where they were received with discerning admiration. Peter Collinson's letters of this period of William's adolescence are full of praise for the boy's "inimitable pencil," his true eye, his delicate touch. In addition to praise there were gifts, as acknowledged in this letter from John to Peter when Billy was seventeen: "Billy is much obliged to thee for his drawing paper. He has drawn many rare birds, in order to send to thee; and dried the birds to send to his friend Edwards, to whom he is much obliged for those two curious books." Edwards was one of the leading naturalists of England and an artist and engraver as well, a distinguished friend indeed for a seventeen-year-old Quaker lad in colonial America.

But, with familiar irony, the more Billy's uncommon talents were recognized, the more intense and persuasive became the efforts to harness this Pegasus to a workaday cart.

One of the first of these ventures seems to have been an apprenticeship to a Philadelphia merchant when Billy was eighteen. John wrote to Peter with relief in 1757: "My Billy comes on fine with Captain Child, who is very kind to him, and keeps him close to business."

The kind Captain Child, in fact, kept Billy so close to business that it was several years before he found a way to break free, leaving Philadephia for his uncle William's home on the Cape Fear River in North Carolina, ostensibly to run a trade store there. A country store and the easygoing home life of his uncle's family offered a generous measure of freedom not to be found in the bustling atmosphere of a city counting house or under the anxious and demanding eyes of his father, and a chance to steal perhaps even a major portion of his time for his true vocation of artist and naturalist. For William had discovered the age-old and potent defense of the artist in the face of social pressures that threaten to destroy him—flight. This was the first time he had used this defense. It would not be the last. For the artist, in so many ways vulnerable and unarmed, has great secret resources, and not the least of these is the fact that he travels light, carrying his world within, poised and winged for flight even when he seems most deeply rooted.

Though the rural store was less demanding than the city trade it could not be neglected with impunity forever, and William was in serious financial difficulties by the time his father's letter arrived, in the spring of 1765, inviting him to accompany him to Florida as assistant to the King's Botanist. Much as John welcomed the help and companionship of his naturalist son on this expedition, he must have been chagrined and dismayed on his arrival at Cape Fear by the woeful evidence of William's utter lack of business competence, even in so simple a role as country-store keeper. It is unlikely that plain-dealing John bore his disappointment in silence. William was now twenty-six. What was to become of him?

Had William been a late-blooming tree, how patiently John would have waited for the promised blossom, seeing and reverencing the hand of God in the yet unformed bud, the fruit withheld until its appointed season. Perhaps, like parents everywhere and in every age, John loved too much and hoped too much to see his son clearly. For, paradoxically, it seems apparent that, with all their differences, William was John's dream made manifest. Yet a dream in human form can be a bit unsettling, especially in the form of a poor farmer's son who must make a living in the world. Many of the lessons that John taught, by precept and example, William had learned, but, perversely, far too well for John's comfort. "Consider the lilies of the field, how they grow," and William indeed considered the lilies, taking "no thought for the morrow, for the morrow shall take thought for the things of itself." Worship God in nature was the core of John's philosophy. William did that too, but he worshiped not only in his leisure time, not just with a part of himself, but with his whole life.

One can imagine the mixture of joy and apprehension with which John had watched, through the years, the progress of this child of his soul, strongly motivated by forces strange to the practical farmer, as the artist and naturalist contended for harmonious development within William, cursed or blessed, as he was, with a minimum of what the world calls common sense to shield him against the harsh realities of life.

Such was the young William Bartram who accompanied his father to Florida in 1765. Such was the "gentle" and "mild" Billy Bartram, the "worthy, ingenious man" whose rescue from his forlorn situation

Mr. Laurens was determined to effect. We don't know just when or how that rescue came about, but the little we hear of him during the remainder of 1766 and until his return to Philadelphia in 1767 indicates that he stayed on in Florida, engaged with a surveying party in the then uninhabited region of New Smyrna. It was probably near there that he was involved in a shipwreck about which we know nothing except that it occurred.

On his return home he had for a while a turn at farming, probably only as a farm laborer. Then again he became involved in a mercantile enterprise with even more disastrous results than his earlier undertaking at Cape Fear. His distracted spirit was too securely in thrall to nature to be mustered to serve the marketplace.

All the while dependable old Peter Collinson was persisting in his efforts to arrange for Billy some source of income more suitable to his endowments. He took every opportunity to show Billy's drawings to his wealthy and influential friends, at least one of whom, the Duchess of Portland, sent a generous sum to the artist for drawings of particular specimens she admired, especially seashells. But Peter persisted in search of more permanent and substantial patronage for his friend's son, and at last, in the final letter he wrote to the Bartrams before his death in 1768, the London merchant announced a measure of success. The letter, addressed to William, was an introduction to Dr. John Fothergill, a neighbor of Collinson on Grace Church Street, a prosperous physician, a philanthropist, and a fellow Quaker, with an avid interest in all facets of natural history. At the time of the letter he was just getting under way with the development of a botanical garden on his newly acquired country estate in Cheshire. This final effort of the kindly Collinson on behalf of his Schuylkill friends planted viable seed from which grew the future happiness and fame of William Bartram.

"This morning," Peter Collinson hastened to write to Billy, from Mill House, his country place, "Dr. Fothergill came and breakfasted here. As I am always thoughtful how to make Billy's ingenuity turn to some advantage, I bethought of showing the doctor his last elegant performances. He deservedly admired them, and thinks so fine a pencil is worthy of encouragement; and Billy may value himself on having such a patron, who is eminent for his generosity, and his noble spirit to promote every branch in Natural History." Dr. Fothergill desired drawings of all American land, river, and sea shells, water and land terrapins and turtles. With concern that Billy might muff this great opportunity, Collinson concludes paternally: "Set thy wits and ingenuity to work, to gratify so deserving a patron."

Here indeed was William's golden opportunity! But, despite Collinson's admonition, he very nearly failed to seize upon it. A year later, in a letter to John Bartram, Dr. Fothergill indicates that he is still waiting for Billy's drawings. Six months later yet another letter with the same complaint.

All the while a quiet desperation was taking hold of Billy. Where was the opportunity to find land, river, and sea shells while he was, six days a week, a prisoner to his accursed store? After months of frustration there came a day when William's silent despair could no longer be contained. William disappeared. Again he fled the marketplace where he could neither understand nor be understood. He was fleeing also the long shadow of his generally prosaic father who, despite his rich endowment of common sense, could not read aright his romantic son. Only in the warm sunlight far beyond the reach of those oppressive shadows could William, the romantic, impractical pantheist, blossom and become fruitful.

Months passed with no word from him. Then one day, from out of his long nowhere, he appeared at the Cape Fear River home of his beloved uncle William. In the undemanding warmth of his uncle's household William's dreams flexed fledgling wings—wings upon which he would soon soar far beyond the horizons of his Carolina aerie. The long-delayed drawings for Dr. Fothergill were completed and dispatched. Apparently the doctor was pleased and impressed with William's talents, but, understandably, he had some doubts of his dependability. He wrote to John:

A few weeks ago I received a letter and some drawings from thy son William, in Carolina. For his sake, as well as thine, I should be glad to assist him. He draws neatly; has a strong relish for Natural History; and it is a pity that such genius should sink under distress. Is he sober and diligent? This may be an uncommon question to ask a father of his son; and yet I know thy integrity will not suffer thee to mislead me. . . . He proposes to go to Florida. It is a country abounding in a great variety of plants, and many of them unknown. . . . I shall endeavor to assist his inclination for a tour of Florida; and if he succeeds, shall, perhaps, wish him to see the back parts of Canada. . . .

This letter was written sometime in the year 1772, a year crowded for the Bartrams with fateful events, whose sequence is uncertain, but it is certain that satisfactory arrangements were made between William and Dr. Fothergill, and equally certain that this was the beginning of freedom for William from all that had held him in bondage. At some time in the past year, tragedy in the form of a rapid succession of deaths, of Uncle William, his wife, and their son, William Bartram, Jr., had already loosed much of the hold his adoptive home on the Cape Fear River had for Billy. For some time he had repeatedly expressed his longing to return to Florida, which, in spite of the misery and defeat of his earlier trial there, still drew him with a strangely potent spell; but John Bartram had met these proposals with indignant letters of outraged protest. Now, although John must still have had secret misgivings and fear, his opposition to the expedition was silenced by the support of such a distinguished patron as Dr. Fothergill.

And William? Something had happened to William, not suddenly or miraculously, except in the sense that the coming of spring is a sudden miracle, though in reality it is merely the flowering debut after slow, unhurried seasons of preparation. For William the fullness of time had come round at last, and he was ready.

2

Thus and then was the stage set for the travels of William Bartram, the account of which was to gain him world-wide fame under the title *Travels Through North & South Carolina, Georgia, East & West Florida*, with a lengthy subtitle according to the fashion of the day, but commonly known today simply as *The Travels of William Bartram*, or even more simply as *Bartram's Travels*.

After a brief return to Philadelphia for his final preparations William set sail for Charleston in March of 1773. When he reached Charleston he found that spring was not sufficiently advanced for his intended trip up the Savannah River to the mountains. To bide his time he acquired a horse to botanize in the Georgia Sea Island country. One of the enigmatic aspects of William's travels is the extent to which the early years of wandering were simply leisurely duplications of the explorations he had already made with his father in the winter of 1765–66. Perhaps William, hitherto always subordinate to his forceful father, needed to gain confidence by retreading the old haunts alone before adventuring on new trails. Perhaps it was the artist in him that hungered to drink more deeply where once he had but sipped. Perhaps the botanist in him longed to study and discover in more detail than the

Portrait of William Bartram by Charles Willson Peale. (Courtesy of the Independence National Historical Park Collection)

rapid early travels had permitted. In any case, this coastal country was familiar territory, as was the Savannah region to which he returned when spring was full blown.

It seems appropriate here in the first reach of his travels to borrow William's eyes and savor, in his words, the excitement of his discoveries; first, some of his observations of the fauna of Georgia's Colonel's Island, near St. Catherine's:

The roebuck, or deer, are numerous on this island; the tyger [puma], wolf and bear, hold yet some possessions; as also raccoons, foxes, hares, squirrels, rats, and mice, but I think no moles: there is a large ground rat, more than twice the size of the common Norway rat. In the night time it throws out the earth, forming little mounds, or hillocks. Opossoms are here in abundance, as are also pole-cats, [skunks], wild-cats, rattlesnakes, glass-snakes, coach-whip snake, and a variety of other serpents.

Here are also a great variety of birds. . . . First, I shall name the eagle, of which there are three species; the great grey eagle [immature bald or golden eagle] is the largest, of great strength and high flight; he chiefly preys on fawns and other young quadrupeds.

The bald eagle is likewise a large, strong, and very active bird, but an execrable tyrant, he supports his assumed dignity and grandeur by rapine and violence, extorting unreasonable tribute and subsidy from all the feathered nations.

The last of this race I shall mention is the false piscatorious, or fishing-hawk: this is a large bird, of high and rapid flight; his wings are long and pointed, and he spreads a vast sail, in proportion to the volume of his body. This princely bird subsists entirely on fish, which he takes himself, scorning to live and grow fat on the dear earned labours of another; he also contributes liberally to the support of the bald eagle.

Water-fowl, and the various species of land-birds, also abound, most of which are mentioned by Catesby, in his *Hist. Carolina*, particularly his painted finch . . . exceeded by none of the feathered tribes, either in variety and splendour of dress or melody of song.

Catesby's ground doves are also here in abundance; they are remarkably beautiful, about the size of a sparrow, and their soft and plaintive cooing perfectly enchanting.

How chaste the dove! "never known to violate the conjugal contract." She flees the seats of envy and strife, and seeks the retired paths of peace.

Leaving the teeming Sea Islands, William turned west toward the interior and Fort Barrington, some twenty-five miles up the Altamaha River. No doubt it was the "curious shrubs," the *Franklinia* and *Pinck-*

neya, then unnamed, which he and his father had discovered there in the early fall of 1765, that prompted this detour from his route. Apparently William sensed the rarity of the plants and the uniqueness of the site. A mere generation later the beautiful *Franklinia* passed from a wild to a domestic plant. It has never been found growing in the natural state in any other place except there by the Altamaha, and it has not been found even there since 1803, though it has been sought by eager botanists through the years and the search continues even today.

On this visit, in the spring of 1773, William lingered to admire and describe the beautiful shrubs, but it was probably not until his return visit, on his way back to Philadelphia several years later, in the fall of the year, that he stopped to gather seeds and plants for himself and his patron.

The next incident of note, as he journeyed south toward the St. Marys River, "about sixty miles through an uninhabited wilderness," was an encounter with an Indian, which, at least in this case, speaks well for the spiritual armor of the pacifist. William tells it in this way:

The gaily attired plants which enamelled the green had begun to imbibe the pearly dew of evening; nature seemed silent, and nothing appeared to ruffle the happy moments of evening contemplation: when, on a sudden, an Indian appeared crossing the path, at a considerable distance before me. On perceiving that he was armed with a rifle, the first sight of him startled me, and I endeavoured to elude his sight, by stopping my pace, and keeping large trees between us; but he espied me, and turning short about, set spurs to his horse, and came up on a full gallop. I never before was afraid at the sight of an Indian, but at this time I must own that my spirits were very much agitated: I saw at once, that being unarmed, I was in his power, and having not but a few moments to prepare, I resigned myself entirely to the will of the Almighty, trusting to his mercies for my preservation; my mind then became tranquil, and I resolved to meet the dreaded foe with resolution and chearful confidence. The intrepid Siminole stopped suddenly, three or four yards before me, and silently viewed me, his countenance angry and fierce, shifting his rifle from shoulder to shoulder, and looking about instantly on all sides. I advanced towards him, and with an air of confidence offered him my hand, hailing him, brother; at this he hastily jerked back his arm, with a look of malice, rage and disdain, seeming every way disconcerted; when again looking at me more attentively, he instantly spurred up to me, and with dignity in his look and action, gave me his hand. Possibly the silent language of his soul, during the moment of suspense (for I believe his design was to kill me when he first came up) was after this manner:

"White man, thou art my enemy, and thou and thy brethren may have killed mine; yet it may not be so, and even were that the case, thou art now alone, and in my power. Live; the Great Spirit forbids me to touch thy life; go to thy brethren, and tell them thou sawest an Indian in the forests who knew how to be humane and compassionate." In fine, we shook hands, and parted in a friendly manner, in the midst of a dreary wilderness; and he informed me of the course and distance to the trading house, where I found he had been extremely ill treated the day before.

When William reached the St. Marys River it was mid-spring. If he was not to miss the spring flowering climax in the backcountry, it was high time he turn back northward to the Savannah. One of his stops along the route toward the Savannah was with the Lachlan McIntosh family at their plantation home near the mouth of the Altamaha. On his southward way a few weeks earlier he had enjoyed the hospitality of the McIntoshes, whose young son, John, attracted by William and his project, determined to join him in his travels. On William's return to the McIntosh home, he "tarried a few days," because, he reported, young John, "being fond of the enterprise, had been so active in my absence, in the necessary preparations, that we had nothing to wait for now but Mrs. McIntosh's final consent to give up her son to the perils and hardships of so long a journey; which difficult point being settled, we set off with the prayers and benevolent wishes of my companion's worthy parents." If the boy is father to the man, John's mother need not have been so fearful for him, for in later years John McIntosh proved equal to the challenge of danger and hardship on the battlefields of the Revolution and of the War of 1812, eventually rising to the rank of major general.

In the latter part of May, William and John reached Augusta just in time to witness the gathering of the chiefs and warriors of the Creeks and Cherokees who had come together for a congress to arrange for another in the long series of land cessions, this one to settle their mounting trade debts to the whites. After the usual rounds of orations and flattery, bribes and threats, a treaty was arranged. Some two million acres more of Indian land was surrendered to the relentlessly encroaching newcomers. William arranged that he and John should accompany the group appointed to lay out the ceded territory. This took them westward from Augusta as far as Athens and from there northwest to the upper reaches of the Savannah River.

For William, the botanist, the expedition was pure delight. All along the Savannah and in the hills of Georgia he was moved to rhapsodies of description. Of the neighborhood of Augusta he wrote: "vegetation, in perfection, appeared with all her attractive charms, breathing fragrance everywhere . . . and although here much delighted with the new beauties in the vegetable kingdom . . . yet, as I was never long satisfied with present possession . . . I was restless to be searching for more, my curiosity being insatiable. . . ."

Near the cataracts of Augusta, "upon the rich, rocky hills," he recorded his first sight of the Carolina rosebay, and the white *Philadelphus,* and his pleasure in the fragrant white spider lilies "which almost alone possess the little rocky islets which just appear above the water."

Not far from the present Washington, Georgia, the survey party came upon a wonderful forest that stood out even in that region of almost unbroken virgin forest. William thought it "the most magnificent forest" he had ever seen. For seven miles their way lay through it. "We . . . entered this sublime forest; the ground is perfectly a level green plain, thinly planted by nature, with the most stately forest trees, . . . whose mighty trunks, seemingly of an equal height, appeared like superb columns. To keep within the bounds of truth and reality in describing the magnitude of those trees, would, I fear, fail of credibility; yet, I think I can assert, that many of the black oaks measured eight, nine, ten, and eleven feet diameter five feet above the ground, as we measured several that were above thirty feet girt, and from hence they ascend perfectly strait, with a gradual taper, forty or fifty feet to the limbs; . . ." In addition to the black oak he listed, in this cathedral forest, tulip trees, black walnut, sycamore, hickory, beech, elm, sweet gum, carefully giving them their full botanical Latin names, as was his almost unvarying custom.

A few days later, crossing the ridge lying between the Savannah and the Altamaha, they came upon a "buffalo lick."

"This extraordinary . . . place, called the Lick contains three or four acres . . . is an almost white or cinerous coloured tenacious fattish clay, which all kinds of cattle lick into great caves, pursuing the delicious vein." However, the buffalo, which half a century earlier Mark Catesby, with Indian companions, had hunted in this same region, no longer came to lick this delicious vein. Already they had been extirpated in the van of the westward-moving settlements of the white men. "The buffalo . . ." observed William, "once so very numerous, is not at this day to be seen in this part of the country; a few elk, and those only in the Appalachian mountains."

He noted, however, the abundance of wolves, bear, wildcats, and "tygers," which he explained was the Carolina name for the creature called panther in Pennsylvania.

With the close of the season, William and John McIntosh returned to Savannah to see to the packing and shipping of their collections to Dr. Fothergill—then on to the McIntosh plantation which probably served as William's headquarters during the ensuing several months. It was the spring of 1774 before he finally freed himself from the spell of Georgia's golden islands and low country and from the warm hospitality of the McIntosh household.

It is evident that William was experiencing a sustained ecstasy in his new-found freedom, and his always catholic interest in nature now lovingly embraced every aspect of the physical world. His rapture spills over into almost every page of the journal, as in this soliloquy on a canoe trip up the river Altamaha:

> I ascended this beautiful river, on whose fruitful banks the generous and true sons of liberty securely dwell, fifty miles above the white settlements.
> How gently flow thy peaceful floods, O Altamaha! How sublimely rise to view, on thy elevated shores, yon Magnolia groves. . . .

He is almost intoxicated by the beauty of his situation and by the perfume of the magnolia blossoms, mingled with that of the balm of sweet gum, and the fragrance from the groves of purple anise, wax myrtle, laurel, and Georgia bark along the shores.

> The air was filled with the loud and shrill whooping of the wary, sharp-sighted crane. Behold, on yon decayed, defoliated Cypress tree, the solitary wood-pelican, dejectedly perched upon its most elevated spire; he there, like an ancient venerable sage, sets himself up as a mark of derision, for the safety of his kindred tribes. The crying-bird [limpkin], another faithful guardian, screaming in the gloomy thickets, warns the feathered tribes of approaching peril; and the plumage of the swift sailing squadrons of Spanish curlews (white as the immaculate robe of innocence) gleam in the cerulean skies.
> Thus secure and tranquil, and meditating on the marvelous scenes of primitive nature, as yet unmodified by the hand of man, I gently descended the peaceful stream, on whose polished surface were depicted the mutable

shadows from its pensile banks; whilst myriads of finny inhabitants sported in its pellucid floods. . . .

. . . Grey pensive eve now admonishes us of gloomy night's hasty approach; I am roused by care to seek a place of secure repose, ere darkness comes on.

My barque being securely moored, and having reconnoitered the surrounding groves, and collected fire-wood, I spread my skins and blanket by my chearful fire, under the protecting shade of the hospitable Live-oak, and reclined my head on my hard but healthy couch. I listened, undisturbed, to the divine hymns of the feathered songsters of the groves, whilst the softly whispering breezes died faintly away.

The sun now below the western horizon, the moon majestically rising in the east; again the tuneful birds become inspired; how melodious is the social mock-bird! the groves resound the unceasing cries of the whip-poor-will. . . .

It is obvious from this passage that William was eagerly responding to the exciting variety of bird life, as well as plant life, in this Southern wonderland, renewing the interest in ornithology he had shown in his boyhood years.

After leaving young John at the McIntosh home, William set out for Florida, and by mid-April he was once more in the area of Cow Ford, on the St. Johns River, not far downstream from his disastrous venture as a planter nearly a decade past. There he equipped himself with a "little vessel . . . furnished with a good sail, and having fishing tackle, a neat light fusee, powder and ball . . ." for his expedition up the wide, north-flowing river.

Here, in this lush and fecund land, with the leisure to observe intently and the mind and temperament to philosophize, an unrestrained Billy Bartram became a pure hedonist, drinking deeply of nature's offerings, often to the point of intoxication. Here is a single morning and evening on that seductive stream, beginning with the brief, nuptial flight of the mayflies:

At the cool eves approach, the sweet enchanting melody of the feathered songsters gradually ceases, and they betake themselves to their leafy coverts for security and repose.

Slowly and solemnly move onward, to the river's shore, the rustling clouds of the Ephemera. How awful the procession! innumerable millions of winged beings, voluntarily verging on to destruction, to the brink of the grave, where they behold bands of their enemies with wide open jaws, ready to receive them. But as if insensible of their danger, gay and tranquil each meets his beloved mate, in the still air, inimitably bedecked in their new nuptial robes. What eye can trace them in their varied wanton amorous chaces, bounding and fluttering on the odoriferous air? with what peace, love and joy, do they end the last moments of their existence?

I think we may assert, without any fear of exaggeration, that there are annually of these beautiful winged beings, which rise into existence, and for a few moments take a transient view of the glory of the Creator's works, a number greater than the whole race of mankind that ever existed since the creation; and that only, from the shores of this river.

No description is complete for William without some philosophical comment, for although his observations were scientific and accurate, his thinking belonged to the great romantic tradition about to flower in Europe. To him indeed "the meanest flower that blows" could give "thoughts that do often lie too deep for tears." And not the flower alone, but every facet of nature must be recognized as significant in the universe and worthy of reverence. He cannot leave even the mayfly without a further thought:

The importance of the existence of these beautiful and delicately formed little creatures, in the creation, whose frame and organization is equally wonderful, more delicate, and perhaps as complicated as that of the most perfect human being, is well worth a few moments contemplation; I mean particularly when they appear in the fly state. And if we consider the very short period, of that stage of existence, which we may reasonably suppose, to be the only space of their life that admits of pleasure and enjoyment, what a lesson doth it not afford us of the vanity of our own pursuits.

Their whole existence in this world, is but one compleat year, and at least three hundred and sixty days of that time, they are in the form of an ugly grub, buried in the mud, eighteen inches under water, and in this condition scarcely locomotive, as each Larva or grub, has but its own narrow solitary cell, from which it never travels, or moves, but in a perpendicular progression, of a few inches, up and down, from the bottom to the surface of the mud, in order to intercept the passing atoms for its food, and get a momentary respiration of fresh air; and even here it must be perpetually on its guard, in order to escape the troops of fish and shrimps, watching to catch it, and from whom it has no escape, but by instantly retreating back into its cell. One would be apt almost to imagine them created merely for the food of fish and other animals.

The next morning he is awakened after a good rest by the "Cheering converse" of the wild turkey cock, "saluting each other from the sun-brightened tops of . . ." the lofty cypress and magnolia. "They begin at early dawn, and continue till sun rise, from March to the last of April. The high forests ring with the noise, like the crowing of the domestic cock, of these social centinels, the watch-word being caught and repeated, from one to another, for hundreds of miles around; insomuch that the whole country, is for an hour or more, in an universal shout. A little after sun-rise, their crowing gradually ceases, they quit their high lodging places, and alight on the earth, where, expanding their silver bordered train, they strut and dance around the coy female, while the deep forests seem to tremble with their shrill noise."

It almost seems that, for William, every day now is a holiday and all the world a circus, infinitely splendid and amusing. Days after the may-fly dances, as he sails along in the quiet reaches of the river, near the present Palatka, he is entertained, as he says, by the floating islands of water lettuce. This plant, now largely supplanted by the water hyacinth, grew in the river in large floating communities, some of them a quarter mile in extent, providing a microcosmic world of their own—a world, according to William, "most picturesque" and replete with "flowery plants, clumps of shrubs, old weather-beaten trees, hoary and barbed, with long moss waving from their snags, . . . completely inhabited, and alive, with crocodiles, serpents, frogs, otters, crows, herons, curlews, jackdaws, etc. . . ."

Here along the low banks were virgin forests of cypress, which William considers "in the first order of North American trees."

Its majestic stature is surprising, and, on approaching them, we are struck with a kind of awe, at beholding the stateliness of the trunk, lifting its cumbrous top toward the skies, and casting a wide shade upon the ground, as a dark intervening cloud, which, for a time, precluded the rays of the sun. The delicacy of its colour and texture of its leaves, exceed everything in vegetation. It generally grows in the water, or in low flat lands, near the banks of great rivers and lakes that are covered, great part of the year with two or three feet depth of water, and that part of the trunk, which is subject to be under water, and four or five feet higher up, is greatly enlarged, by prodigious buttresses, or pilasters, which, in full grown trees, project out on every side to such a distance that several men might easily hide themselves in the hollows between. Each pilaster terminates underground in a very large, strong, serpentine root, which strikes off, and branches every way, just under the surface of the earth; and from these roots grow woody cones, called cypress knees, four, five and six feet high, and from six to eighteen inches and two feet in diameter at their bases. The large ones are hollow, and serve very well for bee-hives; a small space of the tree itself is hollow nearly as high as the buttresses already mentioned. From this place the tree, as it were, takes another beginning, forming a grand strait column eighty or ninety feet high, when it divides every way around into an extensive flat horizontal top, like an umbrella, where eagles have their secure nests, and cranes and storks their temporary resting places; and what adds to the magnificence of their appearance is the streamers of long moss that hang from the lofty limbs and float in the winds. . . .

William observes with delight the vivid Carolina parakeets, which he had first seen in Mark Catesby's paintings, now "commonly seen hovering and fluttering" on the tops of the majestic cypress trees, whose seed, in neat, round burs, were their favorite food. To fell these giant trees it was necessary, he said, to construct, above the level of the buttress, a stage or platform large enough to hold the eight or ten Negroes needed to work upon the trunk with their axes. Some of the cypress trees, William noted, measured "eight, ten, and twelve feet in diameter, for forty and fifty feet strait shaft."

At intervals during his sojourn in this earthly paradise, William shared the company of groups of traveling traders, or now and then that of a lone Indian guide, but, in company or alone, nothing seemed to alter the robust happiness with which he relished each day of adventure, danger, or placid contemplation. One can hardly believe that this confident, capable, assured scientist, explorer, and artist, who moves with such serene authority in this challenging wilderness, is the "poor young man" who was the object of Henry Laurens' compassion in this same wilderness only a decade before.

William assuredly was well aware of the miracle and his pages are fragrant with his lyric rejoicings: "How supremely blessed were our hours"; "What an elysium it is!"; "Seduced by these sublime, enchanting scenes . . ." and like phrases combine with an overflow of praise to celebrate his victory.

Even the villains of the scene compelled his fascinated attention. It was at Lake Dexter, upstream from Lake George, that he encountered the multitude of alligators that gave rise to perhaps the most famous and controversial passages in the *Travels,* passages now substantially corroborated by observations of reliable scientists. William's colorful account is so interesting that no apology is needed for the length of these excerpts from it.

I fixed my camp in an open plain, near the utmost projection of the promontory, under the shelter of a large Live Oak, which stood on the highest part of the ground and but a few yards from my boat. From this open, high situation, I had a free prospect of the river, which was a matter of no trivial consideration to me, having good reason to dread the subtle attacks of the allegators, who were crouding about my harbour. Having collected a good quantity of wood for the purpose of keeping up a light and smoke during the night, I began to think of preparing my supper, when, upon examining my stores, I found but a scanty provision, I thereupon determined, as the most expeditious way of supplying my necessities, to take my bob and try for some trout [black bass]. About one hundred yards above my harbour, began a cove or bay of the river, out of which opened a large lagoon. . . .

The verges and islets of the lagoon were elegantly embellished with flowering plants and shrubs; the laughing coots with wings half spread were tripping over the little coves and hiding themselves in the tufts of grass; young broods of the painted summer teal, skimming the still surface of the waters, and following the watchful parent unconscious of danger, were frequently surprised by the voracious trout, and he, in turn, as often by the subtle, greedy alligator. Behold him rushing forth from the flags and reeds. His enormous body swells. His plaited tail brandished high, floats upon the lake. The waters like a cataract descend from his opening jaws. Clouds of smoke issue from his dilated nostrils. The earth trembles with his thunder. When immediately from the opposite coast of the lagoon, emerges from the deep his rival champion. They suddenly dart upon each other. The boiling surface of the lake marks their rapid course, and a terrific conflict commences. They now sink to the bottom folded together in horrid wreaths. The water becomes thick and discoloured. Again they rise, their jaws clap together, re-echoing through the deep surrounding forests. Again they sink, when the contest ends at the muddy bottom of the lake, and the vanquished makes a hazardous escape, hiding himself in the muddy turbulent waters and sedge on a distant shore. The proud victor exulting returns to the place of action. The shores and forests resound his dreadful roar, together with the triumphing shouts of the plaited tribes, witnesses of the horrid combat.

My apprehensions were highly alarmed after being a spectator of so dreadful a battle; it was obvious that delay would but tend to increase my dangers and difficulties as the sun was near setting and the alligators gathered around my harbour from all quarters; from these considerations I concluded to be expeditious in my trip to the lagoon, in order to take some fish. Not thinking it prudent to take my fusee with me, lest I might lose it overboard in case of a battle, which I had every reason to dread before my return, I therefore furnished myself with a club for my defense, went on board, and penetrating the first line of those which surrounded my harbour, they gave way; but being pursued by several very large ones, I kept strictly on the watch, and paddled with all my might towards the entrance of the lagoon, hoping to be sheltered there from the multitude of my assailants; but ere I had half-way reached the place, I was attacked on all sides, several endeavouring to overset the canoe. My situation now became precarious to the last degree: two very large ones attacked me closely, at the same instant, rushing up with their heads and part of their bodies above the water, roaring terribly and belching floods of water over me. They struck their jaws together so close to my ears, as almost to stun me, and I expected every moment to be dragged out of the boat and instantly devoured, but I applied my weapons so effectually about me, though at random, that I was so successful as to beat them off a little; when, finding that they designed to renew the battle I made for the shore. . . .

On recollecting myself, I discovered that I had almost reached the entrance to the lagoon, and determined to venture in, if possible to take a few fish and then return to my harbour, while day-light continued. . . . I accordingly proceeded and made good my entrance into the lagoon, though not without opposition from the alligators, who formed a line across the entrance but did not pursue me into it. . . . I soon caught more trout than I had present occasion for . . . I now prepared for my return to camp, which I succeeded in with but little trouble, by keeping close to the shore. . . .

I . . . then proceeded to cleanse and prepare my fish for supper, and accordingly took them out of the boat, laid them down on the sand close to the water, and began to scale them, when, raising my head, I saw before me, through the clear water, the head and shoulders of a very large alligator, moving slowly towards me; I instantly stepped back, when, with a sweep of his tail, he brushed off several of my fish. It was certainly more providential that I looked up at that instant, as the monster would probably, in less than a minute, have seized me and dragged me into the river.

This incredible boldness of the animal disturbed me greatly, supposing there could now be no reasonable safety for me during the night, but by keeping continually on the watch; I therefore, as soon as I had prepared the fish, proceeded to secure myself and effects in the best manner I could. . . .

William's position was, to say the least, extremely dangerous. A reconnoitering of his campside had revealed that he was in fact isolated on a small islet, cut off from the mainland by marshes and a flooded cypress swamp. Retreat was possible only by climbing one of the large live oaks or by taking to the river in his boat. No fictional Robinson Crusoe, however, could have shown more presence of mind or been more intrepid than William in this frightful situation. The young man who seemed unable to cope with the simplest problems of business was ob-

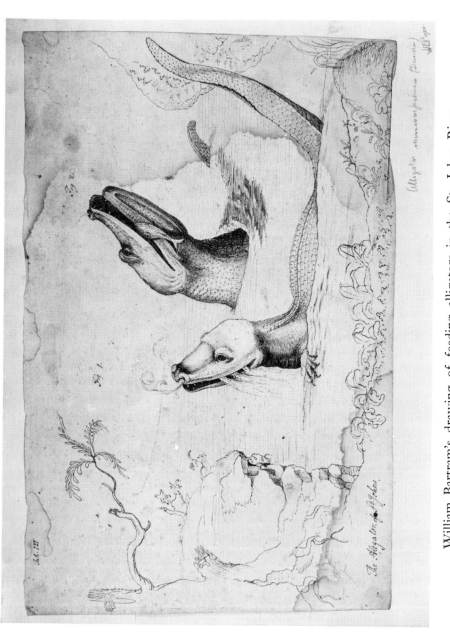

William Bartram's drawing of feeding alligators in the St. Johns River. (Courtesy of the British Museum, Natural History)

viously impressively adequate to the formidable challenges of the wilderness.

It was by this time dusk and the alligators had nearly ceased their roar, when I was again alarmed by a tumultuous noise that seemed to be in my harbour, and therefore engaged my immediate attention. Returning to my camp I found it undisturbed, and then continued on to the extreme point of the promontory, where I saw a scene, new and surprising, which at first threw my senses into such a tumult, that it was some time before I could comprehend what was the matter; however, I soon accounted for the prodigious assemblage of crocodiles at this place, which exceeded everything of the kind I had ever heard of.

How shall I express myself so as to convey an adequate idea of it to the reader, and at the same time avoid raising suspicions of my want of veracity. Should I say, that the river (in this place) from shore to shore, and perhaps near half a mile above and below me, appeared to be one solid bank of fish, of various kinds, pushing through this narrow pass of St. Juans into the little lake, on their return down the river, and that the alligators were in such incredible numbers, and so close together from shore to shore, that it would have been easy to have walked across on their heads, had the animals been harmless. What expressions can sufficiently declare the shocking scene that for some minutes continued whilst this mighty army of fish were forcing the pass? During this attempt, thousands, I may say hundreds of thousands of them were caught and swallowed by the devouring alligators. . . . The horrid noise of their closing jaws, their plunging amidst the broken banks of fish, and rising with their prey some feet upright above the water, the floods of water and blood rushing out of their mouths, and the clouds of vapour issuing from their wide nostrils, were truly frightful. . . .

This extraordinary sight, shocking as it was, brought our lone traveler some reassurance as he concluded the enormous gathering of alligators was primarily in response to the seasonal fish-swarm, which could be expected to keep the fierce predators too busy to disturb his camp. However, the night had other excitement in store for him:

It being now almost night, I returned to my camp, where I had left my fish broiling, and my kettle of rice stewing, and having with me, oil, pepper and salt, and excellent oranges hanging in abundance over my head (a valuable substitute for vinegar) I sat down and regaled myself chearfully; having finished my repast, I re-kindled my fire for light, and whilst I was revising the notes of my past day's journey, I was suddenly roused with a noise behind me toward the main land; I sprang up on my feet, and listening,

I distinctly heard some creature wading in the water of the isthmus; I seized my gun and went cautiously from my camp, directing my steps towards the noise; when I had advanced about thirty yards, I halted behind a coppice of Orange trees, and soon perceived two very large bears, which had made their way through the water, and had landed in the grove, about one hundred yards distance of me, they there began to snuff and look towards my camp, I snapped my piece, but it flashed, on which they both turned about and galloped off, plunging through the water and swamp, never halting as I suppose, until they reached fast land, as I could hear them leaping and plunging a long time; they did not presume to return again, nor was I molested by any other creature, except being occasionally awakened by the whooping of owls, screaming of bitterns, or the wood-rats running amongst the leaves.

With constant vigilance and skillful maneuvers, William managed to continue his voyage of exploration up the river without mishap, in spite of the recurrent danger of having his boat upset by the huge alligators. He even lingered in the area to go ashore, on one occasion, to examine closely a colony of alligator nests.

After some days of sailing in intense and sultry heat, which did not deter the indefatigable William from watching with appreciative eye and recording faithfully the birds and plants along the shores, he reached the entrance "to a beautiful lake, on the banks of which," he noted, "was the farm I was going to visit, and which I designed should be the last extent of my voyage up the river." But nature, in this lovely country, was capricious, capable of sudden and awesome violence; adventures came hard upon each other's heels and William was now caught up in one of the terrifying tropical storms of the southlands, which he describes vividly:

Being heretofore so closely invested, by high forests and deep swamps of the great river, I was prevented from seeing the progress and increase of the approaching tempest, the terrific appearance of which now at once confounded me; how purple and fiery appeared the tumultuous clouds! swiftly ascending or darting from the horizon upwards; they seemed to oppose and dash against each other, the skies appeared streaked with blood or purple flame overhead, the flaming lightning streaming and darting about in every direction around, seems to fill the world with fire; whilst the heavy thunder keeps the earth in a constant tremor.

In an attempt to guide his boat into a small cove for shelter, he was caught up in the turmoil of wind and water:

What a dreadful rushing and roaring there is everywhere around me;
. . . The high forests behind me bend to the blast, and the sturdy limbs of
the trees crack, I had by this time got up abrest of the grove or hommock,
the hurricane close by, pursuing me, I found it dangerous and imprudent
in the highest degree, to put in here, as the groves were already torn up
and the spreading limbs of the ancient Live Oaks were flying over my head,
and carried about in the air as leaves and stubble; . . .

He managed to tie up precariously to a hickory tree leaning over the
bank and rode out the fury of the storm, during which "such floods of
rain fell during the space of half or three quarters of an hour that my
boat was filled, and I expected every moment, when I should see her
sink to the bottom of the lake . . . every object was totally obscured,
excepting the continual streams or rivers of lightning, pouring from
the clouds; all seemed a frightful chaos."

When, after the storm abated, he bailed out his boat and crossed the
lake to his friend's plantation, his host was astounded that William, in
his small boat, had weathered the hurricane, which had devastated the
countryside. "All the buildings on the plantation," reports William,
"except his own dwelling-house, were laid almost flat to the ground, or
the logs and roof rent asunder and twisted about; the mansion-house
shook and reeled over their heads. . . . The great Live Oaks which had
been left standing about the fields, were torn to pieces, their limbs lying
scattered over the ground. . . ."

However, damage from the storm did not diminish the warm welcome and hospitality offered William on the plantation, where he rested
for days, drying his books and specimens and botanizing in the neighborhood with his host. The return journey downriver was leisurely
and serene, long days happily spent watching and sketching the infinite
variety of bird life, plants, and fishes.

By the time he arrived at the entrance to "the little ocean of Lake
George," where he planned to linger, he had just cause for pride in the
arduous and dangerous journey he had completed alone. But William
had his own way of looking at the matter: "I find myself alone," he
wrote on this occasion, "in the wilderness, on the shores of Lake
George. Alone indeed, but under the care of the Almighty, and protected by the invisible hand of my guardian angel."

A few days later he returned to one of the springs which had amazed
both William and his father when the Bartrams had visited the place
years ago. Here John had proudly recorded his son's discovery of the

star anise, one of William's favorites among the Southern plants. The great springs are those known today as Salt Springs in Ocala National Forest. Whereas their flow, depth, and taste of the water absorbed the interest of the older Bartram, to the younger man they were pure enchantment. So rhapsodically did he write of them that the imprint of his enchantment can be traced in the compositions of more than one writer of the romantic era, notably in the lyric magic of Coleridge's *Kubla Khan.*

Here in part are the Salt Springs of Lake George as seen through the romantic eyes of William Bartram:

I seated myself upon a swelling green knoll, at the head of the crystal bason. Near me, on the left, was a point of projection of an entire grove of the aromatic Illisium Floridanum; on my right and all around behind me, was a fruitful Orange grove, with Palms and Magnolias interspersed; in front, just under my feet with the inchanting and amazing crystal fountain, which incessantly threw up, from dark, rocky caverns below, tons of water every minute, forming a bason capacious enough for large shallops to ride in, and a creek of four or five feet depth of water, and near twenty yards over, which meanders six miles through green meadows, pouring its limpid waters into the great Lake George, where they seem to remain pure and unmixed. About twenty yards from the upper edge of the bason and directly opposite to the mouth or outlet to the creek, is a continual and amazing ebullition where the waters are thrown up in such abundance and amazing force as to jet and swell up two or three feet above the common surface: white sand and small particles of shells are thrown up with the waters, near to the top, when they diverge from the center, subside with the expanding flood, and gently sink again, forming a large rim or funnel round about the aperture or mouth of the fountain, which is a vast perforation through a bed of rocks, the ragged points of which are projected out on every side. Thus far I know to be matter of real fact, and I have related it as near as I could conceive or express myself. But there are yet remaining scenes inexpressibly admirable and pleasing.

Behold, for instance, a vast circular expanse before you, the waters of which are so extremely clear as to be absolutely diaphanous or transparent as the ether; the margin of the bason ornamented with a great variety of fruitful and floriferous trees, shrubs and plants, the pendant golden Orange dancing on the surface of the pellucid waters, the balmy air vibrates the melody of the merry birds, tenants of the encircling aromatic grove.

At the same instant innumerable bands of fish are seen, some cloathed in the most brilliant colours; the voracious crocodile stretched along at full length, as the great trunk of a tree in size, the devouring garfish, inimical trout, and all the varieties of gilded painted bream, the barbed catfish, dreaded sting-ray, skate and flounder, spotted bass, sheeps head and ominous drum; all in their separate bands and communities, with free and un-suspicious intercourse performing their evolutions; there are no signs of enmity, no attempt to devour each other; the different bands seem peaceably and complaisantly to move a little aside, as it were to make room for others to pass by.

But behold yet something far more admirable, see whole armies descending into an abyss, into the mouth of the bubbling fountain, they disappear! are they gone forever? is it real? I raise my eyes with terror and astonishment, . . . I look down again to the fountain with anxiety, when behold them as it were emerging from the blue ether of another world, apparently at a vast distance, at their first appearance, no bigger than flies or minnows, now gradually enlarging, their brilliant colours begin to paint the fluid. . . .

This amazing and delightful scene, though real, appears at first but as a piece of excellent painting; there seems no medium, you imagine the picture to be within a few inches of your eyes, and that you may without the least difficulty touch any one of the fish, or put your finger upon the crocodile's eye, when it really is twenty or thirty feet under water.

And although this paradise of fish, may seem to exhibit a just representa-tion of the peaceable and happy state of nature which existed before the fall, yet in reality it is a mere representation; for the nature of the fish is the same as if they were in lake George or the river; but here the water or element in which they live and move, is so perfectly clear and transparent, it places them all on an equality with regard to their ability to injure or escape from one another; . . . here is no covert, no ambush, here the trout freely passes by the very nose of the alligator and laughs in his face, and the bream by the trout.

When he reached the trading post near the present Palatka, a group of Indian traders was just preparing to leave for central Florida to open trade with the natives living in the lake region around the present Gainesville. William joined the expedition.

Upon their arrival at the chief's town they were cordially welcomed and escorted by young Indian men and maidens to the chief's house, where the traditional pipe was filled and handed around, refreshment served, and the usual compliments and inquiries exchanged. The chief was then informed of the nature of their business with which he ex-pressed satisfaction. "He was then," William says, "informed what the nature of my errand was, and he received me with complaisance, giving me unlimited permission to travel over the country for the purpose of collecting flowers, medicinal plants, etc., saluting me by the name of

Puc Puggy or the Flower hunter, recommending me to the friendship and protection of his people."

The Indian conference, terminating in a festive banquet, was followed by a visit to the nearby Alachua Savanna, which inspired William to one of his most memorable and romantic descriptions:

It is encircled with high, sloping hills, covered with waving forests and fragrant Orange groves, rising from an exuberantly fertile soil. The towering Magnolia grandiflora and transcendent Palm, stand conspicuous amongst them. At the same time are seen innumerable droves of cattle; the lordly bull, lowing cow and sleek capricious heifer. The hills and groves re-echo their cheerful, social voices. Herds of sprightly deer, squadrons of the beautiful Siminole horse, flocks of turkeys, civilized communities of the sonorous, watchful crane, mix together, appearing happy and contented in the enjoyment of peace, till' disturbed and affrighted by the warrior man. Behold yonder, coming upon them through the darkened groves, sneakingly and unawares, the naked red warrior, invading the Elysian fields and green plains of Alachua. At the terrible appearance of the painted, fearless, uncontrolled and free Siminole, the peaceful, innocent nations are at once thrown into disorder and dismay. See the different tribes and bands, how they draw towards each other! as it were deliberating upon the general good. Suddenly they speed off with their young in the centre; but the roebuck fears him not: here he lays himself down, bathes and flounces in the cool flood. The red warrior, whose plumed head flashes lightning, whoops in vain; his proud, ambitious horse strains and pants; the earth glides from under his feet, his flowing main whistles in the wind, as he comes up full of vain hopes. The bounding roe views his rapid approaches, rises up, lifts aloft his antlered head, erects the white flag, and fetching a shrill whistle, says to his fleet and free associates, "follow;" he bounds off, and in a few minutes distances his foe a mile; suddenly he stops, turns about, and laughing says, "how vain, go chase meteors in the azure plains above, or hunt butterflies in the fields about your towns."

When William describes the specific he becomes less the poet and more the naturalist, as in some of his observations around Alachua:

Observing a company of wolves (lupus niger) under a few trees, about a quarter of a mile from shore, we rode up towards them, they observing our approach, sitting on their hinder parts until we came nearly within shot of them, when they trotted off towards the forests, but stopped again and looked at us, at about two hundred yards distance; we then whooped, and made a feint to pursue them, when they separated from each other, some stretching off into the plains and others seeking covert in the groves on

William Bartram's drawing of the sandhill crane, which he called "Walloola Great Savannah Crane." (Courtesy of the British Museum, Natural History)

shore; when we got to the trees we observed they had been feeding on the carcase of a horse. The wolves of Florida are larger than a dog, and are perfectly black, except the females, which have a white spot on the breast. . . .

He is far more specific in his description of the sandhill crane in the same area, a bird which was the subject also of one of his most famous sketches.

The wary, sharp sighted crane, circumspectly observing our progress. We saw a female of them sitting on her nest, and the male, her mate, watchfully traversing backwards and forwards, at a small distance; they suffered us to approach near them before they arose, when they spread their wings, running and tipping the ground with their feet some time and then mounted aloft, soaring round and round over the nest; they set upon only two eggs at a time, which are very large, long and pointed at one end, of a pale ash colour, powdered or speckled with brown. The manner of forming their nests and setting is very singular; choosing a tussock and there forming a rude heap of dry grass, or such like materials, near as high as their body is from the ground, when standing upon their feet; on the summit of this they form the nest of fine soft dry grass, when she covers her eggs to hatch them, she stands over them, bearing her body and wings over the eggs.

Another expedition with traders which took him all the way across Florida to the lower reaches of the Suwanee River, which he called the Little St. Juan, rounded out William's summer of 1774. Late fall found him back in Georgia, in the familiar area at the mouth of the Altamaha, where he prepared his collections for shipment and made farewell visits to his "friends and liberal patrons in these parts." "Learning that the honourable Henry Laurens Esq. had a large ship loading at Sunbury for Liverpool," and that Laurens himself was daily expected in a small vessel of his own at Broughton Island, William hastened to meet his friend. Laurens not only saw to it that William's collections were safely consigned on his merchant ship, but he generously gave the young man space in his cabin aboard his own small vessel for the return to Charleston.

⌖ 3

After a winter spent in Charleston and in short excursions in the neighborhood, William Bartram again set out, alone, on April 22, 1775, to visit the mountains beyond the headwaters of the Savannah River. That those mountains were the domain of the Cherokees, a nation then disaffected and bitterly resentful, not without ample cause, of the English colonists, does not appear to have deterred him to any measurable degree. Neither did the impending conflict between the colonies and the Mother Country, the heat of which he must have encountered in Charleston, appear to have given him pause. At that time leading citizens Christopher Gadsden and William Henry Drayton were fanning the flames of conflict in the port city with no less ardor than Samuel Adams in Boston. Only a day or two before William left, a vast store of guns and ammunition had been blatantly taken by "persons unknown" from the royal armory above the Assembly Hall. If William gave thought to these grave developments, he makes no mention of them. Armed only with a few letters of commendation, most notably one provided by Superintendent of Indian Affairs John Stuart, the Quaker naturalist, whose chief armor was always his sublime faith in God and his sincere good will for all his fellow creatures, set out undaunted to follow the spring of 1775 into the backcountry, far beyond any European settlements.

William's way from Charleston to Augusta was one familiar to Mark Catesby, John Bartram, and to William himself. Beyond Augusta to Fort James, his route was along the Georgia side of the Savannah River to its confluence with the Broad, across country most of which now lies deep beneath the waters of Clark Hill Reservoir. The variety of trees and other notable plants he encountered there makes up one of the longest lists in the *Travels,* which one reads with the melancholy nostalgia accorded tales of the drowned and fabled Atlantis.

But there were other and novel observations noted here as well. He describes "chains of hills, whose gravelly, dry, barren summits present detached piles of rocks, which delude and flatter the hopes and expectations of the solitary traveller, full sure of hospitable habitations; heaps of white gnawed bones of the ancient buffaloe, elk, and deer, indiscriminately mixed with those of men, half grown over with moss, altogether, exhibit scenes of uncultivated nature . . . rather disagreeable to a mind of delicate feelings and sensibility, since some of these objects recognize past transactions and events, perhaps not altogether reconcilable to justice and humanity."

Then follows a well-known passage:

How harmoniously and sweetly murmur the purling rills and fleeting brooks, roving along the shadowy vales, passing through dark, subterranean caverns, or dashing over steep rocky precipices, their cold, humid banks condensing the volatile vapours, which fall and coalesce in crystalline drops, on the leaves and elastic twigs of the aromatic shrubs and incarnate flowers. In these cool, sequestered, rocky vales, we behold the following celebrated beauties of the hills, i.e. fragrant Calycanthus [strawberry shrub], blushing Rhododendron ferruginium [rosebay], delicate Philadelphus inordorus [mock orange], which displays the white wavy mantle, with the sky robed Delphinium, perfumed Convalaria [lily of the valley], and fiery Azalea [flame azalea], flaming on the ascending hills, or wavy surface of the gliding brooks. The epithet fiery, I annex to this most celebrated species of Azalea, as being expressive of the appearance of it in flower, which are in general of the colour of the finest red lead, orange and bright gold, as well as yellow and cream colour; these various colours are not only in separate plants, but frequently all the varieties and shades are seen in separate branches on the same plant, and the clusters of the blossoms cover the shrubs in such incredible profusion on the hill sides, that suddenly opening to view from dark shades, we are alarmed with the apprehension of the hills being set on fire. This is certainly the most gay and brilliant flowering shrub yet known: . . .

At Fort James, William crossed over the Savannah River into South Carolina and took the path to the Indian town of "Sinica," the site of which, near Clemson University, lies beneath the waters of Hartwell Reservoir. Thence toward the mountains his path lay through the beautiful "vale of Keowe," the lower part of which already lies beneath Hartwell's waters, and the rest of which will soon be flooded by the reservoir of the immense Keowee-Toxaway hydro-atomic power project.

As he traveled up that lovely vale one peaceful evening, with no sound but the "wary moor fowl [ruffed grouse] thundering in the distant echoing hills," and the "shrill perpetual voice of the whip-poor-will," he seems to have experienced a mood of unaccustomed apprehension: "all alone in a wild Indian country, a thousand miles from my native land, and a vast distance from any settlements of white people. It is true, here were some of my own colour, yet they were strangers, and though friendly and hospitable, their manners and customs of living so different from what I had been accustomed to, administered but little to my consolation; some hundred miles, yet to travel, the savage vindictive inhabitants lately ill-treated by the frontier Virginians, blood being spilt between them and the injury not yet wiped away by formal treaty;

the Cherokees extremely jealous of white people travelling about their mountains, especially if they should be seen peeping in amongst the rocks or digging up their earth." Peeping in among the rocks and digging up their earth was just what William planned to do on this excursion!

However, such moods were rare and, undaunted, he pushed on eagerly toward the purple peaks ahead. Leaving the river, his way lay westward across the Oconee mountain ridge and then down to the Chattooga, and across it back into the extreme northeast corner of Georgia. For William it was a botanist's dream come true. Even as he was feasting his eyes on the magnificent view from the Oconee ridge he discovered a new species of rhododendron among the masses of flame azalea and mountain laurel. Here too were "many trees and plants common in Pennsylvania, New York, and even Canada, . . . but what seems remarkable, the yellow jessamine (Bignonia sempervirens) which is killed by a very slight frost in the open air in Pennsylvania, here on the summits of the Cherokee mountains associates with Canadian vegetables, and appears roving with them in perfect bloom and gaiety; . . ." In this group he noted also the silver-bell tree, the mountain stewartia, wafer ash, and yellow buckeye.

Beyond the eastward-flowing Chattooga loomed a high, narrow ridge of mountains, beyond which the streams flowed northward, their crystal mountain waters starting there on their long, circuitous route to lose themselves in the Gulf of Mexico not far south of their sources here in these hills. This dividing ridge which William thought "the highest ridge of the Cherokee mountains" he named Mount Magnolia for "a new and beautiful species of that celebrated family of flowering trees, which, here at the cascades of Falling Creek, grows in a high degree of perfection. . . ." The beauty of his way along this tributary of War Woman Creek, its lovely falls amid the towering mountain forest, evoked from poet Bartram rapturous response and from botanist Bartram a long list of alpine plant treasures which are sometimes seen romantically as "roving beauties . . . strolling over the mossy, shelving, humid rocks, or from off the expansive wavy boughs of trees, bending over the floods, salute their delusive shades, playing on the surface, some plunge their perfumed heads and bathe their flexile limbs in the silver stream, whilst others by the mountain breezes are tossed about, their blooming tufts bespangled with pearly and crystalline dewdrops collected from the falling mists, glisten in the rain bow arch." The botanist is never long beguiled, however, into neglecting his mission. "Having collected some valuable specimens at this friendly retreat," he concludes the above passage, "I continued my lonesome pilgrimage."

Among the plants he mentioned and may have collected was a wild orchis, probably an Adam-and-Eve or crane-fly orchis, a closely related species of which subsequently contributed much to the modification of Darwin's evolutionary theory, because of the example this plant offers of the necessity of change by mutation. It was found that this temperate zone member of the orchid family had to be cross-pollinated by insects in order to set its seed, but its flowers were observed to be without color, fragrance, or nectar. What inducement, therefore, scientists wondered, could it offer to any insect and how could it lure the visits from the winged creatures necessary for its cross-pollination? Patient observation revealed these facts: the flowers of this orchis closely resemble the female of a certain type of insect, the male members of which species emerge some two weeks before the females; during these two weeks in their female-less world, sex drive keeps the males constantly alighting on these flowers, deceptively resembling the female insect, and coming into full flower at exactly the same time as the emergence of the male insect. With each embrace of the deceiving plant the insect picks up pollen for transport to the next flower lure. The biological significance of these observations to the evolutionary process is based on the fact that this botanical "fraud" could not have been gradually evolved. It had to be achieved in one fell swoop. A less than close resemblance between flower and female insect, or an absence of coincidence in the emergence of the male insect and the flowering of the orchis, would have inevitably resulted in a failure of procreation of the plant species and its subsequent extinction. Ergo, the unavoidable conclusion that the remote ancestor of that orchis plant had to have suddenly, through a mutative "sport," produced flowers not only closely resembling the female insect but timed to greet the male on his emergence.

How that plant and insect vignette would have appealed to William Bartram! The insect sowing his wild oats, the plant reaping its ill-gotten harvest! The marvel of the ways of the Almighty!

From the headwaters of Falling Creek, William moved north through the then unnamed Court House Gap and down into the beautiful valley of the Little Tennessee River. A few days later in company with a young English trader, residing among the Cherokees and familiar with the country round about, William came upon a scene which inspired one of the most idyllic passages in the *Travels:*

[We] began to ascend the hills of a ridge which we were under the necessity of crossing, and having gained its summit, enjoyed a most enchanting view, a vast expanse of green meadows and strawberry fields, a meandering river gliding through, saluting in its various turnings the swelling, green, turfy knolls, embellished with parterres of flowers and fruitful strawberry beds; flocks of turkeys strolling about them; herds of deer prancing in the meads or bounding over the hills; companies of young, innocent Cherokee virgins, some busily gathering the rich fragrant fruit, others having already filled their baskets, lay reclined under the shade of floriferous and fragrant native bowers of Magnolia, Azalea, Philadelphus, perfumed Calycanthus, sweet Yellow Jessamine, and cerulian Glycine frutescens [American wistaria], disclosing their beauties to the fluttering breeze, and bathing their limbs in the cool fleeting streams; whilst other parties, more gay and libertine, were yet collecting strawberries or wantonly chasing their companions, tantalising them, staining their lips and cheeks with the rich fruit.

This sylvan scene of primitive innocence was enchanting, and perhaps too enticing for hearty young men long to continue idle spectators.

In fine, nature prevailed over reason, we wished at least to have a more active part in their delicious sports. Thus precipitately resolving we cautiously made our approaches, yet undiscovered, almost to the joyous scene of action. Now, although we meant no other than an innocent frolic with this gay assembly of hamadryades, we shall leave it to the person of feeling and sensibility to form an idea to what lengths our passions might have hurried us, thus warmed and excited, had it not been for the vigilance and care of some envious matrons who lay in ambush, and espying us gave the alarm, time enough for the nymphs to rally and assemble together; we however pursued and gained ground on a group of them, who had incautiously strolled to a greater distance than their guardians, and finding their retreat now like to be cut off, took shelter under cover of a little grove, but on perceiving themselves to be discovered by us, kept their station, peeping through the bushes; when observing our approaches, they confidently discovered themselves and decently advanced to meet us, half unveiling their blooming faces, incarnated with the modest maiden blush, and with native innocence and cheerfulness, presented their little baskets, merrily telling us their fruit was ripe and sound.

We accepted a basket, sat down and regaled ourselves on the delicious fruit, encircled by the whole assembly of the innocently jocose sylvan nymphs. . . .

After such pleasant companionship in "Elysian fields," as he called
them, and in view of his delight in the natural beauties of this paradise
and the kindliness with which he was received by the Cherokees, it
would be surprising if William had not seriously entertained some
thought of ending here his quest for peace and beauty. But if he did he
gave no hint of it unless there be some suggestion of a stern resistance
to temptation in his decision, unaccountably and suddenly made, a few
weeks after the above interlude, to defer the rest of his mountain researches and to return to Augusta to join a trading expedition soon to
leave there for Mobile.

With the arrival of the summer solstice of 1775, William Bartram
set out from Augusta with a "company of adventurers" bound for West
Florida. Their route across the Creek domain of piedmont Georgia and
lower Alabama was no botanical wonderland comparable with the
mountains and valleys of the Cherokees. There was relatively little
worth recording along their five-hundred-mile trek to Mobile, and most
of that little was unpleasant—the unremitting heat, days when "flying
hosts" of biting flies in incredible numbers "from sunrise to his setting
. . . formed a vast cloud around our caravan so thick as to obscure
every distant object. . . . The head, neck and shoulders of the leading
horses were continually in a gore of blood: . . ." There was a day
when the caravan came across a litter of young wolves, one of which
was caught by one of the party and killed, its brains dashed out with
the butt of a gun. A disgusted William commented, "barbarous sport!
this creature was about half the size of a small cur-dog, and quite
black."

However, although few, there were some intermittent satisfactions
along the way, such as the discovery of the oak-leafed hydrangea which
he found growing in large clumps near the Ocmulgee River in central
Georgia. He made a skillful and detailed drawing of it—one of the most
frequently reproduced of all his botanical illustrations. This "very
singular and beautiful shrub" was covered by several barks, which in
later years earned it its popular name of sevenbark. But, most remarkably, the plant bore two sorts of flowers, panicles of tightly packed, inconspicuous but fruitful flowers, and an overtopping sparse outer cluster
of showy false flowers whose sole *raison d'être* is to advertise to the insect world the nectar and pollen of the plain flowers beneath their
showy canopy.

There was compensation, too, in the beauty and grandeur of some

Hydrangea Quercifolia.

William Bartram's drawing of *Hydrangea quercifolia* (Sevenbark) showing its false flowers advertising the presence of the inconspicuous fertile flowers beneath them. (Reproduced from H. N. Coleridge's copy of the 1792 London edition of Bartram's *Travels* by courtesy of Richard W. Lloyd)

of the forests through which they journeyed, particularly in south central Alabama. For nine or ten miles their path was through a "remarkable grove of dogwood trees, . . . unalterable, except here and there a towering Magnolia grandiflora, . . . their limbs meeting and interlocking with each other, formed a vast, shady, cool grove, so dense and humid as to exclude the sun-beams and prevent the intrusion of almost every other vegetable affording us a most desirable shelter from the fervid sun-beams at noon-day." This dogwood forest was but a small part of a magnificent lofty and colorful forest through which they traveled for seventy unbroken miles. Among its floral embellishments William mentioned silver-bell trees, stewartia, buckeyes, yellow and red azaleas among the shrubs, and American wistaria, yellow jessamine, and coral honeysuckle among the flowering vines.

William described the old French city of Mobile, at which he arrived about the end of July, 1775, as "chiefly in ruins, many houses vacant and mouldering to earth." Nevertheless, it must have provided him with the first opportunity in many moons to enjoy the comforts of civilization. Even so, he tarried but a few days before setting out again, alone, in a canoe headed up through the wide swamps of the lower Mobile River to the confluence of the Tombigbee and the Alabama—an excursion for which he paid dearly, for in the weeks that followed he was ill with a virulent fever that nearly cost him his life. For the botanist, however, the two-hundred-mile canoe trip was eminently successful, as he was able to round out, with his garnerings from the bordering swamps and lowlands, rich shipments of specimens and drawings for Dr. Fothergill.

His journal of the canoe trip recorded such wonders as canes so large that each section could hold a quart, vast areas of the river so thick with American lotus that they appeared as fields "with gay flowers, waving to and fro, on flexible stems, three or four feet high: these fine flowers are double as a rose, and when expanded are seven or eight inches in diameter, of a lively lemon yellow colour"; and a forest in the Tombigbee swamp of cypress, sycamore, sweet gum, and ash, "by far the tallest, straitest, and in every way the most enormous that I have seen or heard of."

He collected many plants of which samples, in the form of seeds, roots, or dried specimens, might be included in the boxes he was preparing for his patron. Among these were the wax tree, *Myrica inordora*, an odorless bayberry which Bartram was the first to introduce to the botanical circle, a new species of silver bell of the two-winged seed variety, a tall sage "of a celestial blue colour," and a plant *Micheliella* (closely related to the plant *Collinsonia*, named by Linnaeus in honor of John Bartram's beloved Peter Collinson), which he was especially desirous of sending to Dr. Fothergill because of its delightful flavor, aroma, and reputedly marvelous medicinal powers.

One of the most exciting of his plant discoveries on this expedition was the giant evening primrose, which William is credited with discovering, naming, and introducing into England. He described it as "perhaps the most pompous and brilliant herbaceous plant yet known to exist," the heavily fragrant flowers of which, "gilded with the richest golden yellow, . . . begin to open in the evening, are fully expanded during the night, and are in their beauty next morning, but close and wither before noon."

The region apparently abounded in animals as well as plants, for William reports spending one night at a plantation whose master, an old man and a famous hunter, was said to kill "three hundred deer annually, besides bears, tygers, and wolves."

No sooner had William returned to Mobile than he was off again in a small coasting vessel headed for Pensacola, the capital of Britain's new holdings of West Florida, extending along the Gulf all the way to the Mississippi. In Pensacola, where his reputation had preceded him, the governor invited him to be a guest in his home and to pursue his botanical work from there at the governor's expense. But William, with his plans to visit lands far beyond the evening sun, could not tarry. After only a few hours he was once more back on shipboard with sails set for Mobile, but in his portfolio he now carried, to augment his accustomed traveling armor of faith and love, the protection of a letter from Governor Peter Chester, proclaiming that William Bartram, botanist, was traveling through the province "for the purpose of collecting rare and useful productions in Botany and Natural History," and commanding "all his Majesty's Servants and Subjects within this Province that they do not interrupt him in his lawful proceedings, but that they be aiding and assisting to him as becometh all encouragers of useful Discoveries."

A royal permit, however, was no magic talisman against the most sinister enemy in this seductive country, the virulent fevers, of which William had more than once been a victim. He was no sooner back in Mobile than he was attacked by some mysterious malady which concentrated its fury on his eyes. Nevertheless he embarked, as planned, on a large trading boat, owned and captained by a French plantation owner and bound for his home on the Pearl River. A day or two after their arrival at this plantation, however, William's condition became so serious that he was carried by his alarmed host to the nearby river home of a neighbor, an "English gentleman who had a variety of medicines." The Englishman, Mr. Rumsey, William reports, "received me kindly and treated me with the utmost humanity during a stay of four or five weeks; the night, however, after my arrival here I sincerely thought would be my last, and my torments were so extreme as to desire it."

When at last his health and his eyesight permitted, William left the kindly Rumsey household and set sail for the Mississippi, via Lake Pontchartrain, into the Amite River, to Manchac, not far below Baton Rouge.

There, in late October, 1775, William Bartram stood at last on a high bluff upon the banks of the great river. "At evening," he says simply, "arrived at Manchac, where I directed my steps to the banks of the Mississippi where I stood as it were fascinated by the magnificence of the great sire of rivers." It was a great moment. To reach the Mississippi had been one of John Bartram's most persistent dreams, which he had shared with his son. During the years 1763 and 1764, almost every letter from John to Collinson contained some echo of this longing. "Oh what a noble discovery I could have made on the banks of the Ohio and the Mississippi," he wrote once. "My William wanted to go as draughtsman." Now, a dozen years later, William had realized the dream alone.

This was, however, to be the westward limit of his travels. His long illness, which had left him with some chronic weakness in his eyes, "contracted," as he said, "the span of my pilgrimage South-Westward." He lingered along the Mississippi for some weeks sailing up and down the river, botanizing, collecting, studying the geology of the riverbanks. He visited several delightful and spacious plantations, and with new-found friends explored some of the river islands and made brief forays across the river. Near Pointe Coupee he noted "great numbers of wild fowl, wading in the shoal water that covers the sandy points, to a vast distance from the shores: they were geese, brant, gannet, and the great and beautiful whooping crane (grus alber)."

In late November he was back in Mobile, preparing his shipments of "growing roots, seeds, and curious specimens" for Dr. Fothergill, and a few weeks later he was once more upon the long wilderness trail back to Augusta and Savannah. The discomforts and dangers of this return trip in the rigors of winter were, if anything, worse than those of the journey down in midsummer. Flooding rivers and streams necessitated the construction of rafts of bundled canes, to be pulled back and forth with grapevine ropes, to move the packs across while men and mounts braved the icy water to effect their crossings. Always present was the danger of serious Indian trouble. The American Revolution was now in full swing and William was traveling from provinces loyal to the British cause into disaffected Georgia and Carolina.

Nevertheless, by the end of February, 1776, William was safely back in Savannah. However, it would be almost another year before the wanderer returned to his home on the Schuylkill. The *Travels* reveals little of his activities during the intervening year. He visited "several districts in Georgia and the East borders of Florida" and prepared and shipped his collections to England. He returned to the spot beside the Altamaha River where the *Franklinia* was now in "perfect bloom, as well as bearing ripe fruit." The *Travels* gives a detailed description of this famous discovery of the Bartrams, which William calls "a flowering tree, of the first order for beauty and fragrance of blossoms . . . which we have honoured with the name of the illustrious Dr. Benjamin Franklin. . . ."

It seems probable that William revisited the McIntosh home at the mouth of the Altamaha before leaving Georgia, but there is no mention of this. The account of his homeward voyage is almost as brief and lacking in detail as the account of his activities during the year 1776. At least we can assume that he set out from Savannah after the south-ward-flying migratory birds had reached Georgia, for, at a plantation about eight miles up the river where he was briefly a guest, several of the servants came in soon after his arrival with "horse loads of wild pigeons (Columbia migratoria) which it seems they had collected in a short space of time at a neighboring Bay swamp." There is no comment in the *Travels* on his visit of several days in Charleston and only a few botanical notes on his visit at the Cape Fear home of his remaining Bartram cousins.

Though the Revolutionary War was in progress all during the last year and a half of the period covered by the *Travels*, the conflict is never mentioned by the author. An acquaintance of William Bartram in later years, with a reputation for veracity, related the story that William briefly joined General McIntosh's militia when rumor predicted an impending invasion of Georgia from St. Augustine, and that the botanist withdrew when the invasion did not materialize. However, there is no confirmation of this in any of William's writings. It seems impossible for the peace-loving Quaker not to have been deeply disturbed by the stress and fever all about him. In early July a fifty-ship British armada made an unsuccessful attack on Charleston, driven off by colonial soldiers in their palmetto log fortress on Sullivans Island, but William, who may well have been in the city at the time, does not refer to even this dramatic battle. The Cape Fear region, once so familiar to him, must have been a place of tension and suspicion at the time of his return trip, for earlier in the year, at nearby Moores Creek Bridge, neighboring Tories and Whigs had clashed in bloody engagement, but the journal has no reference to any aspect of the crisis. Whatever deep convictions William may have held about the crucial and immediate issues of revolution in his own country, he left no specific statement. His whole life, however, was a testament of peace and faith in Quaker principles, which he stated in his own words: "I profess myself of the Christian Sect of the People called Quakers, & consequently am against War & violence, in any form or maner whatever."

⤳ 4

Early in January, 1777, he reached his father's home from which he had set out almost four years earlier. It is pleasant to imagine the joyful reunion between father and son, the many delights which William's return must have given the older Bartram: the vicarious pleasure derived by the old traveler from his son's stories and diaries, the news of their Southern friends, the anticipation of spring inherent in each root and package of seed from William's saddlebags. The return of the wanderer, safe and successful in his quest, brought much needed consolation to the old man, for whom the war, raging ever closer to the nearby capital city, was a constant grief as well as an ever present threat of destruction to his home and garden. One likes to believe that William's return softened the burden of John Bartram's final months, all during the year 1777, until his final brief illness and death in the autumn of that year.

With the death of his father a new life was about to begin for William Bartram. Now, what with manumission from the efforts of others to direct his development, with the self-confidence gained from his expedition, a "success" of sorts to his credit, and the catharsis of his gypsy years, he was in truth a free spirit at last—free to follow his own nature and live a simple life unfettered by the extraneous rules of the marketplace. The struggle had been long. He was nearly forty years old. The serene years ahead, however, were to exceed in number the troubled ones of the past, of which they were the fruit.

Much of his remaining life was given over to the care of his father's beloved garden, to which, although the legal title had passed to John Bartram, the younger, the spiritual title had passed to William. There was no distracting him from that dedication. He continued to live in the family home on the Schuylkill, first with John and his wife, and, after their deaths, with their daughter, Anne, familiarly called Nancy.

He was absorbed, during the first dozen years after his father's death, in revising and editing his diaries into the text of the *Travels*, a demanding task, for he was also preparing, for insertion in the published work, a natural history catalogue, which included the most nearly complete listings of the birds of eastern North America which had yet been published—some two hundred and fifteen species, nearly twice the number included in Catesby's *Natural History*. William Bartram's bird studies were not of the traditional "kill and collect" sort. On the contrary, he was the pioneer of living ornithology with emphasis on what the bird does instead of on its physical specifications alone. His travels had enabled him to observe the phenomenon of bird migration over a wide latitude so that he was able to include in his treatment of birds by far the most advanced discussion of American birds of passage yet to appear.

In addition to an account of his journey and a wealth of natural history lore accumulated during those years of wandering, the *Travels* contained a valuable report on the Indian tribes he had visited. This section, called "An Account of the Persons, Manners, Customs, and Governments of the Muscogulges, or Creeks, Cherokees, Choctaws, etc.," is as revealing of William Bartram as of the aborigines who are his subject. With kindliness, tolerance, and warmth, he discussed those peoples with whom he had spent the better part of the four great years of his life. With a fairness reminiscent of John Lawson, he praised their virtues: their hospitality and liberality, their affection for their children, and their loving natures. In his opinion, "if we divest ourselves of prejudice and think freely," we must conclude that "as moral men they certainly stand in no need of European civilization."

Little green Bittern — half natural size.

William Bartram's drawing of the green heron which he called "Little Green Bittern." (Courtesy of the British Museum, Natural History)

The *Travels* was an impressive achievement whose influence, as with any work of enduring value, was to extend far beyond the limits of its author's life, in space and time. The first American edition, in 1791, was followed by a London edition in 1792, and during the next decade by at least nine or ten European editions, some of which may have been pirated. Its reception in this country was disappointing, but in Britain, France, and Germany, where the romantic movement was coming into full flower, the *Travels* found a public eager for all it had to offer: tropical paradises, peopled by primitive peoples of Rousseauean virtues, dangerous adventures in exotic wonderlands full of strange plants and animals, and the whole picturesque scene presented in poetic, vivid prose. The influence of the *Travels* on English poets, especially Wordsworth and Coleridge, and on French prose writers, notably Chateaubriand, has been the subject of much scholarship and is beyond the scope of this study. On a more scientific plane, William's book remains an amazingly accurate and scientific record of careful observations of a great variety of natural history productions in the wilderness of colonial America, and as such the *Travels* continues to be justly consulted and valued.

But neither the eager reception of his book in Europe nor the meager appreciation in America seems to have disturbed William's happiness. Through those serene years, as the reputation of the botanical garden beside the gentle-flowing Schuylkill grew, so also did the reputation of its gardener, noted also as botanist, traveler, artist, and author. Nothing, however, could induce him to separate himself again from those beloved acres. An offer of the chair of botany at the University of Pennsylvania failed to entice him. He was elected to membership in the American Philosophical Society, but records fail to show that he ever traveled into town to attend a meeting. Even an invitation from President Thomas Jefferson to accompany, as official naturalist, the Lewis and Clark transcontinental expedition—a jewel of an offer for a wilderness naturalist!—could not lure him from his home. He pled infirmities of age. He was not too infirm, however, to prepare illustrations for Dr. Benjamin Barton's book, *Elements of Botany*. Nor was he too infirm to tend his garden, where he entertained an ever growing number of pilgrims, who came as much to see the sage of Kingsessing as to see the botanical wonders of the famed garden.

There, where John Bartram had delighted to entertain his friends, William in turn welcomed such famous visitors as Thomas Jefferson,

George Washington, Alexander Hamilton, John Rutledge, James Madison, and George Mason.

More congenial and enjoyable visits, no doubt, were those from fellow botanists, such as André Michaux and his son, François André, and, most significant for us, the visits of the poor poet and schoolteacher from nearby Gray's Ferry, Alexander Wilson. The latter, thanks in large measure to William Bartram's inspiration, encouragement, and help, was to become famous as the father of American ornithology. There were artist friends too, one of whom, Charles Willson Peale, painted a charming portrait of William Bartram with a gay spray of spring beauties tucked into his cravat. William Dunlap, artist and author, who walked with the novelist, Charles Brockden Brown, early one morning from Philadelphia to Kingsessing to visit the Bartrams' garden, has left a brief pen sketch of the gentle naturalist in 1797:

. . . Arrived at the Botanist's Garden, we approached an old man, who, with a rake in his hand, was breaking the clods of earth in a tulip bed. His hat was old and flapped over his face, his coarse shirt was seen near his neck, as he wore no cravat or kerchief; his waistcoat and breeches were both of leather, and his shoes were tied with leather strings. We approached and accosted him. He ceased his work, and entered into conversation with the ease and politeness of nature's noblemen. His countenance was expressive of benignity and happiness. This was the botanist, traveller, and philosopher we had come to see.

"Benignity and happiness" indeed graced his life, spent to the end in the service of the science he loved. According to a contemporary report: "A few minutes before his death he wrote an article on the natural history of a plant, and, in rising from his desk to take a morning survey of the botanic grounds, he had proceeded only a few steps from his door when he burst a blood-vessel, which suddenly closed his useful life July 22, 1823, in the 85th year of his age." Soon the pilgrims came no more to the banks of the Schuylkill and the garden began its long decline.

Chapter 6

ANDRÉ AND FRANÇOIS ANDRÉ MICHAUX

~ 1

The mountains of North Carolina have long been known as a botanical paradise for nature lovers, and the names of famous naturalists are linked with their awesome beauty. Among these names, none is more revered than that of André Michaux, French botanist and explorer, whose ardent love for the Carolina mountains makes them a fitting stage on which to begin our story of his American adventure. The time: August 30, 1794; the place: the summit of Grandfather Mountain; the characters: André Michaux and his guide Davenport; the dialogue, as given in André's journal entry: "Reached the summit of the highest mountain of all North America, and with my companion and guide, sang the *Marseillaise* and shouted 'Long live America and the Republic of France, long live Liberty, etc., etc.'"

It matters little that Grandfather Mountain is not even the highest mountain in the Southern Appalachians. Rising from a lower base than most of its loftier neighbors and dramatically situated so that its twin peaks and impressive bulk dominate the surrounding landscape, it gives the illusion of unexcelled height, an illusion heightened for the intrepid climber by the breath-taking view from its summit. For the exultant Frenchman, at any rate, it was the top of the visible world—a perfect place to celebrate the glorious triumph of freedom.

This heady perch had been attained only after four days of arduous trail clearing through the tangle of quasi-rain forest, of perilous climbing along precipitous cliffs and up the steep rock faces. No doubt the sharp exhilaration of attaining the great peak was intensified by his fascination with the whole green wonderland lying far below. The surrounding forest within the orbit of his vision was unmatched in variety in all the temperate world. All of Europe from its evergreen forests against the Arctic Circle to the sunbaked Grecian Isles could offer only a little more than half as many species of trees as might be found within a few miles of his lofty aerie. In the nine years that Michaux had already spent in America, this botanical cornucopia had drawn him insatiably back again and again to the wild and dangerous hill country.

Even so, his shouted paeans for the two young republics and for liberty were the spontaneous plaudits of a sincere republican and needed no other stimuli. Although he had come to the fields and forests of the New World as the plenipotentiary of Louis XVI and Marie Antoinette, nine years in the earthshaking young republic, nine years of crisscrossing its dimensions from north to south and east to west, nine years of association with farmers and planters who opened their homes to him, with restless adventurers he met at the inexorably intimate (and often execrable) inns and taverns of the frontiers, with scientists and political leaders to whom he had brought letters of introduction from France and by whom he had been warmly welcomed, hospitably entertained, and generously assisted, had all conspired to subvert this royal emissary, to convert him to an ardent partisan of the inspiring Jeffersonian-Rousseauean philosophy of "liberté, égalité, and fraternité."

This enthusiastic republican had been born on March 7, 1746, in the royal shadow of Versailles, on a farm at Satory, a royal domain entrusted for generations to his forebears. By the time he was twenty his father and mother had died, leaving him with the care of his younger brother and sisters and the family farm. However, nature had given the young Michaux a brilliant and eager mind and an insatiably restless nature, not easily satisfied by the narrow confines of a farm. He sought wider horizons at first through study, striving for mastery of Greek and Latin, indispensable tools of scholarship in the eighteenth century, and in this formidable task he was aided by an extraordinary facility in languages. In 1769 he married Cecile Claye, daughter of a neighboring farmer. Her death, less than a year later at the birth of their son, François André Michaux, plunged him into profound despair and changed the whole pattern of his life. The studious young French farmer, devoted to his fertile acres, would become, in a few years, a wandering naturalist-explorer, infatuated with the whole green world.

The change in his circumstances began with his association with Louis-Guillaume Lemonnier, court physician at Versailles and professor of botany at the king's garden. Near the palace gardens and the Michaux farm the doctor had his own garden, where he experimented in plant breeding and the naturalization of exotics, especially imports from America. In the years following Cecile's death the garden at Montreuil became Michaux's classroom and the learned doctor his tutor. Lemonnier's plant-breeding experiments inspired his pupil to undertake experiments with farm crops, with successful results that brought the young man to the attention of the botanical circle of the palace community. As his mental horizons expanded and his self-confidence increased, the dreams of early boyhood began to awaken again—a world wanderlust—and Michaux longed to escape the grief-haunted scenes of Satory to seek consolation and fulfillment in faraway places.

When he had read, as a boy of fourteen, Quintus Curtius in his school Latin class, he had dreamed of one day seeing the romantic and exotic lands of Alexander's saga of Eastern conquest. Now he studiedly embarked on a course of training and experience that would take him far from France and often far from civilization. His first step outward bound was an appointment to study botany under Bernard and Antoine Laurent de Jussieu, at the gardens of Marie Antoinette's Trianon, where he remained for two years. Then, turning his farm entirely over to his brother, he went to Paris to continue his natural history studies at the Jardin du Roi, where he was soon assigned to collect for the royal gardens. He was on his way.

His first expedition was only as far as England, in search not so much of native British plants as of interesting exotics whose importation, as we have seen in the Catesby and Bartram stories, had long been popular in fashionable and scientific circles alike. The journey served only to whet his appetite. Enchanted by many plants he saw there, he longed even more intensely to visit the distant countries of their origin.

Several other European journeys came first. In 1780 he joined the great naturalist, Jean Baptiste Lamarck, and the botanist, André Thouin, on an expedition into the wild, high region of Auvergne. A contemporary reported that, as soon as these learned men "had quitted the place where they had passed the night, Michaux, furnished with a haversack, a pocketbook, and several tin boxes, would run before them and mount the summit of the hills. He had in his pocket the seed of the cedar of Lebanon, which he sowed in places favorable to it." From afar they saw him "conversing with the shepherds, then heard the discharge of his musket, and at night he returned to the rendezvous, loaded with a collection not only of plants, but birds, insects and minerals."

Other field expeditions, including one to the Pyrenees, only fed the hungry yearning of the young naturalist for faraway countries. At last, in 1781, the brother of the king, mentioned often in Michaux's future letters as "Monsieur frère du Roy," agreed to sponsor him in a botanical expedition to the fabled lands of Alexander's dramatic marches. The fabulous odyssey of André Michaux had begun.

In 1782, 1783, and 1784, such fairy-tale names as Aleppo, Bagdad, and Isfahan became mileposts along the lonely marches of the horizon-bewitched Michaux. Legend takes him far beyond—to the Caspian Sea and even across Afghanistan, in the footsteps of Alexander, all the way to the borders of India and south to the Arabian Sea. In the light of his almost incredible later travels it is easy to give credence to such legends.

In an amazing display of the facility with which he could master strange languages, Michaux, even as he traveled, soon became sufficiently versed in the language of the Persians to complete a French-Persian dictionary. Considering the wild lawlessness then prevalent over much of the country, it is remarkable that he survived his fantastic treks among hostile peoples in an equally hostile physical environment. On one occasion he was waylaid by an Arab band, robbed of everything but his books, and left naked on the desert trail. Miraculously rescued, he remained a prisoner until his release was secured by the British consul. There is also a rumor that he escaped from captivity on another occasion by employing his plant lore to cure the ailing leader of his captors.

After three years of wandering these ancient lands in search of beautiful, interesting, and useful plants, Michaux returned to France, in June of 1785, bringing with him a magnificent collection of dried specimens and a historical collection of seeds. He is credited with introducing to the West many of our favorite plants of Asiatic origin, such as the *Camellia*, the "mimosa" (*Albizzia julibruissin*), the ginkgo, the pomegranate, the tea, the tallow tree (*Sapium sebiferum*), the sweet olive, and the Grecian laurel (*Laurus nobilis*).

Michaux scarcely had time to shake from his shoes the dust of Eastern deserts before he was summoned by Count d'Angeviller, director of the royal parks and gardens, and asked to undertake a botanical mission to

eastern North America. Although he had hoped to return to Persia and
to explore northward to Samarkand and Karakorum, he readily embraced the new assignment presented to him as a mission of pragmatic
urgency.

The urgency behind the mission had welled up in France during
Michaux's years in the East as a concomitant of historical events and
the activities of a group of men, both French and American. The
mounting rivalry between France and England for mastery of the seas,
the almost total exhaustion of France's domestic forest reserves of the
quality required for naval vessels, and her losses under the Treaty of
Paris in 1763 of the forests of Louisiana and Canada, upon which she
had been relying to offset her domestic lack of ship timbers, had significance not only to France and the other nations involved but to the
personal lives and careers of André Michaux and his son François. To
the national interest, restoration of French forests to serve the French
navy, through a massive importation of American trees adapted to the
soil, climate, and needs of France, there was added the powerful incentive of the imperative of fashion.

The enthusiasm for botany and the culture of exotic plants that had
been the fashion for English gentry for several decades had its parallel
in France. But the French had been accustomed to getting by way
of England most of the plants native to Great Britain's American
colonies. The war for American independence had changed all this.
Not only did interest in American plants increase in France as a result
of the close association of the two countries during the war, but the in-
terruption of friendly intercourse between Great Britain and her revolting colonies prevented France from continuing to get American
plants secondhand through England and set the stage for an increasingly
active and direct Franco-American botanical exchange. Benjamin
Franklin and Thomas Jefferson, who successively represented the colonies and the young American republic at the French court, were
notable in encouraging this trend. These two remarkable men, both
popular among the French, shared an avid interest in science and a
special dedication to the support of Franco-American botanical exchange. Perhaps it is worth remarking here that during the height of
hostilities between the American colonies and England, Franklin himself, then an emissary to France from the rebels, continued to aid in
arranging for shipments of plants from America to France and the
sharing of these with fellow naturalists in the enemy country across the

channel. One wonders if such civilized behavior would be permitted in our "more enlightened" century.

Among the many Frenchmen who had significant influence on Franco-American botanical exchange at this time may be mentioned St. John de Crèvecoeur, consul to New York, more interested in the green inhabitants of the New World than in its people, a competent and energetic student of American flora, who early recognized the importance of plant exchange and worked actively to promote it, and the three men who were probably most responsible for the American mission of Michaux: Count d'Angeviller, governor of the royal domain of Rambouillet and special patron of Michaux, l'abbé Nolin, director of the royal nurseries, and André Thouin, in charge of most of the official correspondence between the government and its botanists.

⁓➣ 2

In mid-November, 1785, André Michaux and his son, François, then aged fifteen, with a trained gardener, Paul Saulnier, and one servant, Jacques Reynaud, landed in New York to begin their American odyssey. Barely three weeks later, returns from the mission were already on their way back to France. Despite difficulties "beyond expression," bad weather, "in turn freezing and snowing," Michaux had ransacked the country around New York, the hills across the Hudson, and the Hackensack lowlands beyond, and had succeeded in collecting enough to fill several boxes, one of trees, "very large," others of seeds, cranberries, "from which the people make jam," and "Carolina potatoes" (sweet potatoes). The first shipment of trees and plants was hard to pack properly for he had not yet located suitable moss. Compounding his difficulties was the lack of a "single convenient spot in which to keep our collections" and only one very small room for himself and all his belongings.

The amazing energy and competence with which Michaux began his work in America was characteristic. Before another month had passed, he had found, near Bergen, New Jersey, on a branch of the Hackensack River, a spot suitable for a garden to serve as a way station for his plants destined for France, as a nursery to produce seedlings for shipment, as an exchange depot for Old World plants for barter, and as a home for Paul Saulnier and his helper. He wrote enthusiastically to Lemonnier: "I have acquired a place which unites all the advantages possible for an establishment of this kind, we find there the proximity of great forests for collections of seeds and trees, and the proximity of New York and of the river for connection with packet boats. Then we have the neighborhood of the swamps, a sort of marshy ground, which produces the most sought after trees and plants, a great number of which are probably not yet known."

In order to buy these acres Michaux had to persuade the New Jersey authorities to modify the state law prohibiting alien ownership of land. In March, 1786, the Assembly authorized Michaux, "acting for the King of France," to purchase the land where the naturalist was already busily at work laying out the garden and supervising the construction of the requisite buildings. There was always a fire in his heels, however, and before spring had made its way to New York, Michaux, who had already lingered longer than his wont in one place, set out to meet the season.

First he went to Philadelphia, capital of the new confederation. Although the union of the thirteen insurgent colonies was still so weak that it was scarcely yet a nation, its ally, France, had honored it with a minister to whom Michaux wished to present himself. In Philadelphia was to be found also Mr. Franklin, friend of France, friend of science, with a special interest in international plant exchange. Michaux may have known him years before in France; in any event, a visit to the old inventor was one of the objects of his journey to the capital. Yet another and perhaps the most exciting attraction for the French botanist was the Bartrams' garden and a meeting with William Bartram.

From Philadelphia he continued on south, perhaps as far as Williamsburg. In one of his first letters from America he had mentioned the necessity of a Southern garden to receive such plants as *Magnolia grandiflora* and he suggested Williamsburg as a possible location. In any event, summer found him in northern Virginia, on his way back to New York, as is indicated by this excerpt from George Washington's diary for Monday, June 19, 1786:

A Monsr. André Michaux, a botanist sent by the Court of France to America (after having been only 6 weeks returned from India) came in a little before dinner with letters of introduction and recommendation from the Duke de Lauzen and Marqs. de la Fayette to me—he dined and returned afterwards to Alexandria, on his way to New York . . .

In early September, Michaux and his son sailed for Charleston. The activity of its port and its proximity to the mountains and the less thoroughly explored Southern regions had led Michaux to choose Charleston rather than Williamsburg for his Southern base. By early November he had found and purchased a garden site, one hundred and eleven acres, located ten miles north of Charleston, in an area now occupied by the Charleston Army Air Base. Presumably much of his time during the late fall and winter was spent in developing this new garden and its facilities, but it is always a reasonable assumption that Michaux did not confine himself for long to one area. It seems unlikely that he could have resisted for five months the urge to see the country beyond the estuaries, marshes, and pine barrens of his new establishment; but of such expeditions we have no record, for the surviving journals of André Michaux begin only with his expedition in the spring of 1787, which took him to the Cherokee Indian country, in the neighborhood of the place where North Carolina, South Carolina, and Georgia meet.

These journals are a precious legacy to all lovers of the plant kingdom. Writing by campfire, or *"au clair de la lune,"* in a fine, cramped script, in a series of small, sweat-stained notebooks, he recorded his adventures day by day as he journeyed into the green heart of wilderness America. Though his entries are the orderly and meticulous notes of a conscientious scientist, primarily concerned with accurate recordings of botanical facts and natural history observations, with few expressions of emotion or opinion, and little embellishment of descriptive adjectives, it is impossible not to feel, as one reads, the writer's thralldom to the green world and his warm and single-hearted devotion to all green and growing things. Here and there are anecdotes or comments on fellow-travelers, often with brief flashes of dry wit or irony, many accounts, always restrained and low-key, of dangers and hardships; there are careful records of such facts as might aid other travelers: mileage, condition of roads and rivers, good and bad lodging places. Occasionally the notes refer to beautiful women, encountered at some of the homes which offered hospitality to the lonely traveler, but never does it appear that any such attraction could divert him from or even delay for a day his pursuit of his ever beckoning green mistress.

On this journey, the first his surviving diaries record, Michaux traveled in company with his son and a servant, following the way familiar to Catesby and the Bartrams, across the low country, to Two Sisters Ferry on the Savannah. Also in the company was the Scottish botanist, John Fraser, soon to become a thorn in the side of the French botanist. Along the roadside, in the somber moss-hung forests of live oaks, water oaks, myrtles, and bays, bespangled with dogwood in full flower, through the flat, parklike, grass-covered forests of stately long-bolled pines, and in the wide swamps and marshes bordering the Edisto, the Ashepoo and the Combahee rivers, he noted with suppressed excitement the special glories of each terrain. Near the streams the pervading gloom was touched with flashes of white from the delicate bell-shaped flowers of the two-winged silver-bell tree. In the lower areas of the pine flats the tall, intriguing trumpets of the carnivorous *Sarracenia lutea*, with its foul-smelling, yellow flowers, grew among the inkberries and sweet pepperbushes. On the higher levels two sorts of lupine, one blue and one purple, and two species of verbena colored the forest floor. In the swamps it was the trees—standing in the dark, stagnant-looking water, here and there covered with agglomerations of floating duckweed, the multitude of those tiny plants giving the appearance of green scum—that impressed him with their size and beauty: the cypresses, with their great, flaring bases and delicate fernlike green leaves, and the tupelos with similar bell-shaped bases. Less deep in the swamp, two kinds of pawpaws were in flower, and the red bays, elegant gordonias, and magnolias shone in their polished evergreen foliage. The air was fragrant with a medley of scents, from sweet bays, sweet pepperbushes, and hollies.

Six days after leaving Charleston the party reached the banks of the Savannah, where for two days they tarried to explore and collect in the lush and fecund swamp. Everywhere the wild azalea, sometimes called pinkster, was in full and fragrant blossom. Among less common plants he listed there by the river were the scarlet Virginia pink, several showy species of milkweed, and the thorny water locust. There, too, for the first time Michaux saw the flame azalea, so much admired by William Bartram; and he noted also the colorful little orchids, the *Pagonia*, and the swamp-rose orchis.

However, these swampy Edens also have their serpents, both harmless species and poisonous ones; although Michaux displayed a sensible caution toward the latter, he was fascinated by the variety and beauty of the snakes he encountered. "This morning I killed a very beautiful snake, with vivid red, yellow, and black bands," he wrote. These words may describe equally well the venomous coral snake or its harmless little mimic, the scarlet king snake. "I killed three snakes called mocassin. . . . My son killed another species called the blacksnake which

is the enemy of the serpent sonnette [rattlesnake] but is not venomous. . . ."

After crossing the river the party set out for Savannah, but the road
was incredibly bad and progress was slow. "We found the road so
bad that we made only two miles in five hours time. One must pass
through mud and water to the height of the horses' legs. In one place,
the bridge having broken down, the horses had to swim." He described Savannah as a village of fifty houses situated on sand dunes
overlooking the river. After a day of rest and another of preparation
they continued on down the low country to the Ogeechee Ferry on
their way to the Altamaha River—inspired no doubt by William
Bartram's tales of the rare finds he and his father made there nearly a
quarter century earlier. At the crossing of the Ogeechee he noted
the tupelo known as the Ogeechee lime, the fragrant spider lilies, and
the quantities of wild rice growing in the river shallows.

As it turned out, however, Michaux did not reach the Altamaha until
years later. A little beyond the Ogeechee, at the now abandoned port
of Sunbury, he became ill from the infection of an insect bite. Young
François and their servant traveled on to the region of the *Franklinia*
and the *Pinckneya*, while Michaux remained behind, nursing his swollen
leg, and attempting to arrange passage for them all on a boat to St.
Augustine. He was unsuccessful in this, however, and, as the season was
sufficiently advanced for botanizing in the mountains by the time he had
recovered and the party was reunited, they turned about to follow the
Savannah River up to the Cherokee towns.

It was early May, 1787, when they arrived back at Two Sisters Ferry
and started out up the crude wagon road that had been only an Indian
path when Catesby had known it in 1722 and only a packhorse trail
when John Bartram and his son had first ventured along it in 1765.
Two days up the trail and halfway to Augusta, Michaux lost his
horses, strayed or stolen in the night. He used this misfortune as an
excuse to rid himself of the company of Fraser, who had sworn to
follow him wherever he went. Michaux confided to his journal that, on
setting out from Charleston, he had accepted the company of the Scot
in the hopes that a Briton might be of help in "these little settled
parts," but Fraser had proved so irritating and uncongenial that
Michaux seized with relief the first chance to tactfully send him on
his way, as André and François set out on a futile search for the horses.

After several days devoted to the search they gave up and set out again

P. J. Redouté Del.   Plée Sc.

PINCKNEYA *pubens.*

The rare and beautiful *Pinckneya*, discovered by John Bartram on the Altamaha River, from P. J. Redouté's illustration for André Michaux's *Flora
Boreali-Americana.* (Courtesy of the Caroliniana Library of the University
of South Carolina)

for Augusta, on foot, trundling a cart to carry their specimens. On the way they came upon a group of armed horsemen in pursuit of a notorious horse thief, a certain "Captain." A day or two later they learned that the captain had been caught and shot but an accomplice had escaped with the stolen horses into the country of the Creek Indians. This was but the first of many times during his travels that Michaux lost his horse or horses, sometimes straying away, often stolen.

The way was bad and progress slow, sometimes only two miles, as on the day the wheel of their cart broke, or four miles on a day of especially heavy rains, or ten on the occasion when they had to improvise with logs a way across an alligator-infested stream. Though constantly beset by such difficulties, Michaux's vitality never flagged. He noted the fragrant strawberry shrub displaying its many-petaled brick-red flowers and the rose acacia with its heavily scented blossoms like masses of pink sweet peas. As they moved into the clay hills, yellow lady's-slippers and trilliums began to appear along the trail.

When at length they reached Augusta, they found a village far smaller and poorer than its reputation. Michaux commented on its location, as agreeable as any town "in all North America, but with few houses," a place that could not supply even the basic necessities to the traveler, and "the inhabitants, for the most part, are idlers, gamblers, and addicted to rum, which the inhabitants of every age and class in America drink to excess."

The depressing situation was somewhat relieved for the travelers by a visit to the Hammond plantation, at famous Silver Bluff, where, though Colonel Hammond was not at home, they received "all civilities" from his wife and amiable nieces at his elegant home, and from a lawyer, who was a guest there, a letter of recommendation for use in the Cherokee country.

Although they were able to acquire packhorses, no one in the town, not even the sole baker, would part with any of his meager provisions to sustain them or their poor animals. Undismayed, they left Augusta for the wild and rugged hill country, hoping to get corn at some of the few settler cabins along the newly slashed, stump-studded trail. Thirty-five miles above the town they crossed the river into South Carolina. It was five miles to the first cabin and twelve miles more to the next. There were no bridges across the streams, but Michaux noted with relief that neither were there any alligators in these parts. Everywhere the woods had been burned, following the deplorable custom

of Indian and settler alike, and there wasn't much for a naturalist to
see and even less in the way of food for man or beast until they
reached a clearing, where the mistress of the cabin sold them three
pounds of butter and baked for them some real leavened bread, of corn
meal mixed with flour, upon which they feasted with milk. That a
repast so frugal and simple should earn space in Michaux's terse diary
is an eloquent commentary on the austerity of their usual fare.

This area was known as the Long Cane section, a name drawn from
the larger of two native North American bamboos, the country's largest
grass, sometimes reaching twenty-five feet in height. Incidentally, those
two species are the world's only nontropical bamboos. The night they
spent in this section they were the guests of General Andrew Pickens,
guerrilla leader and hero of the Revolution. The general promised
Michaux to try to secure some wild turkeys for him to carry back with
him on his return from the mountains.

Two days later the mountains were in sight, north and west of them.
Their approach was along the course of the beautiful Keowee to the old
Indian town of Seneca, now abandoned to the settlers who had built a
fort there—a route that could only be followed today by boat on Hartwell Reservoir. The rugged terrain offered new flora and more plentiful fauna, some memorable enough to be noted by the evening campfire: the shooting of a very large owl, carrying a coachwhip snake
(which he called a "veep-coach"), providing two choice specimens
with a single shot, the discovery of quantities of ginseng in the rich
bottomlands along the river, quantities of mountain laurel, hydrangea,
and cornel, all in full flower, adding their contributions to the rare
beauty of this trail which a dozen years earlier had inspired the poetic
William Bartram to torrents of praise.

Another day brought the travelers to the last cabins of the settlers and
the beginning of Indian territory. Here one of the frontier settlers, with
much difficulty, persuaded two Cherokees to join the Michaux party as
hunters and guides into their mountains. An agreement on the terms of
their enlistment was finally reached, after two days of complex negotiations, complicated by the lack of an interpreter and excessive demands
for mounts for each Indian, a supply of rum, and "an exorbitant price."
The neighboring settlers provided a wagon, some bread and corn, and
a young man of one of their households, who spoke a little Cherokee, to
accompany the expedition.

Finally the equipage set out on the trail up the Keowee to the high mountains looming ahead. Obviously the hazards and difficulties in the days that followed were beyond all expectations, as a tone of dismay creeps into Michaux's journal entries. The way seemed an endless series of mountain paths, gorges, and torrents, "which here they call creeks," with beds of "sloping stones covered with slippery moss," making one fearful that the horses would fall. The banks of the creeks were tangles of rhododendron, overhanging the streams themselves. The Indian guides, more adept in surmounting such hazardous terrain, kept leaving them behind, putting the party in danger of separation by mistaking a bear path for the trail. Protests were of little avail—"the savages are not willing to listen to one's reflections in these circumstances." Days passed without any kind of game. All their bread was consumed. Corn meal moistened with creek water was their daily fare.

But for Michaux, ever in pursuit of his green mistress, these hardships were secondary to his "chagrin" that the lush growth constantly impeding his way was not providing him with new and interesting plants. Always, though duty required him to collect, his real joy was in discovery. Ever the unseen beyond, the possible wonders beyond the peaks of the great-toothed western horizon, impelled him on. The "savages" finally redeemed themselves by bringing in a turkey and a deer, but relief from hunger was partly offset by a worsening of the trail. Now it was a jungle of fallen trees, gorges so narrow that the stream bed provided the only passage, now a swamp thick with smilax with its poison-tipped thorns which tore their arms and legs, and always in the dense undergrowth the haunting fear of stepping on a rattlesnake. In the deep ravines the dense growth, the overhanging mountain peaks, and the fogs made a groping nightmare out of traveling in broad daylight. The noise and the spray from the frequent waterfalls and the rains that came down, sometimes for days at a time, increased their discomfort, discouragement, and confusion.

All this Michaux noted in his journal, in his spare, precise prose, refreshingly free of romantic exaggeration, as he chronicles their arduous way up "to the place the river Kiwi begins its bed," and, after resting there to feast on the "wild strawberries which one finds there in abundance," on over the divide "to where the torrents lose themselves in the river Tenasee."

For days now he had been traversing country which, until recently, has remained in almost the same wild state as in the year of Michaux's travels. But if he were to come back now and see it today he would never recognize it, for, even as we write, men with giant logging machines, mammoth earthmovers, and dynamite charges are crashingly, roaringly, screechingly, incredibly remaking the face of the earth there, impounding Keowee waters, which Michaux described as "the purest and best in America," in order that the chill of those mountain waters and their thundering descent, of which Michaux spoke in awe, may be utilized in a gigantic hydro-atomic power project.

Soon after crossing the divide, aiming for the Tennessee River, Michaux noticed that his guides were becoming more and more indecisive in pointing out the way. As the party moved along somewhere between the French Broad River and the Little Tennessee, the young man "who had spent five months among the savages" and "understood a little of the savage language" reported his suspicion, based on what he heard of conversations between their guides, that the Indians were as ignorant as their white companions as to where they were or how to get to the Tennessee River. This disturbing disclosure and the exhaustion of their meager supplies compelled a decision to turn back and return to the frontier settlement of Seneca. After days of gloomy weather the skies cleared, and with the change their spirits lifted. "We have," wrote Michaux in his journal, "for the first time beautiful weather and the clarity of the air produces a charming view of the mountains."

The return journey was fairly rapid as they followed the trading path, a much easier route which they had avoided on the way up, thinking to find more of interest to the naturalist on the little-used trails. In less than two days they were back at the fort at Seneca, from which they had set out nine days before. A pall of apprehension pervaded the place. Word had just arrived of fighting in Georgia between Creeks and whites, causing many to fear an attack by the Cherokees on the Carolina frontier settlements.

A day of rest and two more days of travel found them back at the home of General Pickens. As the general had not yet secured the promised turkeys, arrangements were made with a neighbor to send a supply of the birds to Charleston, so that Michaux could ship them to his royal patrons in France to add variety to the game in the royal forest of Rambouillet. Although Europeans had been familiar with the American turkey ever since the time of Columbus, and in many places it had become a fairly common barnyard fowl, the progenitor of these birds was the Mexican variety, which had long been a domestic fowl there before its introduction into Europe. Believing the larger and more beautiful North American wild species might prove a valuable addition to the game of European forests, Michaux earnestly sought a supply of these magnificent birds.

In a hurry to get back to his garden, Michaux now took, from the Pickens place, the well-worn Charleston trading path, which stayed generally on the ridges, a far more expeditious but less interesting route than that followed on the way to the backcountry. A little more than ten days later he was back at his garden, supervising its reception of the fruits of the expedition, to be nurtured there until the proper season for shipment abroad. Since the theft of their mounts before reaching Augusta, on their way to the Cherokee country, Michaux, his son, and his servant had traveled nearly six hundred miles, mostly on foot, the servant leading the tethered animals, first one, then two, three, and four packhorses, heavy-laden with wilderness bounty, ostensibly for the edification of the ladies and gentlemen of Versailles, but, in fact, even more for the delight of their plant-loving collector and his friends of kindred spirit at the Jardin du Roi and Rambouillet, with whom Michaux unfailingly kept in lively botanical correspondence.

This account of Michaux's nine-hundred-mile expedition into Georgia and up to the Cherokee country represents but eleven weeks of the action-filled ten years he spent in America, mostly devoted to wilderness travels. The summary here presented, of the first of his American expeditions of which there is a surviving journal, represents a drastic telescoping of Michaux's daily chronicle. Space will not permit even so slight a treatment of most of the thousands of miles of travel this horizon-bewitched naturalist recorded during his nine remaining American years: south into Spanish Florida, far, far north to the tundra of British Canada, and back and forth over part at least of the territory now within the bounds of all but a few of the states east of the Mississippi River. Of most of these expeditions sketches and highlights will have to suffice.

After ten days spent at his "plantation" and in Charleston, setting his affairs in order, Michaux embarked on the sixteenth of July by packet for Philadelphia, where he stopped long enough to visit William Bartram and to dine with the French consul before going on by stage to New York. There he divided his time between his botanical nursery in New Jersey, thriving under the competent management of Paul Saulnier, where he arranged for shipments of trees and plants to France, and his business and financial affairs in New York with the French minister.

By the time he had returned to his Charleston garden, after an eighteen-day voyage from Philadelphia, summer was waning and it was seed season again. These tiny packages of dormant life, infinite in variety, became once more the central theme of his activities. Day after day the journal notes: "sowed seed," "labored and sowed," "gathered seed," "Built a seed storage house," or "packed and shipped seed." Interruptions were few: the preparation of a cage for eight wood duck, to be shipped to a patron, a rainy day of letter-writing, a bout of fever and rheumatism.

"Embarked a half-hour after midday for St. Augustine in Florida." With that entry for February 14, 1788, André Michaux's journal begins its daily memoranda of his hazardous three months in the wilds of Florida. Obviously it was Michaux, the exploring naturalist, rather than Michaux, emissary from France, who set out that February afternoon with his seventeen-year-old son and a Negro servant. As humid, subtropical Florida had no climatic counterpart in France to receive botanical introductions from there, the expedition was unlikely to produce the practical benefits that were the purpose of his American mission. For the naturalist, however, especially the botanist, the lush and verdant land was irresistibly alluring.

Their departure from Charleston was far from propitious. What with unfavorable winds and difficulties in retrieving a stuck anchor, they were still waiting to cross the harbor bar into the open sea ten days after going on board. Even when they finally dropped anchor at St. Augustine, it seemed at first as though the voyage might have been in vain, for suspicious Spanish officials sharply questioned Michaux concerning his baggage and his intentions in their territory, forbidding him to travel in Florida without special dispensation from the governor. Fortunately his Excellency did not share the suspicions of his officers and did share the interest in natural history which had brought the Frenchmen to his territory—not only was the license freely given but hospitality as well.

After two weeks devoted to botanizing in the environs of St. Augustine, purchasing and equipping with sails a large cypress "dugout," and gathering supplies, Michaux, with his son, his servant, and two hired Indian rowers, set out southward down the attenuated inlet between the mainland and Anastasia Island known as the Matanzas River. Their second night's camp was at Fort Matanzas, where more than two hundred years earlier the Spaniards under Menéndez, founder of St. Augustine, subjected to holy slaughter several hundred French Huguenots who dared settle there.

Next day adverse winds forced them to take refuge at the home of a Minorcan settler on the bank of a tidal stream which joins the Matanzas at the south end of Anastasia, a few miles below the fort. From his host's place Michaux followed this little river far into the interior and found there a botanist's paradise. On every hand were his old green friends of the Carolina woods, magnolia, gordonia, myrtle and red maple, but here admixed with strange and exciting companions. Some were easily recognized as new species of familiar genera. Among these were species of palms, pawpaws, silver bells, and *Leucothoë* which were easily recognizable to the botanist's eye, although never seen before. Others, such as the primitive anomalous sago palm, the rattan vine, and the *Erythrina*, with its long, scarlet scimitar-shaped blossoms and brilliant scarlet seeds, belonging to families or genera he had never encountered in nature, were even more fascinating. For days the environs of the Minorcan's cabin kept them all busy, drying and mounting herbarium specimens, gathering, digging, and packing seedlings and tubers.

They had great difficulty in getting under way again. High waves running in from the sea through the break in the Sea Islands and hurling their torrents against the sand bars the waves had built up across the Matanzas all but blocked navigation when east winds were blowing. Taking advantage of a lull, the Indians and the Negro, who had been left with the canoe while the Frenchmen botanized, managed to cross the bar, but in accomplishing the passage were twice upset. Despite the difficulties presented by the wide marshes and the mangrove jungles which bordered the shallow Matanzas, the passengers made their way several miles down shore to join the waiting crew and craft. Their Minorcan host, who had provided them with horses for their botanical excursion, and who now accompanied them to their boat, was to be the last person other than those of their own party that any of them would see until their return nearly a month later from their southern expedition, which was to take them as far down the coast as the neighborhood of Cape Kennedy.

The uninhibited wilderness through which they were to pass had been far otherwise at the height of the Spanish power in Florida, when the Spaniards had settled widely over much of the region, and when Indian villages dotted the landscape. After the Spanish decline, when the peninsula fell into British hands, following the French and Indian War, Carolinians invaded the region in search of rice plantations and British entrepreneurs promoted ambitious settlement schemes, most of which became scandalous fiascos. Two decades after the British take-over Michaux noted in his journal only the remains of all those ventures. Governor Moultrie's abandoned plantation, the ruins of Captain Roger's home, a place that was once a sugar plantation, New Smyrna where Michaux counted the foundations and chimneys of more than four hundred houses once occupied by Minorcans, miserably settled there by a ruthless adventurer—these and the spontaneous orange groves were the only tangible memorials to the white man's feeble starts to possess himself of this subtropical wilderness. Sometimes at night, across the Indian River, they could see the campfires of Indian hunting or fishing parties, but, on the advice of their Indian rowers, they avoided any confrontation with them.

About thirty miles south of the present New Smyrna Beach they discovered that the southern reach of Matanzas River, then appropriately known as Mosquito Lagoon (now Indian River Sound), was a cul-de-sac. Michaux was faced with the alternative of turning back or of somehow managing a portage of a mile or more across the sandy isthmus to Indian River. Had he foreseen the difficulties that followed, he would certainly not have chosen to try the portage. Already they were without fresh water, and the supply of rum, a major incentive for the rowers, was exhausted. Recently they had been again overturned in the rough shallows, soaking their food and baggage. The sand barrier they had to cross was covered with a tangled mass of canes, briars, and viciously armed saw palmettos, which sliced their boots and tore their clothing and were so tough they were almost impossible to clear from the path of the roller logs. Indian River, when reached, proved almost as discouraging. Although some six miles wide, it was so shallow that the canoe kept running aground, forcing the passengers to wade most of the way through knee-deep water. Wide marshes and mangrove tangles prevented travel along the water's edge and provided no spot on which to camp. All the while a stiff south wind kept buffeting their craft and soaking its contents. Compensations to offset their troubles were few: the discovery of the beautiful golden necklace-pod tree, and a large, white-flowered pawpaw, and a bountiful supply of fish and waterfowl to augment their short supply of spoiling bread and rice. "We saw many species of waterfowl," he reported, "and my son today killed more than a dozen at a shot, repeatedly." With travel by land impossible and progress by water so painfully difficult, even the usually dauntless Michaux was discouraged by the prospects. At a point approximately opposite Cape Kennedy, they turned about and headed back to St. Augustine.

The day following his arrival back in St. Augustine, Michaux dutifully called on the Spanish governor to report on the expedition. His journal entry for two days later is this:

Sunday, April 20 [1788]. I received a visit from the Governor who came to see my Plants and other collections that I had gathered in my voyage—birds, etc. I was invited to dine at his house and to pass the afternoon in his Excellency's garden with the ladies of his family.

That entry, typical of many that appear all through the journals, suggests a clue to one facet of the personality of this elusive but fascinating French naturalist, whose professional life is well documented, but of whose personal life and nature little is known. What was André Michaux like? No portrait or description of any kind survives. But from entries such as the above we can assume that he was a man of rare social charm, as at ease in the drawing room as in the wilderness, a man for whom any language barrier hardly existed. He seemed to move effortlessly from weeks of botanizing and collecting to a pleasant stop-off for dinner at Mt. Vernon, or from days of arduous camping on the trail to an elegant evening with General Pickens and his ladies.

The governor was not the only person visited by Michaux the day after his return from his canoe trip down the coast. He also waited upon the colonial agent for Indian affairs to forward his plans for another expedition, this one to the interior, "to the home of the Indians." It is a safe assumption that William Bartram had told him of the botanical riches of the St. Johns, the like of which he, Michaux, had failed to find along the salt and brackish streams he had been exploring. Unwilling to leave Florida without seeing the area which had so aroused his friend Bartram's enthusiasm, he made arrangements for his son and himself to travel, with unspecified company, overland to the St. Johns, and by canoe up the river to the neighborhood of the present Sanford. Judging from his journal entries, it was an uneventful but reasonably successful botanical expedition. In the account there is, however, one entry worth quoting as one of the rare touches of self-portraiture:

> We came to a place frequented by the savages. On the bank of the river was a canoe and a big cooking pot, which belonged to them. I put some biscuits, some beans, and some sweet oranges in the pot and we proceeded on our way. We heard two shots which proved that the Savages were hunting nearby.

The return to Charleston was by small boat, navigating by day the channels between the Sea Islands and the mainland, the route of the modern Inland Waterway, camping at night on the islands. Cumberland Island harbored many refugees, whose mainland homes had been destroyed by the Creeks. On St. Simons, the Michaux were welcomed as guests at the plantation of Charles Spalding who had befriended both the Bartrams on their Southern expeditions. Fellow guests were the ladies of the family of General McIntosh, the father of John McIntosh who, as a boy, had traveled with William Bartram. By the time they got back to Charleston and the elder Michaux had recovered from a stiff bout with malaria, the summer had passed and it was seedtime again.

Journal entries become almost wholly seed-centered as he devoted his time, through the blue and golden autumn days, to the gathering, packing, shipping, and sowing of his precious seeds. Enthusiasm for seeds is easily understood. One has only to dwell a bit on the profligacy with which nature produces them, their endless variety in size and shape, the diversity of their devices to disseminate themselves, the compactness of their packaging, and the temporal sense with which they are endowed, and one is almost certainly launched on a voyage into wonder.

Although no seeds of temperate America can approach in size such tropical giants as the coconut or even the avocado, there is dramatic contrast between the size of the walnut, for instance, and the dustlike seed of the orchis, or between the laquered buckeye, big enough to serve the Indian as artificial eyes for his deer-head masks, and its sand-sized replicas that carry forward the generations of the evening primrose. In their shapes, too, seeds dazzle with their incredible variety. Contrast the smooth, hard-shelled, acorn-sized ovals of the lotus, cunningly packed into neat cones, more like wasp nests than seed pods, the equally smooth and polished, fur-tipped chestnut, nurtured in its needle-covered husk, or the shining, plump disk of the persimmon, with the

Pl. 30.
Black Walnut.
Juglans nigra.

Illustration by P. J. Redouté for François André Michaux's account of the black walnut in his *North American Sylva*. (Courtesy of the University of South Carolina Library)

confetti-like wafers of the elm, the tiny rod-shaped tickseed, and the spiny little hedgehogs of the cocklebur.

Not a whit less varied and far more intriguing is the "cleverness" of seeds, a "cleverness" born of necessity in those plants whose survival as a species is not predicated upon a mere profligacy of seed production, but rather on an ability to produce seeds "clever" enough to betake themselves to areas as suitable for germination and survival as those already preempted by their parent plants. Plants, rooted and immobile, must do their traveling to new areas or to repopulate devastated areas through the mobility of the fertilized eggs we call seeds. Some cover themselves with inviting fruit, to travel as stowaways in a bird's crop, but such stowaways must be "clever" enough, also, to provide themselves with shells strong enough to resist a gizzard's grinding sand and a stomach's digestive juices. The seeds of some species which employ the stowaway device have become so "clever" that they refuse to sprout unless they have traveled thus as bird cargo (and been scarified by the sand in the gizzard of the host), thereby avoiding a destructive crowding of the parent plant. More spectacular are those seeds that have developed their own air transport, soaring and gliding through the air by means of their own "clever" devices, such as the propellers of the maple keys, the diaphanous tails of pine mast, the parachutes of thistledown, the gossamer of milkweed. Other seeds achieve the transportation essential to a continuing posterity by "hitching a ride," such as the cocklebur does, and the tickseed, the tick trefoil, and the sandspur. The water lily sets its seed afloat for the wind or current to determine its destiny. The drying pod of the American wistaria, with a sharp report, pops its seed away from the mother vine, while the suddenly coiling springs of the seed pod of the jewelweed, as it ejects its seed, earns that plant its "touch-me-not" alias. Fascinating also is the mysterious time sense which many seeds possess: a built-in awareness of the proper time to sprout, a protective device which, though all other conditions seem propitious, will hold them back from sprouting until their proper season.

No doubt Michaux, like most dedicated gardeners, plunged each year into the glory of the harvest, well aware of the complex wonder of the seeds he handled, but excited and absorbed, as well, by his own participation in the eternal seed time miracle of creation. Once the last of his seed collections had been lovingly given over to the earth's great placenta, there yet remained seedbeds prepared but still uncharged with

hope for spring awakening. To fill these fallow beds, although winter
was fast approaching, Michaux and his Negro helper set out to the
west, aiming again for the headwaters of the Savannah, to gather the
seed and seedling plants they had seen in flower in the spring of the
previous year.

Before setting out for the mountains, he spent some weeks in north
Georgia, returning to Augusta to box and dispatch crates, containing
"eleven hundred and sixty-eight trees and plants," to go by Savannah to
Charleston. It would be redundant to follow him in detail on this
journey to Augusta, the Tugaloo, to Seneca, and to the Keowee. Parts
of this expedition, however, particularly his return to the Keowee-Tox-
away-Horsepasture area, near the line between the two Carolinas, are
so significant to the Michaux story and so eloquently described in his
journal that his own account is here quoted, in an unembellished translation, with a minimum of interpolation, beginning just as he leaves for
the mountains.

December 2, 1788. I left the confluence of the Tugaloo River and the
Kiwi [Keowee], going up the Tugaloo. Slept at the home of Larkin Cleveland, Esquire. 19 miles.

The 3rd. I crossed the Tugaloo at the only place used for fording. It was
so dangerous that two of our horses were in danger of being drowned. I
had breakfast with John Cleveland on the other side of the river. I was told
I would not meet with any more settlements. I crossed through country
completely covered with forest like all the Southern provinces, but it was
very hilly. I slept on the ground at Seneca. 19 miles.

December 6, 1788. I set out for the mountains and slept with my guide at
an Indian village. The chief of this village received us cordially. He told us
that his son, who was to return from hunting that evening, would guide us
into the mountains, to the source of the Kiwi; but he did not return, and
this old man, who seemed about seventy, offered himself to accompany me.
This man, who was born in a village near the source of this river, knew the
mountains perfectly, and I hoped that his son would not come back. He
had a supper served to us of stewed deer meat and bread made of corn meal
and sweet potatoes. I ate with my guide, who served as my interpreter.
The chief ate with his wife at another bench. The mother of his wife, and
his two daughters, one married and the youngest about 14 or 15, sat around
the cooking pot where the meat was cooking. These ladies were naked down
to the waist, having no other clothing than a single skirt.

Sunday, December 7th. The mistress of the house roasted some corn in an earthen pot, using sifted coals, then when it was little more than half roasted the corn was retrieved and taken to a mortar, and, after it was pounded, it was sifted to separate the fine corn meal, which was put into sacks for us to carry. When one is tired, one puts about three spoonfuls in a glass of water, often with brown sugar. This drink, besides being very agreeable, is a restorant, immediately renewing one's strength. The savages never undertake a journey without a supply of this meal. . . . We camped on the bank of the Kiwi at the foot of the mountains among two kinds of rhododendron, Kalmia, Azalea, etc. etc.

December 8th, 1788. The nearer we approached the source of the Kiwi, the more difficult became the way. Our journey was . . . and two miles before arriving I recognized the mountain magnolia, which has been called *Magnolia cordata* or *auriculata* by Bartram. There was at this place a little cabin inhabited by a family of Cherokee Indians. We stopped to camp there, and I hurried out to explore. I gathered a new serrate-leafed plant spreading over the mountainside near the river. The weather changed and it rained all night. Although we were under the cover of a great white pine, our clothes and blankets were drenched and soaked through. About midnight I went into the Indian cabin, which could hardly hold the family of eight people, men and women. There were also six great dogs, who increased the dirt and discomfort of this shelter. The fire was in the middle, without any opening in the ceiling to let out the smoke. There was, however, enough opening to let in the rain through the roof to the house. An Indian offered me his bed, which was a bear skin, and came to take my place near the fire, but, disturbed by the dogs which were continually biting each other to gain their places at the fire, I returned to our camp, the rain having stopped. This spot, which is called the source of the Kiwi, is improperly named. It is the junction of two other rivers or big streams [Horsepasture and Toxaway], which join here but have not been named except as branches of the Kiwi.

The 9th. We set out, guided by my Indian, to visit the highest mountains and to go to the source of the stream, which seemed to be the most precipitous [the Toxaway]. We had to negotiate cliffs and streams overhung with trees where ten times our horses were thrown down and were in danger of perishing. We climbed up to a waterfall, where the noise of the falls resembled distant gunfire. The Indians say that at night fires appear here. I wanted to camp here but, because of the snow which had begun to fall, and the cold wind, we sought out the more sheltered foot of the mountain where there was pasturage for our horses. The night was horribly cold. There was no pine wood to feed the fire which burned badly because of the snow which kept falling. Our blankets, covered with snow, became stiff with ice soon after being warmed.

The 11th. There was a hard freeze. The air was clear and very sharp. I noticed a range of high mountains which stretched from west to east where there was less snow and ice because of the southern exposure. I gathered a creeping juniper, which I had not seen before in the southern part of the United States. But it should be noted that I saw in these parts several other such northern trees as river beech, blue dogwood, white pine, balsam, etc. We travelled three miles through an unbroken grove of Rhododendron maximum. I camped with my guides at the head of the Kiwi, and gathered a great quantity of the toothed leaf plant found the day I arrived. I did not see it on any of the other mountains. The Indians here say that these leaves have a good taste, when chewed, and an agreeable scent, when crushed, which indeed I found correct.

After detailed directions as to the location of the unique toothed-leafed plant the diary continues.

December 12th, 1788. I visited the southern-facing mountains on our way back—our supplies having become so spoiled that we had a very plain breakfast. I gathered a great quantity of mountain magnolia. . . .

We went along the edge of the river and saw several flocks of wild turkeys. Our Indian guide fired, but the gun, which had not been protected from the rain, some days before, misfired. So our supper was some chestnuts which our Indian secured from one of his tribe.

Our journey was 18 miles. The weather was very clear. The freeze set in early in the evening, and, after having asked my Indian the names of several plants in his language, I wrote in my journal by the light of the moon.

December 13th. At daybreak, I tried to kill a wild turkey which were abundant here. I could not succeed and we broke camp without breakfast. Very hungry, we headed for a camp of Indian hunters, and, although the mountains were now less steep, it was one o'clock when we arrived there after a journey of six hours, although we covered only about fifteen miles. They cooked for us some bear meat cut in little pieces, and fried in bear grease. Although it was very greasy, we made a very good dinner of it, and, although I ate a great deal of the greasiest parts of this meat, I was not uncomfortable. The grease of bears has no taste and resembles good olive oil. . . . After dinner we travelled sixteen miles and arrived at Seneca.

Through an amazing coincidence, the above-quoted journal entry for December 8 introduced two intriguing botanical mysteries to take

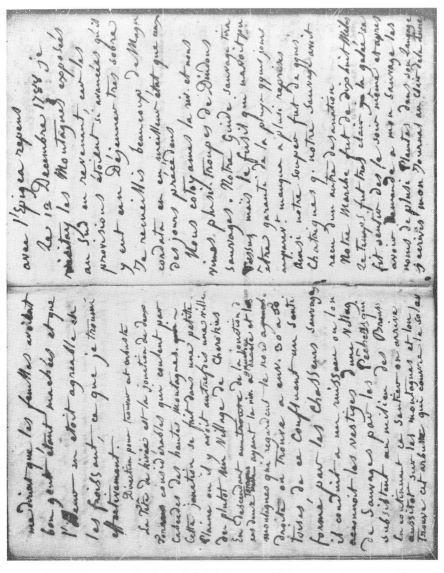

Pages from the journal of André Michaux, which report his 1788 Keowee expedition and the directions for finding the long-lost *Shortia*, and end, "I wrote in my journal by the light of the moon." (Courtesy of the American Philosophical Society)

their places beside the story of the lost *Franklinia alatamaha* of the Bartrams. The magnolia of which Michaux collected specimens that day, the yellow-flowered *Magnolia cordata*, was not found again growing in the wild until a century and a quarter later, when it was rediscovered far away to the south, near Athens, Georgia. Meanwhile, the specimens that Michaux brought back from the Keowee had become the only source of supply for this attractive, commonly cultivated ornamental.

The story of Michaux's other discovery of that day, the plant with the toothed leaves, is far more dramatic, although its final sequel came long before the yellow magnolia's rediscovery. The opening scene is confined to the single sentence recorded in the journal on December 8: "I gathered a new serrate-leafed plant spreading over the mountainside near the river," and two more references on the eleventh, reporting the gathering of quantities of the same plant and giving explicit directions for finding the spot where he had found it growing so abundantly.

The next scene takes place half a century later and three thousand miles away: Paris, 1839. Dr. Asa Gray, famous American botanist, looking through the dried specimens of André Michaux's herbarium, at the Jardin des Plantes, came across an unidentified plant of which only the galax-like, but toothed, leaves and a seed pod were preserved, bearing the notation that they were collected in "les hautes montagnes de Carolinie." Soon after his return to America, Dr. Gray set out for the Southern Appalachians on a futile search for a living specimen of this discovery of Michaux's. His report of the plant in the Michaux herbarium and his frustrated search for a living one proved highly contagious in botanical circles, and soon something akin to a search for a botanical Holy Grail was under way as botanists sought the elusive mystery plant among the high mountains of Carolina. Apparently none of these dedicated seekers was aware of the careful directions left by Michaux in his journal, resting still unpublished in the Philosophical Society in Philadelphia. It was like a treasure hunt, with the main clue missing.

Dr. Gray, wishing to honor an admired fellow botanist, Dr. C. W. Short, had named the new genus *Shortia*, and because of its galax-like leaves, *Shortia galacifolia*. Meanwhile, the hopeful search for a living specimen went on. The first break in the mystery came almost four decades after Dr. Gray's discovery of Michaux's dried specimen. A farm boy, roaming the banks of the Catawba River near Marion, North

Carolina, came on a patch of dark-green, glossy leaves, sporting a showy display of delicate, white, wavy-edged, bell-shaped flowers. He carried home some of the leaves and flowers to his amateur-botanist father, who was interested enough to seek out and determine their identity. Living specimens of *Shortia galacifolia* these were indeed, but they were not found in the high mountains, as Michaux had said, at all. So the *Shortia* quest, far from ending, took on a new life. At last, almost a decade later, an expedition of noted botanists, including Professor C. S. Sargeant (who was to edit three years later an edition of Michaux's journal for the Philosophical Society), found the long-sought plant growing near the Keowee, probably on the same spot where Michaux had plucked the leaves and seed for his herbarium almost a century earlier. Now, from the name of the county where it grew and the shape of its ethereal blossoms, this delicately beautiful and elusive plant became known as Oconee bells.

There was yet another remarkable coincidence, illustrative of another botanical mystery, in that same journal entry of Michaux's for December 8, 1788. Although paleobotanists offer plausible explanations, going back to the ice ages, for the close kinship between the flora of the eastern United States and eastern Asia, more particularly of the Southern Appalachians and Japan, on opposite sides of the world, to laymen it seems a great mystery that the only companion that *Shortia galacifolia* has in its genus is found in the mountains of Nippon. One of the other classical illustrations, among possible hundreds, of that geographically distant but botanically close kinship is the magnolia family. The mountain magnolia, which Michaux collected along the Keowee that cold December day, is one of some twenty-five species of the magnolia, representatives of which are found only in eastern Asia and eastern America. Among the members of that family is our famous tulip tree, of which there are but two species, our own and one in China.

The first six weeks following his return from the Keowee, Michaux was busy planting, packing, and shipping the quantities of plants and seeds collected on that fruitful expedition. Then followed a ten-week voyage to the Bahamas, from which he returned the latter part of April, 1789, bringing a collection of more than nine hundred trees and the seeds of more than sixty species of plants, and leaving for the Bahamians, in exchange, date palms and vineyard stock. A month later father and son were again on the road toward the mountains, this time following much of John Lawson's route up the Santee-Wateree-Catawba, but from

Charlotte they continued their northwest route to the mountains, stopping on the way at Morganton, known to Michaux as Burke Court House. There they were guests at Swan Ponds, the plantation of Colonel Waightstill Avery, who the summer before had faced fiery young Andrew Jackson in a duel, from which both contestants emerged unscathed. Thence their way was across the mountains, by the path along which some eight years before had filed the Tennessee frontiersmen on their way to Kings Mountain to turn back the invading British. It was a rugged trail, along a narrow path hewn through rhododendron jungles, passing beneath the shadows of Mt. Mitchell and Yellow Mountain. For twelve days, there in the mountains, they traveled without coming upon any human habitation.

Across the mountains they turned northeast and followed generally up the Holston River into Virginia, over Natural Bridge, up the Valley of Virginia, and across the Potomac at Harper's Ferry. Along the way from Frederick to Philadelphia the experienced eye of the erstwhile master farmer of Satory noted the productive farms of the industrious Germans. In Philadelphia he visited William Bartram, in whose garden André saw flourishing many of his green friends from Carolina and Florida, along with others he had not yet met in his travels. After a few days of garden-botanizing in the capital he went up to New York and thence to his Bergen garden, in New Jersey, which he found prospering under the capable direction of his gardener, Paul Saulnier. After an uneventful return trip, via Philadelphia, Baltimore, Richmond, and Wilmington, late September found them once more in Charleston.

Two days after their return François, walking along the road near their plantation garden, was wounded in the eye by a stray bullet of a careless hunter and for weeks seemed in danger of losing his sight. Even when this fear was allayed, recovery from the injury was slow, and this no doubt influenced the decision that François should return to France. There were, however, other important considerations, such as the need for formal education for the young man, now nineteen years old, and also the growing concern of both father and son for the fate of their precious plant shipments in a France torn by revolution, reports of which had recently come to them. Uncertainty, too, about the effect of the new state of affairs in France on their own personal concerns and connections at home must have necessitated the return of one of the Michaux to France.

Now there are long and unexplained lapses in Michaux's journal. In the two and a half years following his son's departure, late in 1789, only five months are accounted for in his journal. Except for a late fall collecting trip in 1789 to the headwaters of the Catawba River and the neighborhood of Mt. Mitchell, and another down the coast as far as St. Augustine in the spring of 1791, and three months devoted to sowing, grafting, and scientifically organizing his garden, we have no inkling of the way he employed himself during that long interval. However, one suspects, from what is known of his other American years, that many thousands of miles of American wilderness trails passed under his horse's hooves during those years.

Although his journal makes no mention of it, from other sources we hear of his election to membership in the Agricultural Society of Charleston, to which he made a report, at about this time, on the culture of ginseng, long regarded as a miraculous panacea in China, and on the possibility of growing it in the foothill and mountain regions of Carolina for the China trade. Ginseng, incidentally, is another of the plants common only to the eastern United States and to eastern Asia. For the Agricultural Society, Michaux prepared also a paper on the species of European plants he had found best adapted to American soils and climates and their proper cultivation in this country.

The journal resumes with his departure from Charleston in the spring of 1792 to travel through New England and into Canada. As events dictated, it would be two years before he returned to Charleston—two years devoted mostly to travel, adding up to some seven or eight thousand miles, on foot, by canoe, and on horseback, most of it through uninhabited wilderness. His Canadian expedition, perhaps the most fruitful of his American travels, and certainly the longest and most arduous, took him through New England to Lake Champlain, to Montreal and Quebec, up the Saguenay to Lake Mistassini, and beyond, almost to Hudson Bay, through country even to this day unmarked by road or railroad, regions far beyond the geographical province of this book.

~~~ 3

With his return to Philadelphia in early December, 1792, he appears again on our stage. Although it seems incredible, the tireless and intrepid man had no sooner arrived back in the capital than he was planning an even more extensive and far more hazardous wilderness expedition. Before he had even begun to repack and ship his rich harvest

of the Northern wilds, he was appearing before the learned company
of the American Philosophical Society with a proposal that the Society
underwrite an expedition he planned to make across the continent to
the Pacific Ocean. Despite possible international complications, inherent
in an American-financed, French-led expedition across territories disputed by Spain, Britain, and Russia, the Society agreed to his proposal.
Thomas Jefferson, member of the Society and now Secretary of State
under the new Constitutional Government inaugurated the year before,
was particularly enthusiastic, using his influence to obtain subscriptions
and cooperating in the practical details of the planning.

A few weeks after Michaux first made his proposition to the Society,
Thomas Jefferson was carefully composing "Instructions to André
Michaux for exploring the Western Boundary":

. . . cross the Mississippi and pass by land to the nearest part of the
Missouri above the Spanish settlements, that you may avoid the risk of being
stopped.

You will in the course of your journey, take notice of the country you
pass through, its general face, soil, rivers, mountains, its productions—animal,
vegetable, and mineral—so far as they may be new to us, and may also be
useful or very curious. . . .

The method of preserving your observations is left to yourself. . . . It is
only suggested that the noting them on the skin might be best for such as
may be most important, and that further details may be committed to the
bark of the paper-birch, a substance which may not excite suspicion among
the Indians, and little liable to injury from wet and other accidents. . . .

Ignorance of the country through which you are to pass, and confidence
in your judgment, zeal, and discretion, prevent the society from attempting
more minute instructions. . . .

It is easy to imagine the enthusiasm and excitement with which the
horizon-hungry adventurer-naturalist plunged into preparations for the
most challenging undertaking of his life. It is equally easy to imagine
with what mixed emotions, divided loyalties, and probably suppressed
disappointment he faced the sudden alteration of all these plans, an
alteration heralded by an event noted in his journal thus: "May ———
Citizen Genet, Minister Plenipotentiary of the French Republic, arrived
in Philadelphia." Several entries later: "The ———. Consulted and con-
ferred with Citizen Genet on my mission to Kentucky. . . . The 23,
24, 25, and 26 of June I prepared for my journey to Kentucky." There
follows a listing of letters of recommendation to prominent persons in

Kentucky or to be met with along the way there, a reference to packing his effects, and then the decisive entry: "July 15, 1793. I took leave of Citizen Genet, Minister of the Republic of France to The United States, and I left Philadelphia the same day at ten o'clock at night to avoid the great heat, and to travel by the light of the moon."

Although it was along the road leading to Pittsburgh and the west that Michaux was riding by the light of the moon that July night, this was not the scientific journey of exploration, under the aegis of a group of learned gentlemen, which he had planned. Instead this was an expedition, ostensibly botanical, but secretly political, sponsored by the government of France—a mission of enormous import in the international power struggle of the day. Intrepid and wilderness-wise, renowned as a roving naturalist with extensive personal connections with many of the American leaders, André Michaux was an ideal choice for this secret mission, for which he had sacrificed his dream voyage to the Pacific. Although for him the transcontinental expedition would now never be more than a dream, Michaux's great idea proved fertile seed, bearing fruit a dozen years later when Jefferson, as President, dispatched Meriwether Lewis and William Clark on their famous exploration along the way that Michaux and Jefferson had projected, across the, by then, newly acquired Louisiana Territory to the Pacific Northwest.

Surely it was a tormenting decision for Michaux to make, to forego that expedition for the sake of what was to prove an ill-considered and abortive effort to serve his native land and the cause of "liberté," but one can be certain that it was a carefully considered decision based on sincere convictions. He had now been almost eight years in America. During those years the Constitutional Convention had been held, the Constitution debated and drafted, and the ratification battles fought in each of the states. He had been a frequent guest in the homes of leaders of the new republic whom he held in high esteem. It would have been strange, then, had he not developed a considerable degree of republicanism; and that he had done so is evident from the alacrity with which he embraced the revolution in France when word of it reached American shores. Prior to this time there are no political allusions in his journal, but after Genet's arrival they become frequent and partisan.

Although the picture of Genet's scheme is still somewhat clouded, it appears that Michaux was to serve as courier and coordinator of a planned attack against upper Louisiana, then in the hands of the Spanish. American personnel was to be employed under the command of the embittered and disaffected George Rogers Clark, whom history credits with winning the Ohio country from the British, and who felt, with some justice, that he had been unappreciated by the American government. Many of the leading citizens of Kentucky, impatient with the American government's failure to secure from the Spanish a free passage for them along the Mississippi, were sympathetic to the plan. The French-financed expedition of Americans and Indians against the St. Louis area was to be coordinated with a French attack from the Gulf, with the hope that France might recover the whole of Louisiana and open the Mississippi for free navigation.

At the time of Michaux's departure, official Philadelphia's policy with regard to the plan seems to have been one of looking the other way. Thomas Jefferson, however, viewed the scheme with sufficient favor to give Michaux an introductory letter to Governor Isaac Shelby of Kentucky, one of the heroes of the dramatic Battle of Kings Mountain, presenting Michaux not only as a friend and traveling naturalist but also as a Frenchman enjoying the special confidence of the French republic. When he left Philadelphia on July 15, 1793, he carried as well, in his saddlebags, letters of introduction to dozens of other prominent persons in the frontier areas.

Two weeks after leaving Philadelphia he arrived at Pittsburgh, presented his letters of introduction there, and arranged to travel by drifting flatboat down the Ohio, or, as Michaux liked to call it, the Belle Rivière. During the days of waiting he herborized along the banks of the Monongahela, noting in his journal a rich profusion of plants. No political mission could alienate or distract him from his absorption in the green world, and these pages in his daily chronicle are especially detailed in observation and listing of plants along the way.

At Maysville, Kentucky, he left the flatboat, arranged for horses, and took the road to Lexington. En route he stopped to inspect a salt lick, where, but a few years earlier, vast herds of buffalo used to come for the saline waters of its springs. After visiting in Lexington two unnamed persons, to whom he had letters, he continued on to Danville. There he called upon General Benjamin Logan, to whom he confided the commission entrusted to him, and was told that the general "would be delighted to take part in the enterprise." He visited also Governor Isaac Shelby with Jefferson's letter of introduction and was likewise warmly received by him.

Then on to Louisville, through "country very interesting for a botanist to visit," to confer with General Clark: "I handed him the letters from the Minister and informed him of the object of my mission. He told me that he was very eager for the undertaking . . . but that fresh circumstances seemed to oppose an obstacle to it."

Those "fresh circumstances" may have had reference to the leaking out of word of the plot, alerting the Spanish along the Mississippi, news which sent Michaux back down the road to Danville and thence on to Lexington. On the way his horse strayed off during the night, an experience so common that it comes to seem characteristic of a Michaux journey. While he "spent the whole day looking for him," he botanized as well, carefully noting the type of soil favored by each species of plant.

For six more weeks he shuttled back and forth between Louisville, Danville, and Lexington, dispatching and receiving letters at each place, some by special messenger. About the middle of November he started back to Philadelphia, choosing the route which carried him down into Tennessee to the Holston River and thence up the Shenandoah Valley.

In December, 1793, he arrived in Philadelphia to make his report to Genet, whose mounting arrogance and indiscretion were rapidly making him *persona non grata* in the capital. President Washington, aware of the domestic and international dangers in the situation, was bringing his opposition to bear on Genet's plan and would eventually request the government of France to replace their too ambitious envoy.

While all this was simmering in official circles, Michaux lingered on in Philadelphia, paying official and unofficial visits, and engaging, as always, in his natural history pursuits. Some of his activities seem to indicate a hope that his Pacific expedition might now be revived. There were conferences with Jefferson and the president of the American Philosophical Society, and visits with botanists Bartram and Barton, the latter lending him a copy of Linnaeus' *Systema Naturae*, from which he spent days copying the sections on quadrupeds and birds, as he sought, perhaps with the Pacific enterprise in mind, to widen his natural history lore. Birds for a time became his dominant interest.

For a few days Genet talked of sending Michaux on an important mission to Charleston, but, as this failed to materialize, the minister agreed to Michaux's departure for the South on his own natural history researches. Turning away from the confusion and conflict of the capital, Michaux started south, once more along the familiar road, dull and wintry in the January cold, but leading to his beloved garden and his American home.

Michaux leaves no record of his activities in the year following his return to Charleston in March, 1794, except for two and a half months devoted to an expedition to the North Carolina mountains, and a few weeks' illness with malaria, which he calls "the fever of the climate." This expedition to the mountains was the one on which he and his friend, Davenport, shouted their praise of liberty and sang the "Marseillaise" from the top of Grandfather Mountain. He had reached there by following the road up the Santee-Wateree-Catawba River Valley. His return was across North Carolina to Fayetteville and thence down to Charleston. It was his first late summer visit to these mountains, the paradise of botanists. Perhaps that explains the great number of plants new to him and even many new to science that he notes in his journal account: a new kalmia near Camden (white-wicky), a new stewartia between Charlotte and Lincolnton, lily of the valley on the mountainside of Linville, where he measured a tulip tree twenty-five feet in circumference, a new flame azalea, white alder and mountain cranberry near Crabtree, *Diphylleia* (pixie-parasol) on Mt. Mitchell, several azaleas new to him on Roan Mountain, along with that beautiful miniature rhododendron, sand myrtle, and false pennyroyal, a new species, where he forded the Catawba on his return trip.

It was April, 1795, before he resumed his customarily terse memoranda of his daily activities. That month, his republican enthusiasm revealed in his dating, he recorded his departure on a new and major expedition: "The 30th Germinal in the 3rd year of the French Republic, One and Indivisible, started to go and herborise in the high mountains of the Carolinas and afterward to visit the Western territories."

Another April would be in flower before Michaux would again return to his Charleston "Garden of the Republic" from this expedition across the Old Northwest Territory to the Mississippi. On his way up to the Carolina mountains, the hosts he mentioned were fellow republicans, heroes of the American Revolution that, in part at least, inspired the revolt of the masses in his homeland: Colonel James Crawford, uncle and foster father of Andrew Jackson, Colonel William Hill, who showed him his ironworks on the right bank of the Catawba, and his host on previous occasions, Colonel Avery.

There in the piedmont spring was in full flower. On an unplanned

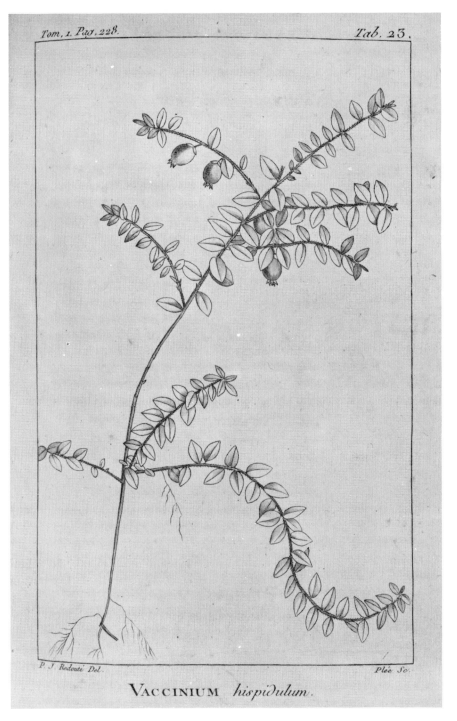

P. J. Redouté Del. *Plée Sc.*

VACCINIUM *hispidulum.*

The botanical artistry of P. J. Redouté is exemplified in this delicate deline-
ation of a creeping snowberry (*Gaultheria hispidula*) from André Michaux's
Flora Boreali-Americana. (Courtesy of the Caroliniana Library of the University of South Carolina)

side trip, when once more his horse "strayed away during the night" so that he was "obliged to look for him all day," he noted, beneath a canopy of blossoming dogwood, crab apple, and waning Judas, the rare shooting star (*Media*), wild ginger, (*Asarum*), spring beauties (*Claytonia*), and dogtooth violets, all in full bloom. But two weeks later, in Gillespie Gap, flanked by the majestic bulks of Roan and Yellow Mountains, their forested slopes barely showing touches of the early greens of cherry trees and the ambers of the burgeoning oaks and chestnuts, there were only those daring advance guards of spring, shadblow, pale blue hepaticas, showy formal bloodroots, fragrant lilies of the valley, and the white bells of the May apples, each protected from late frosts by its own special green parasol. Less common and more exciting were the occasional groups of yellow lady's-slippers and slopes covered with that most delicate of native rhododendrons, *Rhododendron minus,* a Michaux discovery, displaying at this season its shell-pink flower clusters.

Across the mountains he received the hospitality of yet another colonel, lost his horse again, and devoted two days in a futile search for it; bought another, and moved on to the newly laid-out village of Knoxville. For a week he botanized in the neighborhood, awaiting the accumulation of twenty-five westward-bound travelers, the minimum number considered safe to travel the Nashville trail where it crossed the region only recently seized from the Cherokees and still in dispute. Along the way he was the guest of Colonel James Winchester for two days, then of Andrew Jackson, at his pre-Hermitage plantation, Hunter's Hill, on the Cumberland River. Nashville is in limestone country, a fact of major significance for a soil-wise searcher for trees adaptable to the calcareous soils of France. Now, and throughout this expedition, his new interest in birds persisted and grew. His collection of bird skins shared space with his plants and seeds. He contented himself with observing and listing the "quadrupeds" seen around Nashville: "musk-rat, beaver, elk, dwarf deer, bears, buffaloes, wolves, small grey squirrels."

From Nashville his way was across the empty, Indian-haunted Barrens, to Louisville, by way of Danville, where he again visited Governor Shelby. This and other visits he made in Tennessee and Kentucky lead us to believe that Michaux still entertained a hope that the Louisiana scheme might yet have life in it, although it is possible that they may have been purely in the interest of his projected great expedition up the Missouri to the Pacific Northwest, a dream he definitely continued to harbor, despite the fact that his financial situation was extremely uncertain. The French Revolution had canceled his royal contract and with it any hope of collecting the unpaid salary of years back, and his new republican patrons now seemed little more dependable financially than their royal predecessors. At the same time his political involvement with the discredited Genet had probably foreclosed any American support for a Western expedition.

Mid-August found Michaux in the company of an Indian and his wife on the bank of the Wabash, on the Indiana side of the river. This country only the year before was the scene of bloody battles with the Indians of the region. Besides hazarding his scalp, there were other drawbacks to travel here:

Of all the Journeys I have made in America in the past 10 years this is one of the most difficult, owing to the quantity of Trees overturned by storms, to the thick brushwood through which one is obliged to pass; to the numbers of Flies by which one is devoured, etc. . . . The 14th, 15th, and Sunday the 16th of August I was obliged to rest having arrived almost ill. My horse, while trying to jump over the trunk of a large fallen tree, fell and threw me a great distance and I suffered for several days from an injury to the lower part of the Chest on the left side because the trigger of my gun had struck there.

While he convalesced, Michaux herborized and prepared a list of "Plants Observed on the Wabash," five species of verbena, six of sunflower, several oaks, and Indian pink, from which the Miami Indians prepared "a decoction of the root [which] is a sovereign remedy for several diseases and for long-continued venereal disease."

From Vincennes, then but a military outpost, where they crossed the Wabash, Michaux and his Indian companions headed southwest, aiming for the Mississippi. Across Illinois intermittent prairies made for easier travel, and the devastation, which followed the white man's gun, had not yet had its full impact in those unsettled parts.

The 26th . . . An hour after camping the Savage came back laden with a Bear cub and with the two hams of another and much older one. We boiled the pot twice and had enough to satisfy us. We roasted what remained.

The 27th. The Savage killed two stags. We halted very early to dry the skins and to eat, for the Savage and his wife ate five meals a day. Moreover, they regaled themselves with the marrow of the bones which they ate raw. . . .

By the end of August they had reached the Mississippi, at the village of Kaskaskia, which was then on the east side of the river but now occupies that bit of Illinois lying west of the river, which has since changed its course. Kaskaskia had been settled by the French almost a century earlier but had fallen on evil days after the cession of Louisiana to Spain had deprived them of their fur trade. Of this village of forty-five families Michaux writes:

> It is agreeably situated . . . but nothing is to be seen but houses in ruins and abandoned, because the French of the Illinois country, having always been brought up in and accustomed to the Fur trade with the savages, have become the laziest and most ignorant of all men. They live and the majority of them are clothed in the manner of the Savages. They wear no breeches but pass between their thighs a piece of cloth about one third of an ell [in length] which is kept in place before and behind above the hips by a belt.

Michaux spent the whole autumn roaming western Illinois, traveling up the trail along the Mississippi as far as St. Louis, and downriver to the mouth of the Ohio, and up the Ohio to Fort Massac, the post General Anthony Wayne had manned the previous year to block the Louisiana scheme which had first brought Michaux to the Ohio. For many of those autumn days there are no journal entries. There are occasional observations on the trees of the region—pecans, hickories, oaks, locusts, and gums—and on the game: "My guide killed an elk, called cerf by the Canadians and French of Illinois," an animal "thrice the size of the European stags"; and two days later, "my guide killed a Buffalo which he considered to be about four years old. . . . It seemed larger than any oxen in France."

As the frosts moved south across Illinois, so did the water birds, and the journal now and then records "duck hunting" or "goose hunting." Grebes, kingfishers, a white pelican, and a blue goose were added to his collection of bird skins. Turkeys were so plentiful that one day five were shot from the canoe without landing. However, these activities were but interludes, for it appears more than likely that many of those autumn days in Illinois were devoted to seeking out the erstwhile traders of the region for information about the Missouri River country and the lands beyond the western horizon, which Michaux continued to dream of exploring. Consistent with that dream, in mid-December he disposed of his horse, acquired a canoe, employed oarsmen, and set off on a long river voyage which, despite the hindrances of winter storms and cold, and upstream navigation most of the way, would take him all the way back to mid-Tennessee—a good, dry-run training expedition for a possible ascent of the Missouri.

The second day after setting out from Kaskaskia to travel down the Mississippi to the mouth of the Ohio, they camped on the west bank of the river, near Cape Girardeau in Spanish territory. Next evening they made camp on the American side "where the Belle Rivière falls into the Mississippi. On the opposite bank was camped Don Gayoso, Governor of Natchez and upper Louisiana. He sent a boat to find out who we were and, learning that I was a passenger, he came to see me. He told me the news of the Peace between France and Spain. He offered me his services."

After four days ascending the Ohio, they had passed Fort Massac and the mouth of the Tennessee and entered the Cumberland a few miles farther upstream. Heavy rains, sleet, snow, wintry blasts, and floods made progress upstream slow and painful, sometimes forcing them to stay all day in camp. That was the way they spent Christmas Day, 1795. "Rain continued to fall, mixed with hail," he wrote, as always without distinguishing the day in any other way than as December twenty-fifth. It took more than three weeks to reach Clarksville, twenty miles short of Nashville. Almost immediately after leaving his canoe there, the tireless naturalist secured a horse and turned northward again along the road to Louisville, traveling in bitter cold weather over frozen and often snow-covered roads. He spent several days gathering the collections he had left there with a French acquaintance, and, after visiting General Clark and the general's father, he set forth again to return to Nashville.

After a few days at the home of Colonel Robert Hays, brother-in-law of Andrew Jackson, Michaux purchased another horse to carry his collections and set out eastward for home. A steady, bone-chilling winter rain began to fall, and to shelter himself and his precious baggage which had already cost him so much effort and hardship he sought refuge in a roadside farmhouse. To his chagrin, his host, Colonel Mansko, turned out to be a "declared enemy of the French, because," he said, "they have killed their king." Michaux recorded his own response: "Although I had not dined I would not accept his supper, believing that a Republican should not be under obligations to a fanatical partisan of Royalty. I was greatly mortified that the night and the rain should compel me to remain in his House. But I slept on my Deer Skin and paid for the Maize he supplied me with to cross the Wilderness."

Snow, bitter cold, and flooded streams. A week after leaving Nashville he had only made it as far as Fort Blount, sixty miles away. Although a two-day accumulation of snow forced him to stop at this newly established post, it did not deter him from wintry botanizing. Near the fort he discovered a new tree, the beautiful yellowwood (*Cladrastis lutea*) which biennially adorns itself with showy panicles of fragrant, white, pealike flowers. As the name indicates, its bark produces a yellow dye. Michaux observed this characteristic and was so impressed by its possibilities as a practical source of dye that he promptly reported his find in a letter to Governor Blount at Knoxville. A young captain at the fort helped him to cut down a tree to get seed pods and to dig beneath the snow for roots of the tree to plant in his Charleston garden.

At Knoxville he tarried a week, awaiting the dawn of spring, before venturing into the mountains. It was in mid-March, while exploring along the Holston River, that he saw those traditional and symbolic harbingers of spring, hepaticas, dogtooth violets, and spring beauties, thrusting their new leaves and delicate flowers above the brown detritus of last summer's green. Blossoming there with these well-known wild flowers were masses of the equally beautiful but far less common twinleaf, with its delicate, daisy-like, white flowers. Michaux had discovered this plant years before in the mountains of Virginia. He had taken a specimen to William Bartram in Philadelphia and it had been named *Jeffersonia* in honor of their friend. Since then, only one other species of *Jeffersonia* has been discovered, and that one in faraway China.

These flowers were the awaited signals, nature's all clear for the homeward-bound naturalist to be on his way. As Michaux took the trail into the mountains, following the narrow valley of the Nolichucky, and back into winter, through Iron Mountain Pass, and down into a much more advanced and intoxicating springtime on the other side, one suspects that he somehow sensed that this was to be his last visit to his favorite region. Day after day the journal records a lengthening testament of beauty, seen now everywhere he looked—spring beauties and bloodroot, flame azalea and *Rhododendron minus*, aromatic strawberry shrubs, silver bells and big-leaf magnolia, yellow violets, and arbutus, verbena and phlox, and lupine. He notes them all, calling over their names with loving care, perhaps with a hint of nostalgic leave-taking, perhaps only with the floral rapture of an exceptionally vital man in tune with the symphony of spring.

A last farewell it was, however. Four months after his return to Charleston, a period of silence for his journal, André Michaux boarded the *Ophir* to return to France. Although he does not tell us what precipitated the decision to return at this time, we know that for some time his financial situation had been increasingly unsatisfactory. For almost seven years, ever since the revolution in France, he had received little or no financial support from that country, forcing him to use, with no guarantee of repayment, his own resources to maintain the two American gardens, to cover costs of packaging and shipping collections, and for his own expenses in the field. A close friend, in a posthumous memorial, wrote that Michaux had all but exhausted his own modest fortune in supporting his country's American enterprises. Even more distressing was the realization that his financial sacrifice may have been fruitless. Word reached him, probably from his son, that of the sixty thousand trees and plants, so laboriously gathered, transported, packed, and shipped to France, only a few still survived. During the time of his royal patronage most of his shipments had been sent on, by Marie Antoinette, to her father's Austrian gardens, or given to court favorites. Few reached their intended destination, the Rambouillet nurseries, where they would have received expert care; and most of those few were lost in the plundering of the royal gardens in the chaos following the revolution, as were also many of the shipments he continued to dispatch during the years of the Republic. A return to France offered a hope of remedy for his financial distress, perhaps a chance to rescue some of his collections, and an opportunity as well to establish a more vigorous and dependable basis of support for his future enterprises. It was probably with mixed emotions of discouragement and eager hopes that the French naturalist, after eleven years of eventful exile, saw the Carolina shoreline drop below the horizon that August day in 1796.

Three weeks later the *Ophir* encountered a furious tempest and was driven onto the shore of Holland. Several hours after the wreck, as the ship was being battered to pieces by the waves, Michaux was rescued, unconscious, by the townspeople of a nearby village. Washed ashore and recovered were almost all the boxes and chests containing his collections of plants, animal and bird skins, and seed packets, and all of his journal notebooks except those covering the activities of his first year in America.

Early in December he reached Paris, where, in spite of all his difficulties, he appears scarcely to have missed a beat in the vital progress of his life. There was a round of calls on old friends and associates, including Thouin and Lemonnier, and visits to the scientific leaders at the museums, among them Lamarck and Jussieu. He went also to see the Redoutés, famous natural history artists, and several times he visited his American friend, General Charles Cotesworth Pinckney, then on a touchy mission to France.

Most of these visits were probably concerned with forwarding the plans he had already resolved upon: the publication of a work on the American oaks, which in his opinion offered the most valuable possibilities for French forestry, and, a far more ambitious project, the publication of an illustrated work on North American flora. He hoped to return to America to continue his work there after these books were well launched.

After a brief visit to Satory, Michaux returned to Paris and, with characteristic energy, plunged into preparation of his proposed publications. Meanwhile the French authorities had not yet agreed to subsidize a new expedition to America, but in 1800 he was offered, instead, an opportunity to accompany a scientific expedition to the East Indies. It is not altogether clear why he accepted this, unless he had indeed given up hope of returning to America to continue his work there and so thought this offer his only immediate prospect of resuming his most congenial role of voyageur.

At any rate, he sailed with the expedition in October, 1800, and, during a stopover in Madagascar, he became so interested in the natural history of that island that he decided to leave the expedition and to remain on Madagascar for botanical research and collection. He died there of tropical fever in November, 1802.

Meanwhile, back in Paris, his son, François André, had seen through the press his father's book on American oaks, treating thirty-six species, and beautifully illustrated in color by the Redoutés. Two years later his two-volume work on North American flora was brought to completion through the devoted efforts of his able fellow botanist, Claude Richard. These landmark works are the only surviving tangible memorials to André Michaux. The Museum of Natural History in Paris voted that a bust of the great voyageur be placed in its garden, but those were still parlous times in France and the bust never appeared. His name survives, however, in mediums far more enduring than stone, not only in the significant pages of his botanical works, not only in the speaking words of his inimitable journals, but alive in every green and flowering plant that bears his name or imprint in gardens and forests throughout the world.

⟆ 4

At the very moment that André Michaux drew his last fevered breath of dank, tropical air in Madagascar, his son, François André, through a peculiar twist of fate, was in the region of America to which his father had longed to return—in the heart of "les hautes montagnes de Carolinie." There François was the guest of his father's old friend and guide, Davenport, who had been André's companion on that memorable and ecstatic September day, eight years before, when they struggled to the peak of Grandfather Mountain, there to shout to the surrounding wilderness the strains of the "Marseillaise." One would have difficulty in dreaming up a more symbolic coincidence, a more perfect seizing of the torch from the failing hand; for, if ever a son was the extension of his father's life and work, François André Michaux was that son; two lives, like the work of a master joiner, bonded so perfectly that the finished surface appears all of a single beautiful piece.

In the four years he had spent as a youth in America, before his return to France following his eye injury in 1789, the son had served his apprenticeship in wilderness travel, natural history, and horticulture under the able tutelage of his father. Back in France he resumed his formal education and studied under the botanists at the Museum, gaining the esteem of his scientific colleagues. When political turmoil subsided sufficiently to permit official attention to other matters, not the least of which was concern for the future of the depleted French forests, both his name, aggrandized by his American experience, and the respect of his colleagues made the thirty-year-old François André the natural choice for a new mission to the United States, an appointment his father had sought in vain. François' assignment was to report on the condition of the nursery gardens established by his father in New Jersey and Carolina and, primarily, to make a careful study of the trees that might be useful in enriching the forests of France.

He sailed from Bordeaux in August, 1801. His arrival in Charleston in early October was an inauspicious and disappointing return to the

François André Michaux, from a portrait by Rembrandt Peale. (Courtesy of the American Philosophical Society)

scene of his growing-up years. As soon as they dropped anchor, the passengers were told that the town was in the grip of a yellow fever epidemic, prompting the captain to land his fourteen passengers on Sullivans Island. This island, "almost bereft of vegetation" and all but treeless since its slow-growing palmettos had been sacrificed for the construction of Fort Moultrie in the early days of the Revolution, was not to the liking of the young student of trees. He soon left that "dull and melancholy place" and went on to the stricken city. A few days later he had reason to regret his temerity when he came down with the "dreadful malady, under which [he] laboured upward of a month." As soon as he had recovered sufficiently he moved out to the botanic garden, where, years before, he and his father had worked together so long and so lovingly.

The five years which had passed since the *Ophir* dropped behind the eastern horizon on her last voyage, carrying with her the devoted master of these Carolina acres, had been quite long enough for the notoriously voracious Southern weeds and shrubs, ever jealous of every open spot and ruthlessly intolerant of any exotic in their midst, to have repossessed the Jardin du Roi, once a mecca for the Charleston gentry who drove out in their carriages on Sundays. Much of the garden, however, had withstood the siege, and to his pleased surprise François found "a superb collection of trees and plants that had survived almost total neglect . . . likewise a great number of trees belonging to the old continent that my father had planted, some of which were in the most flourishing state." He noted especially the good condition of such exotics as Persian pomegranates, varnish trees, ginkgos, and "mimosas" which had managed to survive the embrace of the hardy native stock. Using the relict garden as his headquarters, François spent the winter collecting seeds in the low-country forests.

In the spring he sailed for New York to visit the Jersey garden. He found it thriving under the devoted and skillful hand of Paul Saulnier. Now, having visited his father's gardens and made his report on them, François was ready to set out on his second and principal mission—a search for desirable trees for introduction into French forests. To begin that search he went first to Philadelphia, then the horticultural and scientific, as well as the political, capital of the country. There he visited the gardens of William Hamilton and the Bartrams, which were, in fact, artistically arranged arboretums rather than gardens as we

think of them today, for they featured variety and exotics rather tha
showy effects.

From Philadelphia he set out, in late June, 1802, for Pittsburgh an
the Ohio River Valley, to follow generally the routes his father ha
taken at the behest of Citizen Genet, at this same season, nine years be
fore. François Michaux's account of this expedition, which carried hii
down the Ohio to Mayesville, across Kentucky to Nashville, thence east
ward across the mountains, and back to Charleston, where he arrived i
October, was published in Paris two years later with the title *Voyag
à l'ouest des Monts Alléghanys.* It proved so popular that, in the ne:
few years, it reappeared in several editions, in French, German, an
English.

Although the work of François André Michaux is as important to th
progress of botanical science and to American natural history as th:
of his father, perhaps of even more ultimate significance, he was as yr
only beginning his career, and this particular account does not hav
for us anything like the relevance of his father's journals. In it Franço
concerned himself with information more of interest to the historia
and to the sociologist than to the naturalist. His report offers, howeve
an entertaining and revealing look at frontier America and its peopl
as well as some insight into the personality of the young author hin
self, as is indicated by the sample potpourri of his observations th
follows.

All through the length of the hinterland of the southern and centr
states, beyond seventy or eighty miles from the sea, he noted that '
third of the inhabitants reside in log houses." These dwellings, oft
windowless, have chimneys of clay. Two men can build one of tl
cabins in four or five days. "Inns are very numerous in the Unit
States—yet almost everywhere, except in the principal towns, they a
very bad, notwithstanding rum, brandy, and whiskey, are in plenty.
fact, in houses of the above description all kinds of spirits are consider
most material, as they generally meet with great consumption." Brea
fast fare was "indifferent tea or worse coffee" with slices of fried hai
dinner, salt beef or roast fowl, with rum; supper, tea, coffee, and ha
again. ". . . seldom do you meet with clean sheets. Fortunate is tl
traveller who arrives on the day they happen to be changed; althoug
an American would be quite indifferent about it."

He observed with interest that the green cones of the cucumber tr
were infused in whiskey to make a remedy "much esteemed . . . as

preventive of intermittent fever; but I have my doubts whether it would be so generally used if it had the same qualities when mixed with water. . . . A passion for spirituous liquors is one of the features that characterize the country people belonging to the interior of the United States . . . in fact, I do not conceive there are ten out of a hundred who have resolution enough to desist from it a moment provided they had it by them . . ." At a village in western Pennsylvania he found the people celebrating the suppression of the tax laid upon whiskey distilleries: "The public houses . . . were filled with the lower class of people who made the most dreadful riot, and committed the most horrible excesses. . . ."

In the realm of commerce he noted "the conveyance of merchandise from Philadelphia to Pittburgh is made in large covered wagons, drawn by four horses. . . . They reckon it to be three hundred miles . . . and make it a journey of from twenty to twenty-four days." The wagons returned empty except during the season for furs from the West or ginseng from the hills. In Kentucky corn and wheat were the only significant crops, the former on new ground producing seventy-five to a hundred bushels an acre worth twenty-five cents a bushel. These grains were sent down the river on flatboats, capable of carrying three hundred barrels, manned by five men, who either returned home on foot, or by sea around Florida, to Philadelphia or Baltimore, and on foot from there. The freightage for the thirty-day, fifteen-hundred-mile voyage, which included the boat, for it was abandoned in New Orleans, was about one hundred dollars. Michaux was surprised to find shipyards at Pittsburgh and Marietta producing seagoing, three-masted vessels, to export both vessel and cargo of regional produce, by way of New Orleans, to the West Indies or Atlantic ports. In those shipyards he took particular note of the species of timber employed and the qualities and special uses of each, for trees producing shipbuilding timber were of primary importance in his assignment. With the same careful and detailed observation he also noted the methods of maple sugar production. He not only observed but speculated thoughtfully on what he saw. The ignored outcroppings of rich veins of coal intrigued him with their possibilities, in the light of the fact that he had noted the coal used in the East was brought there all the way from England.

Trees in all their aspects of growth and usefulness were his constant concern. He recorded that the canoe in which he and a chance companion navigated the Ohio was "twenty-four feet long, eighteen inches wide, and about as many in depth," fashioned from a single log. In the Ohio region both pine and tulip-tree logs were used for canoes. Along the river the soil was extraordinarily rich and big trees were common. Near a hut where they stopped one night they measured a sycamore forty-seven feet in circumference—more than twice the size of any known today.

The inhabitants along the river seemed to him in no way in harmony with the beauty all about them. They spent most of their time stag and deer hunting, for the sake of the skins which they sold, and they paid little attention to cultivation of the land or to building attractive houses, content to live in squalor in miserable windowless log cabins, with little or no furniture. They received travelers, however, with the rough-and-ready hospitality of the frontier—"they give them a lodging, that is to say, they permit them to sleep upon the floor wrapped up in their rugs. They are accommodated with bread, Indian corn, dried ham, milk and butter, but seldom anything else. . . ."

Occasionally he had the company of some of the frontier settlers for a day or two of travel. One such, who accompanied him for two days on the river, was headed downstream for the Missouri and the Mississippi, to select a suitable spot in which to settle, attracted by "the quantities of beavers, elks, and more especially bisons" to be found there. ". . . his costume, like all American sportsmen, consisted of a waistcoat with sleeves, a pair of pantaloons, and a large red and yellow worsted sash. A carbine, a tomahawk or little axe, which the Indians make use of to cut wood and to terminate the existence of their enemies, two beaver-snares, and a large knife suspended at his side, constituted his sporting dress. A rug comprised the whole of his luggage. . . . Such were the first inhabitants of Kentucky and Tennessea."

Crossing Kentucky from Lexington to Nashville, Michaux's way led across the Barrens or Kentucky Meadows. For the traveling tree-lover, "nothing can be more tiresome than the doleful uniformity of these immense meadows where there is nobody to be met with; and where, except for a great number of partridges, we neither see nor hear any species of living beings, and are still more isolated than in the middle of the forests." Only a few years earlier, in that rolling grass country, elk and buffalo had been common, the latter in herds of several hundred, but soon after the advent of the white man they had been reduced to rarities, and with their passing the white hunters had moved on westward to not yet decimated hunting grounds. In this prairie country, near "Bear-Wallow," Michaux came upon a settler's cabin, where the mistress of the house told him that he was the first white person seen there in eighteen months. The prairie was not entirely a dull interlude for Michaux, however, for he remarked: "amidst these pasture lands I discovered a great variety of plants, among which were the gerardia flava. . . . The flower season was over with three parts of the plants, but the time for most of the seeds to ripen was still at a great distance; nevertheless I gathered about ninety different species of them which I took with me to France."

Of the Kentucky people, in general, Michaux reported that they had brought with them from the "remotest parts" of Virginia, from which most of them had come, "the passion for gaming and spirituous liquors [which] is carried to excess, which frequently terminates in quarrels degrading to human nature. . . . Horses and law suits comprise the usual topic of their conversation. If a traveller happens to pass by, his horse is appreciated; if he stops, he is presented with a glass of whiskey, and then asked a thousand questions. . . ."

The young Frenchman remarked also on the various religious sects existing among the Kentuckians with the greatest degree of religious tolerance. Methodists and Anabaptists were the most numerous, and he described the open-air camp meetings or revivals, to which many thousands sometimes came from as far as twenty miles away. "The clergymen are very vehement in their discourses. Often in the midst of the sermons the heads are lifted up, the imaginations exalted, and the inspired fall backwards, exclaiming, 'Glory! Glory!' This species of infatuation happens chiefly among the women, who are carried out of the crowd, and put under a tree, where they lie a long time extended, heaving the most lamentable sighs."

Between Nashville and Knoxville, in crossing the Cumberlands, it was still deemed reckless to travel except in large groups to provide protection from possible Indian attacks. Farther on, Michaux found that the trail across the Appalachians through Iron Mountain Pass was so little traveled that it was extremely difficult to follow, "encumbered by forests of rhododendrum, shrubs from eighteen to twenty feet in height, the branches of which, twisting and interwoven with each other, impede the traveller every moment, insomuch that he is obliged to use an axe to clear his way." Part of the way the trail was mostly the bed of a wild mountain stream, "the winding course of which cut the path in twelve or fifteen directions . . . the entrance of which was frequently concealed by tufts of grass or branches of trees, which have time to grow and extend their foliage, since whole months elapse without it being passed by travellers." That was the road to the "charming plantation" of his father's old friend and guide, Davenport, a welcome place on the Toe River for the weary traveler to rest and reprovision for the remainder of his crossing of the mountains. Michaux spent a week there with his father's friend. "I was at that time very far from thinking," he wrote after his return to France, "that, at the same time when this worthy man was entertaining me about his old travelling companion, I lost a beloved father, who died a victim of his zeal for the progress of natural history, upon the coast of the island of Madagascar!"

During the rest of his journey back to Charleston, except for the German settlements along the upper Catawba, there was little to please the traveler, plantations few and poorly cared for, the soil abused, little diversity of crops, many farms already worn out and abandoned. Between Chester and Columbia "the country grows worse in every respect. The traveller no longer meets reception at plantations; he is obliged to put up at inns, where he is badly accommodated both in point of board and lodging, and pays dearer than in any other part of the United States."

In Columbia, the new capital of South Carolina, "the legislature . . . meets annually on the first of December, and all the business is transacted in the same month; it then dissolves, and, except at that time, the town derives no particular advantage from being the seat of government." Between there and Charleston the road was terrible. Along it "every two or three miles we met with a miserable log house . . . surrounded with little fields of Indian corn . . . that do not yield more than four or five bushels per acre. . . . The extreme unwholesomeness of the climate is clearly shown in the pale and livid countenances of the inhabitants, who . . . are almost all infected with tertian fevers. . . . The major part of the inhabitants do not even cultivate vegetables. . . ."

In the plantation country of the coastal region, he wrote that "the agricultural labours are performed by negro slaves, and the major part of the planters employ them to drag the plow; they conceive the land is better cultivated, and calculate besides that, in the course of a year, a horse, for food and looking after, costs ten times more than a negro, the annual expense of which does not exceed fifteen dollars. I shall bstain from any reflection concerning this, as the opinion of many people is fixed."

Although it would be ten years more before his monumental landmark on American trees was completed and published, and yet another five years before its appearance in English, rewarding its author with the undisputed title of "Father of American Forestry," there was much in his account of his Western travels indicating the direction and aim of François André's genius. In addition to careful observations on the quality and uses of every species he found being utilized by the inhabitants, he noted that the species of trees indigenous to an area was a reliable index of the quality and value of the soil. He observed the contrast between the nature of a forest surrounding an abandoned clearing and the one beginning to grow up in the clearing, and in this he anticipated what is now a well-known tenet of forest management, the sequence of species domination. Related observations led him to the conclusion that the prairie regions of Kentucky and Tennessee owed both origin and continued existence to repeated wildfires. He noted the rapidly mounting timber shortage in the east, and recommended elimination of the less desirable species, and encouragement of the better sorts, to offset the timber drain.

Thinking and writing scientifically about the future of the American forests was something new. Americans had grown accustomed to regarding their forests as impediments to be surmounted, as nuisances in the way of cultivation of land or building a road. When the practice of burning virgin timber or girdling the trees and leaving them to die was commonplace, any thought of encouraging the growth of trees seemed fatuous. Literally speaking, Americans of the eighteenth and nineteenth centuries could not see the forest for the trees. However, to venture another aphorism, it was already later than they thought. It would take a full century after Michaux's pioneering concepts for them to awaken to a sufficient realization of that sober truth to begin to study and apply the science and wisdom of François André Michaux to their, by then, sadly manhandled forest heritage.

After a few months in Charleston, Michaux sailed back to France in March, 1803. Now his course was clearly charted, his life work laid out for him. Two years later, the year after the first publication of his *Voyage*, he made a thirty-six-page report on the naturalization of North American trees to France, complete with a tabulation of sixty-eight species (nearly twice the number of native French trees) he considered useful and adaptable to French conditions, detailing the size, uses, preferred locations and soils of each. This report so impressed the Administration of Waters and Forests that he was given a major role in the government's efforts to stem the encroachment of the sandy wastelands below Bordeaux, on the Bay of Biscay, which were then inexorably overwhelming the rich farmlands of southwest France. The wasteland area, now largely reclaimed and in productive forests, and no longer encroaching on its neighboring regions, stands as a monument to the skill and devotion of Michaux, a skill and devotion which gave him, in the natural history of France, an even more distinguished place than the recognition accorded him in America as the Father of American Forestry.

In pursuit of his dedication, in 1806 he sailed once more for America. En route, the American ship on which he had sailed was stopped and searched by a British warship. As England and France were then at war, Michaux was taken into custody. However, as usual in those days, in this respect more civilized than our own era, the pursuit of science was not held subject to military hostilities. The vocation of naturalist was sufficient passport so that, after a few pleasant weeks of internment on Bermuda, which gave him the opportunity to study the flora of an isolated bit of land, with few native trees, Michaux was permitted to proceed to New York.

There the personable Frenchman was cordially and admiringly received. During his visit to New York, Robert Fulton's *Clermont* made its maiden voyage up the Hudson, with Michaux and a fellow countryman as the only two passengers. In Philadelphia, the scientifically elite, many of them old friends and admirers of his father, were sufficiently impressed by the son's ability to elect him also to membership in the American Philosophical Society. Among the personal friends he made was a fascinating fellow naturalist, a romantic figure, artist, ornithologist, poet, and erstwhile schoolteacher, now connected with the city's leading publishing house, Bradford and Inskeep. This new friend, Scottish-born Alexander Wilson, was himself, like Michaux, in the process of writing a landmark multi-volume, illustrated natural history work. Their shared interests, and the interrelationships of Wilson's birds and Michaux's trees, closely cemented their friendship. Wilson endeavored to bring about arrangements for his employers, who were also the publishers of his own series of volumes, already beginning to appear, to undertake also the English-language edition of Michaux's volumes, but in this he failed. Michaux's work, in three volumes, magnificently illustrated in color by the Redoutés, was first published in French, between 1810 and 1813, by a Paris firm, under the title *Histoire des Arbres forestiers de l'Amérique Septentrionale*, and did not appear in an English edition until 1817, when another Philadelphia publisher brought it out under the title *The North American Sylva*.

In these volumes Michaux treated his trees much as Wilson did his birds, not only as scientific specimens to be accurately identified and precisely described, but as friends, to be warmly remembered, with personal comment and anecdote rounding out many of his accounts. It was not only his scientific knowledge of trees but his appreciation of their importance, his recognition of the impending necessity for forest conservation and tree culture, and his full awareness of the as yet nameless science of ecology that lifted François Michaux above the category of dendrologist alone and dignified him with the greater historical significance of forester, America's first.

Here, for example, is part of his discussion of the palmetto or cabbage palm:

The base of the undisclosed bundles of leaves is white, compact, and tender; it is eaten with oil and vinegar, and resembles the artichoke and cabbage in taste, whence is derived the name of cabbage-tree. But to destroy a vegetable, which has been a century in growing, to obtain three or four ounces of substance, neither richly nutritious nor peculiarly agreeable to the palate, would be pardonable only in a desert destined to remain uninhabited for ages. With similar prodigality of the works of nature, the first settlers of Kentucky killed the buffalo, an animal weighing 1200 to 1500 pounds, for the pleasure of eating its tongue, and abandoned its carcass to the beasts of the wilderness.

Likewise he deplored the waste of wood in supplying tanbark—magnificent trunks of oak and hemlock left to rot after removal of the bark—and the enormous waste of fuel wood in firing the inefficient furnaces of the potters and smelters and in the crude distilleries and the evaporators used in salt and sugar production. To ameliorate this forest drain, he suggested the employment of a coppice system for a more efficient production of fuel wood.

Michaux foresaw the day when forest managers would be selecting the species for their acres. With that day in view he suggested that the areas occupied by the red maple could be better utilized by oaks, ashes, and sugar maples. Although he was a theorist in the best sense, he was

White Oak.
Quercus alba.

Typical of the fine, hand-colored illustrations in *North American Sylva* by François André Michaux is this of the white oak by P. J. Redouté. (Courtesy of the University of South Carolina Library)

not a mere visionary. On the contrary, he was a realist when confronted with situations that, although they made him unhappy, appeared to be irremediable. "It would be unavailing," he wrote, "to recommend the preservation and multiplication of the cypress in the maritime districts of the Carolinas and Georgia; though for an extent of more than 900 miles they have neither stone nor slate for building, it becomes daily more profitable for the increasing population to convert the marshes into rice grounds. . . . It is highly probable that in less than two centuries the cypress will disappear from the southern states."

Thus was the trail blazed through the American forests, through the leaves of Michaux's *Sylva*, a trail with markings still clear a century later when, born of the "imperious necessity" he foresaw, the professional forester appeared on the American scene.

In 1822 Michaux retired to a country estate near the village of Vauréal, beside the beautiful river Oise, not far from Paris. His life during the following decades, though relatively rooted for a nomadic Michaux, was one of continuous active experimentation with forest trees and forest management. It was during these years also that he married his wife, a distant cousin.

The death of François André Michaux, in 1855, brought to an end the lifework, but not the influence, of the father-son team who had contributed so immeasurably to the botany and forestry of the two great Western republics and to Franco-American botanical exchange. He was buried on the grounds of his estate, beneath the shade of American trees he had planted there.

Even death did not, however, still the Michaux's active advancement of forestry. A substantial legacy, left by François André to the American Philosophical Society for the encouragement of forest studies, enabled the Society to support studies which played no small part in the creation of the Pennsylvania Department of Forestry, a department which was the stimulus as well as the seedbed and nursery of the forestry services of the several states during the early years of this century.

~~ Chapter 7

ALEXANDER WILSON

~~ 1

In the great harbors and wide estuaries along the coast of the eastern United States, in the latter part of the eighteenth century, sailing vessels riding at anchor were a common sight, many with a sea-weary load of European exiles, bearing their burdens of hopes and sorrows and usually little else. For a few years after the terrible epidemic of yellow fever in Philadelphia in the summer of 1793, vessels bound for that city sailed into the beautiful estuary of the Delaware River to land their passengers at the old Swedish town of Newcastle.

One such vessel was the *Swift*, out of Belfast, which dropped anchor in the Delaware on a mid-July afternoon in 1794 with a cargo of 350 immigrants, including two young Scots, deck passengers, with hardly a shilling between them. They were Alexander Wilson, twenty-eight, weaver, poet, libertarian, and his nephew, William Duncan, age sixteen.

No doubt the tall, romantic-looking Wilson was noted with approval by his fellow passengers, one of whom, on landing, loaned him a few shillings; perhaps he had entertained his shipmates during the long summer days at sea with his flute and his ballads. None on shipboard, however, least of all Alexander Wilson himself, could have suspected the prophetic symbolism for him of the name emblazoned across the broad stern of their vessel: *Swift*. In the relatively few years left to him, Alexander Wilson was to become a competent artist and naturalist and the foremost ornithologist of his adopted country—author and illustrator of eight, out of a projected ten, volumes of *American Ornithology*, a stupendous accomplishment that earned him posterity's acclaim and the title: "Father of American Ornithology."

Nothing in his past life hinted at this destiny. His early years had been marked by hardship and tragedy. Haunted by an intense desire to achieve greatness in the eyes of future generations, he had spent his early youth in a frustrating search for some channel of expression suited to his passionate spirit, only to be met with disappointment again and again. Now, penniless and almost alone in a strange land, he felt his heart lift with hope. As he walked that July day along the green and shady meadows beside the Delaware, heading toward Philadelphia, perhaps he, like other exiles, sensed the promise in the very air of the fresh, young nation he would some day make his own; perhaps, almost unaware, he sensed within himself the courage, the resolution, and the vitality to make his dream come true. But as yet he did not even know the shape of that dream—he had years more of trial before he saw it clearly.

The fabric of Wilson's life, prior to his departure for America in 1794, had all the subdued but varied color and the apparent lack of design of a paisley shawl, a peculiarly appropriate metaphor for his Scottish years, for it was in the town of Paisley, in a house by the foaming Cart River, that Wilson was born on July 6, 1766. He was one of a numerous tribe born to sometime weaver and sometime smuggler Alexander (Sanders) Wilson, several children by young Alexander's mother, who died when he was nine, the rest by his stepmother who took over the household a few months later. By the standards of eighteenth-century Paisley the elder Wilson was a successful businessman and a responsible citizen of the community despite his smuggling activities, which after all, were calculated to keep Scottish shillings from London pockets—in Scottish eyes a laudable, if illegal, activity.

It had been the hope of Alexander Wilson's devout Presbyterian mother that her only son should become a minister and, until her death, his schooling was directed to that objective. With her death and his father's remarriage to a widow with several children of her own, all formal schooling ceased for Alexander. The schoolboy now became a herd boy or herd "callan" in the rugged mountain country southeast of Paisley. The three years he spent there in the wild, misty hills and moors, through which turbulent streams tumbled on their courses from the mountains to the Firth of Clyde—with no other company but his dull-witted charges—no doubt served to awaken the lad's curious and alert mind to nature's rather parsimonious offerings in that harsh country. Certainly he seems to have learned to endure and enjoy solitude, an essential lesson for the future naturalist, and to delight in wild creatures and the natural world about him.

It must have been a dismal change for the nature-loving lad when, at thirteen, he was brought back to town and apprenticed to his brother-in-law, William Duncan, a Paisley weaver. It was a tedious and exacting trade, and the life of an apprentice in eighteenth-century Scotland was not an easy one, especially for a boy tuned to very different music from that of clattering looms. At about this same time the elder Wilson had another turn at smuggling, now made highly profitable by the war with the American colonies, and, as a safer, more discreet base for his activity, he moved his family away from town to the hill country where his son had spent his herd-boy years. A forbidding, square gray stone tower, once the home of William Wallace, Scotland's greatest hero, became the Wilson home. To this austere but romantic refuge, every summer Saturday the weaver's apprentice trudged the seventeen miles that lay between Paisley and the Tower of Auchinbothie.

Alexander Wilson was now growing into a tall, darkly handsome young man, with a taste for books, an ability to dance, like most young Scots, and a flair for verse writing and flute playing. When he finished his apprenticeship in the summer of 1782, he marked the end of his bondage with a verse, endorsed on his indenture paper:

> Be't kent to a' the warld in rhime,
> That wi' right meickle wark and toil,
> For three lang years I've ser't my time,
> While feasted wi' the hazel oil.

Now a full-fledged weaver, he joined the family at the Tower of Auchinbothie, weaving now and then with his father or neighborhood weavers. It is said, however, that most of his time during his two or three years at home was spent in roaming the country, climbing Misty Law, skating on nearby Lock Semple, and making verses and love—and all the while, unconsciously and without benefit of indenture papers, serving a significant apprenticeship for his lifework as a naturalist.

Youthful restlessness and probably a longing for friends to share his love of poetry and books brought Wilson back to Paisley in 1785, where he gained his daily bread, for the next few years, at one or an-

other of the town's many looms. One of his fellow weavers, David
Brodie, was as literary, studious, and ambitious as Wilson himself, with
dreams and abilities, like Wilson's, far beyond his humble calling. The
two encouraged and stimulated each other in serious study, especially
in classical and English literature. They soon became members of a
literary set, largely inspired by Robert Burns, whose first book of
poetry had appeared in 1786, beginning the love affair, still ardent
today, between the Scottish people and the poet whose genius gave
such perfect expresson to their hopes, their joys, their sorrows.

Wilson's working partnership, though not his friendship, with Brodie
and his literary friends was interrupted by a call from William Duncan,
his brother-in-law, to help him out with his weaving business near
Edinburgh. Wilson's principal role was as peddler of the woven materials, and for the next four years he wandered with a pack on his back
from village to village and cottage to cottage, traveling, as he put it,
"beneath a load of silks and sorrows" eventually over almost the whole
of Scotland. The long journeys were rare, however, and most of his
peddling was within a limited radius and was interrupted by intervals
of living briefly at the Tower of Auchinbothie again or working for
short periods at the looms. Happily, too, he was preparing, all unaware,
for his destiny as a great ornithologist. These tramping days accustomed
him to living out of doors, often sleeping by the roadside, and sharpened
his already deep interest in nature. Nature, indeed, dominated the
poetry he was constantly writing, often in conventional and hackneyed
verses, but sometimes with fresh and haunting lines. Wilson's verse had
sufficient merit to persuade a local printer to bring out an edition of
his collected poems—for whose publication the poet desperately solicited
subscriptions along his peddling route and for which he sought in vain
financial patrons. Perhaps the most appropriate comment on these poems
is his own inscription, written sixteen years later, in a copy of this
volume: "I published these poems when only twenty-two—an age more
abundant in sail than ballast. Reader, let this soften the rigour of criticism
a little."

During the next few years most of the significant events of young
Wilson's life involved his poetic efforts. The persistent attempts he had
made to obtain subscriptions for his work over a wide area of Scotland,
and, where obtained, to follow up with delivery and collection, the
constant dread of failure to meet his debt to the publisher, combined
with crushing discouragement over the pallid reception of his poems,

brought about a physical collapse which drove him back to the care of his family at the Tower of Auchinbothie, where for months he lay bedridden and helpless with "inflammation of the lungs." Back on his feet once more, he returned briefly to Edinburgh and his peddling job, trying to collect from the subscribers to his book, but trade was petering out with the beginning of war with France and Wilson soon gave up his peddling and returned to a loom job in Paisley, living quietly, but continuing a devout follower of the poetic muse. A chance to take part in a poetry contest in Edinburgh inspired him to a 210-line composition and a midwinter walk of fifty miles to Edinburgh to deliver it. While he failed to win the contest he came in second, and, perhaps even more gratifying, he received enthusiastic ovations from the general audience and welcome attention from a literary group who invited him to cooperate with a literary magazine then being planned.

Shortly after that, back in Paisley, he achieved the only really popular poetic success of his life, a comic, dramatic ballad called "Watty and Meg," and this was published anonymously, thus depriving him of the literary recognition for which he longed. The poem, excellent of its kind, was generally thought to be by the idolized Robert Burns, which may account somewhat for its huge sale of one hundred thousand copies. Wilson's material return from "Watty and Meg" was a greatcoat, a gift from the satisfied printer, a most appropriate and useful form of royalty for the poet who, by the winter of 1792, was a wretched prisoner in Paisley's tall gray stone jail, the Tolbooth. Behind this sad turn of events lay another poem and a strange and puzzling affair.

These were the years of the French Revolution. Beginning with the fall of the Bastille in 1789, the upheaval in France had steadily escalated in aims and intensity. By 1792 it was displaying a terrifying vitality, simultaneously successfully resisting formidable invasions, overturning the old order and the monarchy, and substituting rule by the Committee of Public Safety. Across the channel, the power structure in England watched fearfully. To protect the bastions of privilege, a sort of eighteenth-century McCarthyism was loosed on the land. In panic, the British government set incredibly severe penalties for any seditious writing, any criticism, or any combination of employees against an employer. Informers were everywhere. Anyone so indiscreet as to propose the old waggish toast to "George the Third and last" might soon find himself on a prison ship headed for the penal colony at Botany Bay. The impact of these harsh measures was especially severe in Scotland where many had little affection for the English crown and little respect for English laws. This was particularly true in the textile regions where the weavers were a notoriously stiff-necked lot with many a reformer and revolutionary among them. Wilson had sincere sympathy with liberal views and a warm friendship with some of the more radical weavers. He had even expressed in verse an admiration of that well-known in-spirer of revolutions, Tom Paine:

> The "Rights of Man" is now weel kenned,
> And read by mony a hunder;
> For Tammy Paine the buik has penned,
> And lent the Courts a lounder;
> Its like a keeking-glass to see
> The craft of Kirk and statesmen;
> And wi' a bauld and easy glee
> Guid faith the birky beats them
> Aff hand this day.

Those were bold words in the all-pervading atmosphere of suspicion, tension, and unrest; but worse was to come. William Sharp, one of Paisley's leading mill owners, notorious for his oppression of workers, received an anonymous letter enclosing a poem which patently de-scribed him and accused him of defrauding his weavers by short-measuring them. The letter demanded five guineas as the price for sup-pression of the poem. As the town's best-known poet and a weaver of liberal leanings, Wilson was promptly arrested. He readily admitted that the letter and poem were in his handwriting but steadfastly refused to make any statement beyond that admission. The logical conclusion seems to be that he was protecting, by his silence, other weavers involved in the affair, perhaps weavers already suspected of seditious acts, for whom disclosure would mean death or deportation. However, nothing about the affair is clear, neither the facts, nor Wilson's motives, nor the behavior of the authorities. The initial arrest and detention were fol-lowed by other charges—contempt of court, sedition, extortion, and libel —until the bewildered young man was as entangled in legal ramifications as a gnat in the syrup and tentacles of a sundew leaf. During the next two miserable years he was in and out of the Tolbooth cells. Bonds were posted, fines and damages paid. Finally the wretched poet was required to burn, publicly, the offending stanzas on the Tolbooth balcony over-looking the public square.

The penalty may seem a mild one in view of the hysterical temper of the times, but the long-drawn-out harassment, the threats, the humiliation, the repeated imprisonments and abuse had shaken and bruised the youth's sensitive nature and traced upon his spirit the shadow of melancholy which was never wholly to leave him again. The experience cut deeply and painfully into the very stuff of Alexander Wilson's life, especially into the vulnerable fabric of the one really serious and passionate love affair of his youth. Martha M'Lean, the girl to whom most of his love poems refer, was the daughter of a prominent Paisley family and by all accounts a beautiful and intelligent girl of fine character. She seems to have made a loyal and persistent effort to support the poet all during the disastrous proceedings, but her kindness only served to accentuate the wound to his damaged pride. To him it seemed impossible that there could ever be friendship, not to speak of marriage, between a M'Lean and a convicted blackmailer. At whatever cost, he closed the door upon his dearest hopes; he was never again to write a love poem.

He faced his bleak prospects with heroic determination, as he was to do again and again in the years to come. Bitter and resentful against his repressive homeland, he resolved to put a wide ocean between himself and the scenes of so much grief and suffering. Intent on this purpose, he returned to the monotony of the loom, for four months saving almost every penny he earned until he accumulated enough to buy deck space on a westward-bound vessel for himself and young William Duncan, son of his sister and the weaver to whom Wilson had been apprenticed as a lad. It was in May, 1794, that they left Paisley, in secrecy, for Wilson felt himself a marked man politically, and crossed over to Ireland. In Belfast they had the good fortune to secure deck passage on the *Swift*, then loading for Philadelphia.

∼ɔ◌ 2

In mid-July, when the *Swift* dropped anchor in the Delaware estuary at Newcastle, the first introduction the Scottish youths had to their new homeland was not the busy port city of Philadelphia, which was their destination, but a thirty-mile walk up the right bank of the Delaware in "the intolerable heat of a scorching sun," shocking to their Northern bodies. However, after weeks confined to the deck of a crowded sailing vessel, it was a relief to be on land, and joyous indeed, to the ambitious and adventurous youths, to be at last in the land of their hopes. Everything at first was a source of interest—the tree-shaded countryside, the new and vivid flowers, the novelty of the farmhouses in the clearings, still almost without exception made of round logs, the industries, already built or in process, textile and flour mills in Wilmington, a paper mill farther along the way to Philadelphia. They were excited most of all by the birds, the number and variety and strangeness of them. One, a red-headed woodpecker, which Wilson shot so that he might inspect it in detail, he thought the most beautiful bird he had ever seen.

They had little time to feast their eyes on the wonders of America once they arrived in Philadelphia, for they desperately needed to find employment to provide them with more substantial fare. Jobs were plentiful in the city, where the inhabitants, who had fled the terrible plague of the preceding summer, were slowly trickling back. Wilson found work in an engraver's shop. It was a good start. In the months that followed, however, his initial exhilaration and delight in his new country fought a losing battle with homesickness, an illness to which transplanted Scots are particularly subject. But he had burned his boats. A return to Scotland was out of the question. To assuage his loneliness and longing, he sought the company of fellow Caledonians and the kind of work he had done at home. Giving up his job in the engraver's shop and leaving the city, he found work on a Scot's looms and a room in a Scot's home in the country north of the city. The lure of the familiar persisted, and spring found him with a pack on his back once more selling cloth from door to door across the Jersey hill country. Another year passed before his restlessness and misery permitted him to settle down to anything more demanding than temporary work.

Somehow the autumn of 1796, however, found the erstwhile weaver, peddler, poet filling the role of schoolmaster in the predominantly German village of Milestown (now part of Bristol), about fifteen miles up the Delaware River from Philadelphia. As German was the language of most of his pupils, he had to learn the language, a process made easier by his lodging in a German household. Now again, as in his youth in Scotland, he turned with passionate dedication to books, studying far into the night after his long day in the schoolroom.

For five years Wilson remained in Milestown as schoolmaster, a long time for the restless Celt to stay in one place and on one job. During these years his industry and his natural hunger for learning led him into many fields of study. He acquired also some practical skills, mastering enough mathematics, for instance, to accept surveying commissions. His

Portrait of Alexander Wilson by Rembrandt Peale. (Courtesy of the American Philosophical Society)

interest in America inspired him to read whatever was available on the brief history of his new country. Slowly the young Scot was becoming a well-educated and accomplished man, by the standards of eighteenth-century America. So it was natural that he should be chosen to make the patriotic address on the occasion of the town's celebration of Thomas Jefferson's inauguration in March of that year, an address in praise of liberty and Jefferson which received warm praise far beyond Milestown itself. Though he did not formally become an American citizen until 1804, several years after he had left Milestown forever, it is clear, from his Inauguration Day address, that Wilson was already at heart an American, the countryman of his revered hero, Jefferson.

However, Milestown's greatest significance in Wilson's education was a mere matter of geography, since it lay in the Delaware Valley which is a part of the flyway, twice annually, for the world's most concentrated bird migration. For one who, as a boy, had become an intimate of nature in the hills of Renfrewshire and, as a young man, had filled his poetry with bird references, such as the "Lines to the Disconsolate Wren": ". . . bonny, wee, bit wren, Lone on a fuggy stane" (mossy stone), the winged myriads, passing spring and fall to and from their breeding grounds, were endlessly fascinating. For one so attuned there was no ignoring the flashes of yellow in the trees as the feeding warblers prepared for their long flight in the dark of night, the bands of waxwings, elegant in posture, dignified in their dove-brown coats, with red and yellow trimmings, freely fraternizing and traveling with red-breasted bluebirds, or the plain little slate-colored juncos, flashing the white feathers of their tails as they flitted in short flights from the roadside hedgerows. From him even the secretive cuckoo and the shy, swamp-loving woodcock were not hidden.

Even more exciting were the millions of transient waterfowl along the river. A friend owned Duck Island, a long island in the Delaware up near Trenton, a favorite haunt for prodigious flights of ducks. Frequently Wilson went to the island in the company of hunters, an exceptional opportunity to learn to distinguish the dozens of species then common transients there, feeding in the river's shallows or beneath the oaks and beeches of the island. One could watch most of the duck kind flying by day on their long journeys north and south, and so also with the swifts, swallows, and whippoorwills. The night-flying warblers and songbirds, on the contrary, must be observed as they rested and fed, by day, in preparation for their mysterious flights through the darkness.

For the romantic Wilson, the northward flights of spring were more appealing: through some mysterious selection system, male and female, already paired, hastened toward their wide northland breeding grounds to nest and nurture broods in the long daylight hours of northern latitudes, guided there, even to last year's nesting bush, by the mysterious compasses with which nature endowed them. For some the Delaware Valley itself was the nesting ground, the home destination of their flight. Among these were the fish hawks, who each year returned to their great nests perched high in tall riverbank trees, a common sight in Wilson's day. In later years Wilson would compose a poem to that superb harbinger of spring:

> True to the season, o'er our sea-beat shore
> The sailing osprey high is seen to soar,
> With broad unmoving wing, and circling slow,
> Marks each loose straggler in the deep below;
> Sweeps down like lightning! plunges with a roar!
> And bears his struggling victim to the shore.
> The long-housed fisherman beholds with joy,
> The well-known signals of his rough employ;
> And as he bears his nets and oars along,
> Thus hails the welcome season with a song: . . .

The time when Wilson could dedicate himself entirely to birds was still some years away. Teaching in a country schoolhouse was at best a dreary drudgery of long hours with few compensations. The pay of a country teacher in rural America at that time was barely more than a starvation wage, even that not always forthcoming. Wilson had contracted, about a year after he came to Milestown, to purchase a hundred and fifty acres of wilderness, far to the north between Cayuga and Seneca lakes in New York, to be developed into farmland by his nephew William Duncan, with the hope that the place could become a refuge and home for his sister and the rest of her Duncan children who now wanted to join their two kinsmen in America. To meet this additional burden and to pay the cost and keep of the horse he acquired, Wilson turned to "moonlighting," adding tutoring, summer teaching, and surveying to his regular job.

He was beginning to come out of his shell, taking part more and more in community life, where he was respected for his intelligence and integrity of character and valued for his accomplishments. In his lonely hours he had mastered the violin, whose melancholy sweetness alternated with the haunting strains of the flute to companion his sorrows, and he began occasionally to take part in musical evenings with congenial neighbors. Fortune seemed to be turning upon him a more smiling countenance than she was wont to bear for him, and for a brief while she seemed almost to be beckoning him down a road he had abandoned all hope of traveling—the road of traditional success and domestic happiness. In a light-hearted mood he wrote to a friend, in a letter facetiously headed "Milestown Monastery":

An old bachelor, . . . and clusters of dimple-cheeked, soft-eyed females, in every log hut around, and sighing for a husband . . . We must make advances in some one or all of these important duties, which Mr. Sterne says, devoid of, a human being is undeserving of the name Man. That is, to write a book, plant a tree, beget a child (I ought to have said marry a wife first), build a house, and learn something every day that he did not before know.

Whatever reality there may have been in his dreams and plans for marriage, suddenly all such hopes were ended. On May 1, 1801, Alexander Wilson disappeared from Milestown, leaving secretly at night, on horseback, abandoning all his possessions but his greatcoat. There is no conclusively proved explanation for the debacle, but vague hints in distraught notes to a trusted Scottish friend suggest a possibility of romantic involvement with a Milestown matron. Through the same confidential correspondence we learn that he spent most of the remainder of that year teaching in a log-cabin school in a village in northern Jersey. In his self-imposed exile, fierce despondency gripped him. He had nowhere to turn. In his bitterness he longed at times to return to Scotland, but that was impossible. His situation in New Jersey was so wretched that any move seemed desirable, and early in the new year, in a mood of somber despair, he returned to Philadelphia. He had to find a job. When he heard somehow that a school at Gray's Ferry, four miles on the other side of Philadelphia from Milestown, was in need of a master, Wilson, in the same mood of dull hopelessness, applied for the position and was accepted. In his words, he returned to "that painful profession with the same sullen resignation that a prisoner re-enters his dungeon."

There was nothing to tell him that he was about to enter upon the happiest and most fruitful period of his life, or that he was soon to find the long sought direction and motivation of his genius. It is true that there were some pleasant surprises almost at once. His hundred-dollar-a-quarter salary was munificent compared to his earlier stipends. The schoolhouse was attractively located, his own lodgings comfortable and cozy, the surrounding country verdant and flowering. Soon, in metered lines and stanzas, in his poem "The Solitary Tutor" he would be praising his new situation: "A neat stone school-house on a sloping green . . . near the Schuylkill's winding tide" . . . with "tufted cedars scatter'd round," . . . "stripling poplars planted in a row," "some old, gray white-oaks" overhanging, the whole scene "resounding with the songs of warblers"; nearby the wayside tavern, the Sorrel Horse, with black-smith shop adjacent; the road in front crowded with traffic headed to and from the city beyond the Schuylkill Ferry. His rooms were in the nearby "yellow-fronted cottage" of William Jones, "nestled in en-clust'ring trees . . . walled from the road," surrounded by tall poplars and catalpas with their candelabra of white blossoms.

His natural need for solitude, intensified since his flight from Miles-town, found leafy refuge in a sequestered glade close at hand:

> Around on Nature's scenes he turns his eye,
> Charmed with her peaceful eve, her fragrant morn,
> Her green magnificence, her gloomiest sky,
>
> . . . .
> Adown each side of his sequester'd cot,
> Two bubbling streamlets wind their rocky way,
> Round many a moss-grown rock they dimpling play,
> Where laurel thickets clothe the steeps around,
> And oaks thick, towering, quite shut out the day,
>
> . . . .
> The air serene, and breathing odours sweet,
> The sound of falling streams, and humming bees,
> Wild choirs of songsters round his rural seat,
> To souls like his have ev'ry pow'r to please.

In such idyllic retreats he spent long hours of his leisure time, some-times reading his favorite English poets, sometimes watching the birds he had never ceased to love and which now, in his first lonely months, seemed his best and sometimes his only friends. A great many of the birds he was later to describe most lovingly in his *Ornithology* were visitors or residents of the Schuylkill area, and during his slow climb upward from the valley of despair, their innocent companionship, their beauty, and their music were daily solace to him. And even in his rooms he surrounded himself with the healing company of nature's wild children, keeping not only caged birds but "opossums, squirrels, snakes, lizards, etc., so that my room has sometimes reminded me of Noah's ark; but Noah had a wife in one corner. . . ."

Gradually and very cautiously his spirit began to revive. Again he dared to dream of fame through poetry. As his spiritual recovery progressed, his naturally warm nature reached out for human companionship once more. To one friend he now wrote exultantly: "My heart swells, my soul rises to an elevation I cannot express . . ." He felt, he said, that he was a harp "new-strung."

In nothing was he more fortunate, at this time, than in the quality of his friends. One of the most significant friendships was with Alexander Lawson. Wilson had met the tall, athletic artist-engraver shortly after their almost simultaneous arrivals in America, but until his move to Gray's Ferry he had been only an acquaintance of Lawson. Lawson had become the center of a group of Philadelphia artists and scientists, and, moved either by a sympathetic liking for his lonely fellow Scot or by a recognition of Wilson's talents, or perhaps by both, he urged the young tutor to join the intellectual group. At the same time, seeking to distract him from his melancholy, the kindly engraver suggested that Wilson try his hand at drawing. Wilson not only tried his hand but became so intensely interested in drawing and painting that, by the spring of 1804, he was all but a slave to this new art. "I have no more time than just to swallow my meals," he wrote to Lawson, in explanation for not seeing him more often, because of "that itch for drawing which I caught from your honourable self."

He had other friends equally encouraging and helpful, and closer at hand than Philadelphia. The famous garden of the Bartrams was only a little more than a mile away from Gray's Ferry. One could always count on finding there, in loving attendance, William Bartram, artist, naturalist, author of the famous *Travels*. Between the Scottish schoolmaster, now in the prime of life, and the gentle botanist, entering upon his autumnal years, there developed a deep, abiding friendship. Diverse as were their personalities and their backgrounds, they had in common an intense love of nature and a romantic turn of mind. William, whose own youthful years had been spent in long and painful struggles to find and claim his true vocational heritage, understood and sympathized with Wilson's frustration, his tormented efforts to find the proper focus for his life. Their two minds supplemented and enriched each other. The younger man brought the vitality and fire of his passionate eagerness to enliven their common interests, while the older man lent steady encouragement and advice and, specifically, the valuable instruction of a skilled artist and naturalist. The Bartrams' gray stone house on the brow of the hill, overlooking the garden, held now another artist as well, Nancy Bartram, William's niece, whose special subject was flower painting, and who, like her uncle, delighted in teaching friend Wilson to draw and paint from nature.

It seems impossible to overestimate the importance of William Bartram in the metamorphosis of the nature-loving and poetic tutor into an accomplished naturalist and artist. Over and over in the *Ornithology*, Wilson refers to Bartram as a respected authority and as a cherished friend. But it is in the latter capacity that he was first of profound value to the young Scot, whose defeated spirit rallied and gained new strength in the serenity and affectionate companionship of the kindly Quaker. Some hint of the easy intimacy between the two is glimpsed in a gay, playful letter of Wilson's in rhyme in which he postponed a planned outing together until better weather, when, he concluded:

> Then in whirling Chariot seated
> With my friend I'll gladly go
> With his converse richly treated
> Happy to be honoured so.

Encouraged and inspired in his new venture, Wilson intensified his efforts. To learn to draw birds as Bartram had done, he shot and mounted an owl to serve as a model for his early attempts. This was during his second summer at Gray's Ferry, in 1803.

During the summer and early fall he devoted every spare moment to preparing a collection of drawings of the birds about the secluded cottage in which he lived and those that haunted the mossy brookside of his nearby sylvan retreat. His students and neighbors began to supply him with specimens, living and dead. He began to keep many kinds of birds in cages as ready models, and to attempt to raise others from fledglings, in order to study their habits and changing plumage. He even succeeded in raising a hummingbird, brought in, as a nestling, by one of his pupils. Soon his rooms were a veritable aviary and museum so that indoors or outdoors he was completely absorbed in his new interest. He continued to receive constant help and encouragement from the Bartrams in whose garden he found many of his subjects, and at intervals he submitted collections of his drawings to William for professional criticism. One such was accompanied by the modest note: "I am almost ashamed to send you these drawings; but I knew your generous disposition . . . They were chiefly coloured by candle-light. Be pleased to mark on the drawings, with a pencil, the names of each bird, as, except for three or four, I do not know them." These words from a man who, less than a decade later, would be recognized as the greatest American ornithologist of his time suggest the stupendous accomplishments ahead of him in the next few years.

By late winter, 1804, he thought his collection creditable enough to risk a judgment from friend Lawson. He even dared to confess to the engraver his bold dreams: "Now, I don't want you to throw cold water," he wrote. "Quixotic as it may appear . . . I am most earnestly bent, on pursuing my plan of making a collection of all the birds of this part of North America." Lawson did indeed think the scheme quixotic and said so, with such emphasis that Wilson decided to wait a little longer before confessing his hopes to William Bartram.

He had not yet abandoned his dreams of becoming a great poet, and Lawson's cold-water response to his bird project may have served to drive him back for a time to his early muse. In the spring he sent a few more drawings to Bartram with the words: "The last I shall draw for some time, as the employment consumes every leisure moment, leaving nothing for friendship, or those rural recreations which I so much delight in. Even poetry, whose heavenly enthusiasm I used to glory in, can hardly ever find me at home, so much has this bewitching amusement engrossed all my senses."

That summer he must have been torn between his rival muses. Three of his poems, "The Invitation," "The Rural Walk," and "The Solitary Tutor," appeared in *The Literary Magazine and the American Register*, then edited by Charles Brockden Brown. This was a taste of the recognition he had hungered for since his early youth and for which he still longed. He must have been sorely tempted to abandon his new love and embrace again the muse that had dominated him for most of his adult life. But he had steeped himself too deeply in his bird study, drawing, and painting to be willing or even able now to turn away. Was it possible to combine all his talents and interests in some way that would bring him artistic fulfillment and yet earn him a living? With characteristic intensity he determined to try.

Although it was almost time for him to ring the bell for the opening of the fall session in the schoolhouse across the way, early autumn found him, instead, setting out on foot for Niagara Falls. Between the Falls and Gray's Ferry lay six hundred miles, much of it through sparsely settled wilderness. There were rivers, lakes, and mountain ranges to cross and long treks through dark boreal forests. Such an expedition would test the physical stamina he knew he would need to go forward with his ambitious bird-collecting plan. He would observe and collect birds along the way. He would keep a journal of the expedition—in poetry—and illustrate it. Thus he would retain his harem of muses.

With two companions, his nephew, Will Duncan, who had come down from their farm near Seneca Lake to accompany him, and a teen-age boy from Milestown, Wilson set forth early one "soft, meek-eyed Indian summer" day, all three bravely accoutered in white breeches, short coats, and high-crowned beaver hats. A fowling piece, powder horn, shot, a dirk in belt, and a knapsack, stuffed with drawing and writing materials and victuals, rounded out Wilson's equipment. All this, and many an incidental detail, helped to fill up the twenty-one hundred lines of *The Foresters*, his poetic chronicle of the expedition. What they met with in the settled parts of their route was unpleasant enough to make the wilderness a relief: "Black wet bread, with rancid butter spread" and "beastly drunkards who beside us fed." Far better to lie wrapped in a blanket beneath a stormy sky than "beds with fleas and bugs accursed . . . from every seam its tens of thousands poured. . . ."

But whatever the hardships of frontier settlement or unspoiled wilderness, from the beginning birds were the most memorable feature of the account. There were the pair of grouse they shot for food, and that tiny feathered jewel, the ruby-crowned kinglet, which Wilson called a wren, the crossbill with its mandibles peculiarly crossed instead of neatly meeting, presumably an adaptation to facilitate the removal of mast from the cones of conifers. The great slit-eyed owl, as adept as the osprey at snatching fish from the river, was even more memorable. And there was the blue and white Canada jay, which Wilson thought a new species and so rare that, when he returned to Gray's Ferry, he sent a drawing of it to President Jefferson, always keenly interested in ornithology. Most exciting of all, perhaps, were the bewildering variety of waterfowl encountered on Lake Cayuga. When they reached the lower end of that long, slim body of water and saw it veritably teeming with

ducks and geese, Wilson rented a skiff to go along the shore to observe
the great avian show and to collect specimens. In his excitement he
overstayed the daylight hours and overburdened himself with specimens, a variety of ducks and plovers, herons, and a large hawk. But
worst of all, he missed his way back to the path. The cry of a cougar
and the howling of wolves added to his dismay until, after ten miles of
stumbling through the forest and many a signal shot, he succeeded in
rejoining his young companions.

From Lake Cayuga they crossed over to Lake Oneida and acquired
a small skiff to carry them down the Oswego River to Lake Ontario.
Although they almost lost their tiny craft at the falls of the Oswego,
they made it to Fort Oswego at the river's mouth, and there, with more
daring than discretion, they rigged a blanket sail for their skiff and set
out to sail westward the two hundred miles of inland sea between the
old fort and the Niagara gorge. When a violent storm struck, a tragic
end to their folly was barely averted by rescue by a lake sloop, which
not only saved their lives but took aboard their skiff and sped them on
their way to Niagara.

The magnitude and power, the beauty and wonder of the great falls
were an overwhelming and unforgettable experience for the poet and
artist in Wilson. And when, holding hands to reduce the risk, the companions climbed down the slippery rocks and across the narrow ledges
to enter the caves behind the wall of tumbling water, there was hazard
enough to satisfy momentarily Wilson's adventurous thirst for danger.

For the apprentice ornithologist, too, the falls offered special interest.
The gorge below the falls was a superb place from which to watch the
bald eagles, attracted there by the numerous carcasses of squirrels, deer,
bears, and various other animals that, in attempting to cross the river
above the falls, were "dragged into the current and precipitated down
. . . among the rocks . . . below." Years later, when Wilson drew
his excellent illustration for his account of the eagle in his *Ornithology*,
although he used as a model a fine specimen taken on the Jersey shore,
he gave it a Niagara background in recognition of its special appeal for
the great bird.

Soon after the travelers reached the falls, the weather turned bitterly
cold, speeding their departure homeward, Duncan for the Cayuga farm,
Wilson and the lad for Philadelphia. The bitter weather forced them to
take transportation on stagecoach and boat when possible, but Wilson,
who had no money beyond a minimum for food and to replace his

tattered clothing, depended, for most of the journey homeward, solely on his own striding pace, a pace that covered forty-seven miles on the wintry December day he reached the yellow cottage at Gray's Ferry.

His spare time, for the remainder of the winter, had to be spent in composing and revising *The Foresters*, but with spring the poet turned once more with concentration to the feathered choristers acclaiming the season all about him. Inspired with renewed resolve to move forward with his "quixotic" scheme, he set to work on another collection of bird pictures to give some substance to his dream when he confessed it to his mentor in the garden down the river. By early summer he was ready. A note to Bartram accompanied the new set of drawings:

I dare say you will smile at my presumption, when I tell you that I have seriously begun to make a collection of drawings of the birds to be found in Pennsylvania, or that occasionally pass through it: twenty-eight as a beginning, I send you for your opinion. . . . Any hint for promoting my plan, or enabling me to execute better, I will receive from you with much pleasure. I have resigned every other amusement, except reading and fiddling, for this design, which I shall not give up without making a fair trial. Criticise these, my dear friend, without fear of offending me. . . . For there is not among all our naturalists one who knows so well what they are, and how they ought to be represented. . . . To your advice and encouraging encomiums I am indebted for these few specimens, and for all that will follow. They may yet tell posterity that I was honoured with your friendship, and that to your inspiration they owe their existence.

⌖ 3

Alexander Wilson had crossed his Rubicon. In doing so he had assigned himself a stupendous undertaking, requiring the combined skills of naturalist, artist, writer, and businessman. He had simultaneously to continue to support himself, to perfect himself in the skills he needed, and to apply them in the preparation of his projected work. In addition to the talents, the time, and the drudgery essential to produce the ten-volume illustrated ornithology Wilson envisioned, the financial problems presented by a work of that magnitude, when one considers the relative value of a dollar in 1805, would appear to have been enough to doom the project in its planning stage. The experienced engraver, Alexander Lawson, thought it an impossible undertaking for any publisher. He figured that the blank copper plates for the illustrations would take more money than Wilson had ever grossed in one year, that the engraving would cost fifteen times that, and each illustration in each volume would have to be individually hand colored by an artist—another enormous expense. All in all he estimated that each volume would have to bring twelve dollars, making the cost of the planned ten-volume work a total of one hundred and twenty dollars, half the annual income of a rural schoolteacher. How many people in largely bookless America could be interested in such a work? Not enough, thought Lawson, to interest any publisher. Such were the cold facts of Lawson's "cold water." Wilson, however, intent now on his dream, was in no mood to be deterred by mundane statistical facts, however realistic and formidable.

He determined to circumvent the most costly feature of the work, engraving the plates. After all, that was what Mark Catesby had done, and his great *Natural History*, generations later, was still the finest and most elegant work on American birds. Wilson greatly admired Catesby's illustrations and frequently consulted the set owned by the Bartrams. The trouble with Catesby's work was that more than half the birds of eastern America could not be found in it. Wilson wanted to prepare a work along similar lines but including all the birds of the country, if possible. Inspired by Catesby's determination in the face of financial difficulties, he set about mastering, as Catesby had done, the difficult art of engraving. Under Lawson's tutelage, he progressed so well that in a few months he had some creditable examples to show for his efforts.

But all the while the distracted schoolmaster was struggling to master these new skills, there was the daily confrontation with the realities of his situation. How could he follow his dream while fettered to his classroom? Yet, without its sustaining income, how could he live to follow that dream?

In the winter of 1806 word leaked out that President Jefferson was planning a southern supplement to the Lewis and Clark Expedition. Zebulon Pike was to lead an expedition to the Southwest, up the Red River to Colorado and the borders of Mexico's Texas. Seeing here an opportunity to free himself from his dilemma, Wilson carefully composed a letter to the President, asking that he be included in the expedition's company as its artist-naturalist. This letter is particularly interesting because it shows something of the pace of Wilson's progress in his newly chosen field. "Having been engaged, these several years," he wrote, "in collecting materials, and finishing drawings from Nature, with the design of publishing a new Ornithology of the United States of America, so deficient in Catesby, Edwards, and other Europeans, I have . . . Collected many birds undescribed by these naturalists. Upwards of one hundred drawings are completed. . . ." William Bartram, who had been a personal friend of President Jefferson for many years, forwarded the application with a warm recommendation. Weeks passed, but there was not even an acknowledgment from the White House. With the coming of spring the brief flare of hope kindled by news of the expedition flickered out. Years later, after Wilson's death, the aging Jefferson denied any knowledge of the application, and, in the light of recent scholarship, it seems unlikely that Wilson's letter ever reached the President.

Though failure to get this appointment and the lack of even a courteous response from Jefferson, whom he deeply admired, was a bitter disappointment to Wilson, fortunately another avenue of escape presented itself. Bradford and Inskeep, Philadelphia's leading publishing house, offered him the editorship of their proposed revision of the twenty-volume *Rees's Cyclopaedia*. Although the position offered release from classroom drudgery and penury, with a salary of nine hundred dollars a year, by far the most munificent he had ever known, his bird work would still have to be an after-hours activity. Nevertheless, he jumped at the opportunity, and in April, 1806, in the fortieth year of his life, schoolmaster Wilson left Gray's Ferry and moved into Philadelphia to become editor Wilson. His new lodgings were in the town house of his Gray's Ferry landlord, William Jones, a large brick house near the Delaware River, on Spruce Street. That the Jones family continued to want him under their roof, in spite of the moods of deep depression that must often have made him a melancholy companion, is one more evidence of Wilson's magnetic attractiveness to those who knew him well.

Early in their association, young Samuel Bradford learned of Wilson's ambition to produce a comprehensive American ornithology. Captivated by the enthusiasm of his new associate and impressed by samples of his work, he unhesitatingly committed Bradford and Inskeep to its publication. Wilson was elated. Although Bradford's commitment was soon reduced to a single trial volume, it was still enough to launch Wilson into a period of incredible effort and accomplishment. Even as day after day he dutifully gave to his editorial job its full measure of his time, he gave to ornithology at least as much and probably a greater measure of his thought.

Bradford's commitment was valuable also in allaying Lawson's skepticism about the project sufficiently for him to agree to do the engraving for Wilson. Soon the artist-author, engraver, and printers were busily engaged in preparing a handsome, illustrated prospectus describing the projected *American Ornithology*. This prospectus was to be mailed to likely subscribers throughout the country. It was essential to the success of the project that at least two hundred subscribers be secured, for although Bradford had agreed to finance that many copies of the first volume, he would not go on with subsequent volumes without the security of advance subscriptions. So, from the very outset, artist-author Wilson had to double, or shall we say triple, as book-salesman Wilson. The plan called for ten folio volumes to be published over a five-year period. Each volume was to include ten plates, each picturing in color from one to six different birds, followed by a full descriptive text of each species.

Although by 1806 modern bird taxonomy had been pretty well established, it was obvious, from the outset, that this taxonomic order, beginning with the loons and ending with the sparrows, could not control the order of treatment in Wilson's work. There were still too many yet undiscovered and undescribed species. A new member of the loon family might be found long after volume one was completed. An even more commanding reason for not attempting to construct his *Ornithology* in taxonomic order was the simple and practical exigency of the state of Wilson's advancement in the science. He began with the common neighborhood birds, the goldfinch, blue jay, oriole, nuthatch, robin, and wood thrush, because specimens, usually live ones, were readily available as models, and they were birds whose habits he already knew well. In treating others, he had to spend long hours collecting, learning, and drawing species after species, often as chance provided, all the while feeding the results to engraver Lawson, the colorists, and printers, as they demanded copy. Perhaps one might liken his situation to that of a cartographer with an exploring expedition, whose map can only delineate the expedition's discoveries when and in the order that the discoveries are made. American ornithology before Alexander Wilson was still largely an uncharted wilderness. He was to be its most productive cartographer.

Naturally, as he launched his work, intended to "comprehend a description of every species of our native birds, from the shores of the St. Lawrence, to the mouth of the Mississippi, and from the Atlantic

Ocean to the interior of Louisiana," he began with those familiar birds who had shared his room at Gray's Ferry or those met with in his nearby solitary retreat. Of such old friends he could write with ease and confidence. The ubiquitous blue jay could be found "frequenting the thickest settlements, as well as the deepest recesses of the forest, where his squalling voice often alarms the deer, to the disappointment and mortification of the hunter." In spring, "among his fellow musicians," the jay "is what the trumpeter is in a band. . . . When he hops undisturbed among the high branches of the oak and hickory they [his notes] become soft and musical; and his calls of the female a stranger would readily mistake for the repeated creakings of an ungreased wheelbarrow." The clever ruses of the jays to conceal the location of their nests, their enmity for owls, whom they aggressively torment until they drive them from their "jurisdiction," their propensity to plunder the nests of other species and feed upon their eggs and young, their talent for mimicry, their ability, like that of a parrot, to learn to speak, their food caches—all this and more had been carefully observed. Now Wilson, at last able to fuse literary, artistic, and scientific talents, could share such observations with the world in lucid and lively prose that sometimes takes wing like its subjects.

He displayed the same love and mastery of his field as he moved on through the list of his well-known feathered friends: the Baltimore oriole, whose hanging nest was a marvel of weaving, especially to one who had been three years apprenticed to learn a human version of the same skill that the oriole carries intuitively in his tiny brain; the robin, which was then being decimated to supply a popular demand for its small but tasty body ("two young men, in one excursion after them, shot thirty dozen"); the wood thrush he had grown to know and love in a glen he frequented years before, a bird which he had identified for President Jefferson; and the waxwings, wayfarers welcomed in their passage by the hunters and "in great numbers are brought to the market in Philadelphia, where they are sold from twelve to twenty-five cents per dozen."

Wilson often varied his vivid prose accounts with poems of his own, lyric descriptions of the rare beauty and interesting habits of his birds, such as his poems to the dainty and colorful orioles and bluebirds, among others. Or he enlivened his text with anecdotes about the birds, from his own or a friend's experience, as, for instance, a letter from William

1. *Corvus cristatus.* Blue Jay. 2. *Fringilla Tristis.* Yellow Bird or Goldfinch.
3. *Oriolus Baltimorus.* Baltimore Bird.

The first plate in Alexander Wilson's *American Ornithology*, showing the goldfinch, blue jay, and Baltimore Oriole. (Courtesy of the Columbia University Libraries)

Bartram, which he quotes, giving a romantic description of the courtship of the bluebird.

The homebody house wren called up a recollection of a pair of these small birds nesting in his window box: when the female was devoured by a cat, the male mourned briefly but soon brought home a new wife, removed the old eggs and the nest lining, and was, in due course, proudly proclaiming the arrival of a new set of eggs.

The red-headed woodpecker, with which he closed the first volume, the bird he had so greatly admired on the roadside between Newcastle and Philadelphia just after he first set foot on American soil, evoked an authoritative ecological defense. After commenting that some husbandmen had developed such an antipathy to the woodpecker for his occasional raids on fruit and grain that some states "in former times offered premiums to the amount of two pence per head for their destruction," Wilson, with a bit of simplistic teleology, appealed the woodpecker's case: "But let us not condemn the species unheard. They exist; they must therefore be necessary." More convincingly, he cited the results of his studies of their food habits, which proved that insects made up two-thirds of their diet, and effectively demonstrated the woodpecker's usefulness to man.

Thus, bird by bird, did the first volume slowly come into being. Largely a product of time spared from his job as editor of *Rees's Cyclopaedia*, the first volume of the *Ornithology* was well behind the schedule that contemplated ten volumes in five years. Volume One did not appear until the fall of 1808, some two years after the project was launched, and this in spite of the fact that it contained to a large degree material long familiar to Wilson, and in spite of the fact that, except for a brief and largely fruitless trip farther east, in search of subscriptions solicited on the basis of the prospectus, Wilson had stayed faithfully on the job, six days a week at Bradford and Inskeep at work on the *Cyclopaedia;* nights and Sundays on the *Ornithology*. Notable among the few subscribers obtained on the brief foray east were King's College, New York (now Columbia University), and Robert Fulton, whose *Clermont* had just begun to ply the Hudson between New York and Albany. The discouraged Wilson, who returned to his Philadelphia office in November, 1807, could at least take pride in the quality of his subscribers. In his absence a subscription had arrived from President Jefferson himself.

There were other factors involved in the tardiness of the first volume in addition to the lack of spare time of the author. In fact, before Volume One appeared, Wilson already had much of the material for the second volume prepared. Lawson, however, was having difficulty in finding competent craftsmen to complete his engravings, or colorists with sufficient skill to match the accurate, lifelike colors of Wilson's guiding prototypes. Wilson himself, by candlelight, did some of the routine coloring. Nancy Bartram and a girl friend did some. But the best of them all was a seventeen-year-old apprentice in Bradford's shop, Charles Leslie. The finest coloring in the *Ornithology* is that which came from his brush during the three years he worked on it, an employment which terminated when Wilson joined other friends of the talented youth in buying a release from his apprenticeship and sending him to study under Benjamin West in London. Years later their faith in the youth was well justified when he became court painter to Queen Victoria. In his old age, looking back on his early years of association with the *Ornithology* and with the man who had played such an important role in his own career, Leslie recalled Wilson as a man of singular distinction. "He even looked like a bird," he remembered. "His eyes were piercing, dark and luminous, and his nose shaped like a beak. He was of spare, bony frame, very erect in his carriage, inclined to be tall; and with a light, elastic step, he seemed perfectly qualified by nature for his extraordinary pedestrian achievements. . . . I remember the extreme accuracy of his drawings, and how carefully he had counted the number of scales on the tiny legs and feet of his subject."

The appearance of the first volume of the *Ornithology* in the fall of 1808 signaled for Wilson the greatest challenge of his lifetime. Embued now with confidence in the merit of his work and its importance to the country, he saw, latent in the project, a measure of the fame in the eyes of posterity for which he hungered. It lay now within his grasp, if only he could get recognition and support enough among the living to see his enormous task through to completion. As yet he could not see his way clear, financially, even one volume ahead. The material already prepared for the second volume must remain unpublished unless at least two hundred subscribers could be promptly secured. Faced with this challenge, Wilson lost no time in setting forth in an all-out effort to meet it.

No sooner had the binder finished a copy of Volume One for him to take along as a sample for prospective subscribers than he was on his way. There was not even time to afford a farewell visit to the

Bartrams. A note had to suffice: "In a few minutes I set out for the Eastern States, through Boston to Maine and back through the State of Vermont, in search of birds and subscribers. . . ." Both, as it turned out, would be hard to come by. It was an ill-chosen season to search for birds in those parts. Almost all the migrants, except waterfowl, had already left for more hospitable climes, and in the plan of the *Ornithology* waterfowl were to be dealt with in the later volumes. Also, for some unaccountable reason, subscribers proved as hard to find as new birds. His high hopes for subscriptions at Scottish-oriented Princeton and again at nearby Rutgers were soon dashed. Compliments were the only currency the scholars were willing to expend.

After a discouraging start his New York efforts proved more fruitful, thanks largely to the well-known naturalist, Dr. Samuel Mitchill, who, although he himself did not subscribe, assisted in getting other prominent New Yorkers for the subscription list. Moreover, Dr. Mitchill was extremely helpful with ornithological facts. There in New York, Wilson visited also one of his political heroes, Thomas Paine, who signed his name as a subscriber, but, already an ailing and broken man, he did not live to fulfill his contract.

Beyond New York, it was mostly a steady fare of discouragement. Many compliments, few subscriptions. On north, despite the wintry weather, he crossed on foot through the Maine woods to Dartmouth, where, for a change, he received substantial support, and thence to Albany, where the glow of Dartmouth was quenched by the New York governor's ice water in the form of a glance at the sample volume and a dismissal with the comment that he "would not give . . . a hundred dollars for all the birds you intend to describe, even had I them alive."

Back at home with only forty-one subscriptions to show for his efforts, Wilson was burdened with doubts as to the prospects for his great work. Although generally admired, it was deemed too expensive— "a fault," he commented somewhat bitterly, "not likely to be soon repeated, and will pretty severely correct itself." Despite the discouragement of poor sales, Wilson's determination to continue with his great undertaking was unflagging. Where he had failed to get subscribers he had succeeded in getting correspondents in those "northern regions, like so many pickets and outposts, so that scarcely a *wren* or a *tit* shall be able to pass along, from New York to Canada, but I shall get intelligence of it."

However, without more, many more subscribers, any number of pickets, even ornithological omniscience, would be of little avail. With a desperation born of that realization, and true to his resolve not to "sit down with folded hands, whilst anything can be done to carry my point: since God helps those who help themselves," Wilson, almost immediately after returning to Philadelphia, set out on horseback to solicit subscribers and correspondents in the Southern regions. Unaccountably, as he made his wintry way to Baltimore and Washington, the climate of response changed for the better. In the capital President Jefferson's warm support helped recruit the signatures of many of the nation's high officials. This initial success continued and even increased as the itinerant ornithologist made his way down through Richmond, Norfolk, Wilmington, to Charleston and Savannah. Also, as he moved slowly southward, the hardships of frozen roads and execrable taverns had other compensations, in addition to the financial support, in the increasing variety and numbers of birds. He rejoiced in meeting once more the long loved summertime friends of his Gray's Ferry glen, along with many seen there on their way to and from more northern breeding grounds. But here also were some entirely new to him. Most notable of these was the ivory-billed woodpecker.

It was in North Carolina, near Wilmington, where the road circuited a swamp-filled "bay" that he came upon the ivory-bills. Hearing their resounding hammering on the tall cypresses and their single clarinet-tone cries, he dismounted and followed these sounds through the gloom of the moss-hung forest to their source. Of the three birds he shot, one was only winged. Using his coat as a net, he succeeded in capturing the injured bird for use as a live model. From time to time, as he continued along the road to Wilmington, the weird cries of the imprisoned bird so frightened his horse that it became almost uncontrollable. The resemblance of the bird's cries to those of a human baby suggested a prank. When he reached the inn with the screaming bird swaddled in his greatcoat, he requested accommodations for himself and his baby; only when the consternation of the bystanders reached menacing proportions did he reveal the source of the cries. A little later on, his elegant, crow-sized, red, white, and black prisoner very nearly escaped. On his return to his room, after a brief absence, he found his captive on the point of completing a hole through plaster, laths, and outer boards. On his next absence from the room he took the precaution of securing the bird by a stout string tied to the mahogany table, only to

The ivory-billed woodpecker, pileated woodpecker, and red-headed woodpecker, drawn to scale by Alexander Wilson, engraved by Alexander Lawson, for the *American Ornithology*. (Courtesy of the Columbia University Libraries)

find, when he returned a little later, that the table had been turned into a pile of chips. In spite of painful wounds from a beak powerful and sharp enough to splinter mahogany, Wilson made several drawings of his handsome captive before it died for want of food of the specialized sort essential to its survival.

Below Wilmington his way was near the ocean, through the rice plantations along the Waccamaw River. There he met with success in both his objectives. The planters were especially receptive to the *Ornithology* and the country had bountiful offerings for the ornithologist. Most exciting were the flights of the great white whooping cranes, as tall as a man, with a wingspread of eight feet and more, "the mingled noise of their screaming, even when they are almost beyond reach of sight, resembling that of a pack of hounds in full cry. . . . At times they utter a loud, clear and piercing cry. . . . They have also various modulations of their singular note, from the peculiarity of which they derive their name. When wounded they attack the gunner or his dog with great resolution; . . ." In winter residence there on the rice plantation these giant birds fed upon grain and insects.

Farther down the road he came on a sight that evoked an eloquent appeal for ecological understanding. His way lay through the remains of a once magnificent forest:

Would it be believed that the larvae of an insect, or fly [pine bark beetle], no larger than a grain of rice, should silently, and in one season, destroy some thousand acres of pine trees, many of them from two to three feet in diameter, and a hundred and fifty feet high! Yet whoever passes along the high-road from Georgetown to Charleston, in South Carolina . . . can have striking and melancholy proofs of this fact. In some places the whole woods, as far as you can see around you, are dead, stripped of their bark, their wintry-looking arms and bare trunks bleaching in the sun, and tumbling in ruins before every blast, presenting a frightful picture of desolation. And yet ignorance and prejudice stubbornly persist in directing their indignation against the [woodpecker] . . . , the constant and mortal enemy of those very vermin, as if the hand that probed the wound to extract its cause should be equally detested with that which inflicted it; . . . I would humbly suggest the propriety of protecting and receiving with proper feelings of gratitude the services of . . . the whole tribe of woodpeckers, letting the odium of guilt fall to its proper owners.

After a week or ten days in Charleston, Wilson's attitude toward the city was ambivalent. Nowhere else had he as readily obtained subscribers for the *Ornithology*. Even so, this warm reception of his work was insufficient to offset his disapproval of the indolent, slave-based society and his revulsion at the sight of human beings offered for sale in the market, like cattle.

Though Charleston and its environs were the highlight of the journey for book-salesman Wilson, the Savannah area was the most fruitful for the naturalist. In nearby Beaufort lived Stephen Elliott, a botanist without peer in his region. Both at his home and his Georgia plantation Elliott extended to Wilson a warm welcome and valuable assistance, sharing with him not only his home and his ornithological observations, but continuing to befriend him and to send him valuable information and bird specimens through the years.

But if Stephen Elliott was a rich lode for Wilson, John Abbot, a talented recluse, whose plantation lay a day's ride up the Savannah, was a diamond strike. British-born Abbot, who in his lifetime produced an incredible volume of magnificent natural history drawings and paintings, especially of insects in the various stages of their development, together with the plants each fed upon, only a few of which have ever been published, was also an authority on the birds of the area. Abbot's work was known to Thomas Jefferson, with his always keen interest in natural history, and it was the President who had suggested to Wilson, during his visit at the White House on his way south, that he visit Abbot, thereby rendering Wilson a great service. Abbot had literally stacks of bird paintings, each shown with the plant most associated with it—some of birds so rare that his remains the only recorded report of them in this region. He too was unstintingly generous to his fellow toiler in the natural history of his adopted country. Henceforth the names of both Elliott and Abbot, particularly Abbot, would make frequent appearances in Wilson's writing.

Ornithologically and commercially then his excursion into the South was highly successful—but apparently at an unpleasant price personally. In a letter from Savannah to William Bartram he complained of the discomforts, fatigue, insults, and impositions he had suffered in the region. "I have, however, gained my point in procuring two hundred and fifty subscribers . . ." So it was a triumphant but somewhat disgusted Wilson who set sail for Philadelphia in the early spring of 1809.

Back in Philadelphia, with the continuation of his project now financially secured, he plunged into the production of Volume Two. He opened it with an accurate, detailed, and generous treatment of his favorite among all American birds: the inimitable mocker. "This celebrated and very extraordinary bird, in extent and variety of vocal powers stands unrivalled by the whole feathered songsters of this or perhaps any country. . . ." Its intrepidity as a warrior he illustrated by his observations of its defense of its nest against a marauding blacksnake.

Whenever the insidious approaches of this reptile are discovered, the male darts upon it with the rapidity of an arrow, dexterously eluding its bite, and striking it violently and incessantly about the head, where it is very vulnerable. . . . As the snake's strength begins to flag, the mocking-bird seizes and lifts it up, partly from the ground, beating it with his wings, and when the business is completed, he returns to the repository of his young, mounts the summit of the bush and pours out a torrent of song in token of victory.

That song, the whole amazing repertoire and musical virtuosity of the mockingbird, filled Wilson with boundless admiration:

A voice full strong and musical, and capable of almost every modulation, from the clear, mellow tones of the Wood Thrush, to the savage scream of the Bald Eagle. In measure and accent he faithfully follows his originals. In force and sweetness of expression he greatly improves upon them. . . . Neither is this strain altogether imitative. His own native notes, which are easily distinguishable by such as are well acquainted with those of our various song birds, are bold and full and varied seemingly beyond all limits.

It was no wonder, in a day when music was not available at a mere turn of a dial, that captive "mockers" were in lively demand. Taken young, usually from the nest, the ordinary price in 1808 was from seven to fifteen dollars each, but choice singers sometimes brought from fifty to a hundred dollars. Captivity did not apparently lessen their urge to sing. Even as his free brother is wont to do, the performing prisoner "spreads his wings, expands his tail and throws himself round the cage, in all the ecstacy of enthusiasm, seeming not only to sing but to dance, keeping time to his own music. Both in his native and domestic state, in the solemn stillness of the night, as soon as the moon rises in solemn images, he begins his delightful solo, and serenades us the live long night. . . ."

Another of the "universally beloved" birds that especially inspired Wilson to wonder and awe was that ornithological jewel, the hummingbird, whose beauty and rapid migratory flights evoked from him a poem of praise, well balanced, however, with a careful account based on sound scientific observations. John Abbot's records of the spring arrival date of the ruby-throated hummingbird in Georgia were coupled with Wilson's own Pennsylvania observations to calculate the hummer's northward migratory progress. "The wonder is excited how so feebly constructed and delicate a little creature can make its way over such extensive regions of lakes and forests among so many enemies, all its superiors in strength and magnitude. But its very minuteness, the rapidity of its flight, which almost eludes the eye, and that admirable instinct, reason, or whatever else it may be called, and daring courage, which heaven implanted in its bosom, are its guides and protectors. . . ."

Although he had successfully kept caged hummingbirds, supporting them entirely on nectar and sugared water, his observations, confirmed by studies of the stomach contents of dissected specimens, convinced him that they fed also on insects. He concluded that, although insects did comprise a significant part of the hummer's fare, nectar sipped from a succession of wild flowers was always its dominant food. Cosmopolitan as these birds were in their nectar tastes, they had special favorites among the plants, most notably the little orange or yellow, hanging, horn-shaped flowers of the jewelweed. "In some places where these plants abound you may see at one time ten or twelve Hummingbirds darting about and fighting with and pursuing each other. . . ."

It was Wilson's policy, throughout his *Ornithology*, to allot space to each species of bird in proportion to the appeal and special interest of each species. In contrast to the long and loving accounts of the mockingbird and the hummingbird, with twelve pages devoted to the former and eight to the latter, there are less than three for the towhee, which he found less interesting and less attractive. This personal approach is one of the things which gives his *Ornithology* a warm and appealing quality and a readability no purely technical ornithology can offer.

Volume Two gave especially generous space to the cardinal, the scarlet tanager, the bobolink, the kingbird, and the cowbird, with, as was his common practice, accurate scientific descriptions enlivened with anecdotes and unusual particulars; such as the fact that the cardinal was very popular as a caged bird at that time, not only in America, but in France and England as well, valued not only for its beauty, but for its willingness, like the mockingbird, to sing even in captivity; or that the cowbird, in spite of its habit of providing neither nest nor care for its young, continued to thrive as a species and to migrate in such great flights that, in 1809, strings of them were commonly offered in the Charleston market.

Mockingbird, hummingbird, and towhee, drawn and colored by Alexander Wilson, engraved by Alexander Lawson, for the *American Ornithology*. (Courtesy of the University of South Carolina Library)

Also commonly for sale in the markets of the day were the bobolinks or ricebirds, as they were then called:

About the middle of August [they] arrive in great multitudes along the shores of the Delaware and Schuylkill. These are halcyon days for our gunners of all descriptions and many a lame and rusty gun barrel is put in requisition for the sport. The report of musketry along the reedy shores of the Schuylkill and Delaware is almost incessant, resembling a running fire. The markets of Philadelphia at this season exhibit proofs of the prodigious havoc made among these birds. . . .

His defense of the kingbird or bee martin, that valiant little tormentor of crows and hawks, is revealing, in its intensity, of his sympathy with a quality he himself had had to develop, courage in the face of great odds. After praising its loyalty to its family, usefulness to man, and courage in guarding its area against predators, Wilson finds it incredible that farmers persist in destroying it because honeybees are a part of its diet. "Man arrogates to himself, in this case, the exclusive privilege of murder; and after putting thousands of these same little insects [bees] to death, seizes upon the fruits of their labour. . . . I honour this little bird for his . . . unexampled intrepidity; for his meekness of behaviour when there is no call on his courage, a quality which even in the human race is justly considered so noble. . . ; but, above all, I honour and esteem this bird for the millions of ruinous vermin which he rids us of; whose depredations in one season, but for the services of this and other friendly birds, would far overbalance all the produce of the bee-hives in fifty." Wilson's esteem for the kingbird is further emphasized by a long poem in its honor.

His essay on the scarlet tanager has personal overtones not only of the author but of his friend, William Bartram.

Passing through the orchard one morning I caught one of these young birds that had lately left the nest. I carried it with me about half a mile, to shew it to my friend, Mr. William Bartram; and having procured a cage, hung it up on one of the large pine trees in the botanic garden within a few feet of the nest of an Orchard Oriole, which also contained young; hopeful that the charity or tenderness of the orioles would induce them to supply the cravings of the stranger. But charity with them, as with too many of the human race, began and ended at home. The poor orphan was altogether neglected, notwithstanding its plaintive cries; and, as it refused to be fed by me, I was about to return it back to the place I found it; when towards the afternoon, a Scarlet Tanager, no doubt its own parent, was seen fluttering round the cage, endeavouring to get in. Finding this impracticable, he flew off, and soon returned with food in his bill, and continued to feed it until after sunset, taking up his lodgings on the higher branches of the same tree. In the morning, almost as soon as day broke, he was again seen most actively engaged in the same affectionate manner; and notwithstanding the insolence of the Orioles, continued his benevolent offices the whole day, roosting at night as before. On the third or fourth day he appeared extremely solicitous for the liberation of his charge, using every expression of distressful anxiety, and every call and invitation that nature had put in his power for him to come out. This was too much for the feelings of my venerable friend; he procured a ladder and mounting to the spot where the bird was suspended, opened the cage, took out the prisoner, and restored him to liberty and to his parent, who with notes of great exultation accompanied his flight to the woods.

The happiness of my good friend was scarcely less complete, and shewed itself in his benevolent countenance; and I could not refrain saying to myself—If such sweet sensations can be derived from a simple circumstance of this kind, how exquisite, how unspeakably rapturous must the delight of those individuals have been, who have rescued their fellow beings from death, chains, and imprisonment, and restored them to the arms of their friends and relations! Surely in such godlike actions virtue is its own most abundant reward.

Thus, page by page and plate by plate, the second volume of *American Ornithology* emerged not simply as the best work on ornithology yet produced anywhere in the world but as, much more than that, a work of vastly wider compass than its predecessors in the field. As the colorists tinted the final plates and the printers locked the forms for the final pages of the text, Wilson composed the introduction to the new volume.

"As far as the acquisition" of living models and accurate observations, he wrote, "depends upon his personal exertions in ransacking our fields and forests, our sea shores, lakes, marshes, and rivers . . . the author pledges himself that no difficulty, fatigue, or danger, shall deter him. . . ."

~~∂∾ 4

True to that pledge, as soon as the printers delivered to him the first bound copy of the second volume, so that he could display Volumes One and Two as samples in soliciting new subscribers, with the land still hard in the tight grasp of winter's frost, Wilson took the westbound coach and headed across the mountains to Pittsburgh and the Ohio River country. Stops along the way in quest of subscribers and his decision to walk much of the way slowed his westward progress so that it was near the end of February, 1810, before he left Pittsburgh, where the response to his solicitations had been unexpectedly enthusiastic for a raw and booming frontier town. There had been a thaw, and masses of ice sometimes nearly choked the river when he set out alone in a little skiff across the stern of which he had inscribed *The Ornithologist*—a name one of the residents on the Ohio took to be a "droll Indian name."

Through sleet, snow, and floating ice, it was a rigorous and lonely four-hundred-mile voyage down the river to Cincinnati where the Miami joined the big stream. Across the river in Kentucky, about ten miles up Big Bone Creek, lay Big Bone Lick—a place long famous in natural history circles. Peter Collinson, excited by reports and sometimes wild rumors of the bones found there, repeatedly questioned John Bartram about it. It seems likely that Wilson had heard descriptions and speculations about the place from William Bartram, who was interested in all natural history curiosities.

In any event, he rowed up Big Bone Creek as far as he could go and then continued on to the famed spot, which apparently for eons past, through the lure of its saline waters, had attracted a variety of wildlife in great quantities, some of which fell victim to the tenacious mire, leaving their skeletons preserved there. Fossil remains of mammoths and buffaloes abounded. When he waded into the morass to recover a duck he had shot, Wilson came close to contributing his bones to their company when he became dangerously mired in the binding quagmire. The duck, a gadwell, very rare in the East, was some compensation for his fright, and the next morning the lick provided him with a thrilling ornithological experience in the arrival of a great flight of the now extinct parakeets, beautiful, pigeon-sized, bright green birds, with heads of yellow and red, the only parrots native to the United States.

They came screaming through the woods in the morning about an hour after sunrise, to drink the salt water, of which they, as well as the pigeons, are remarkably fond. When they alighted on the ground, it appeared at a distance as if covered with a carpet of the richest green, orange, and yellow. They afterwards settled in one body, on a neighbouring tree, which stood detached from any other, covering almost every twig of it, and the sun shining strongly on their gay and glossy plumage, produced a very beautiful and splendid appearance. . . . Having shot down a number, some of which were only wounded, the whole flock swept repeatedly around their prostrate companions, and again settled on a low tree, within twenty yards of the spot where I stood . . . looking down on their slaughtered companions with such manifest symptoms of sympathy and concern, as entirely disarmed me. . . . They fly very much like the Wild Pigeon, in close compact bodies, and with great rapidity, making a loud and outrageous screaming, not unlike the Red-headed woodpecker. . . . They are extremely sociable with and fond of each other, often scratching each other's heads and necks, and always at night nestling as close as possible to each other. . . .

One of the fallen parakeets was only slightly injured. Wilson caught it and carried it back with him to his boat. Soon tamed, it became his traveling companion all the way to New Orleans and beyond. Under every roof that sheltered them along the way, "Poll" paid with his amusing and talkative ways for his share of the shelter. One of those shelters was the cabin of an old hunter who entertained him with stories of wolf trapping and bear and bobcat hunting while "all the night long the howling of the wolves kept the dogs in a perpetual uproar of barking."

A hundred miles downstream were the falls, actually only rapids, and Louisville, a community for which Wilson had great expectations. He had letters of introduction to several of the prominent residents there and he hoped to be able to duplicate his Pittsburgh success in subscriptions. It was not to be. He could not garner even a single subscription in the booming and brawling town. Also in Louisville he experienced not merely disappointment but a dramatic encounter with reverberations continuing right down to the present.

Among those he solicited was a young merchant, John James Audubon, at that time only twenty-five years old and struggling to make a living for himself and his family by running a trade store in the frontier town, giving drawing lessons, and painting an occasional portrait. On Wilson's visit to the store, the young proprietor, after examining the two sample volumes of the *Ornithology*, took from a shelf and displayed to his visitor some of his own bird drawings. Thus, fortuitously, on such a chance exchange, was planted the seed of the Audubon-Wilson controversy, a bitter wrangle involving disputed priorities, ideas, and discoveries, charges and countercharges of artistic and ornithological plagiarism, and aspersions on the integrity of those involved. It was a controversy, however, to which Wilson was never a part. It did not even begin until after his death and after the rise of Audubon's fame as a bird artist and ornithologist, when the battle was joined between Audubon and his admirers on the one hand and Wilson's biographer and admirers on the other. Wilson's diary is evidence enough that he had no part in the dispute. Of the meeting with Audubon he reports only: "Examined Mr. Audubon's drawings in crayons. Very good. Saw two new birds he had . . . both motacillae . . . Went out this afternoon shooting with Mr. A. Saw a number of Sandhill Cranes. Pigeons numerous." In all his many letters written on this journey there is no mention at all of Audubon. These two men, destined to lasting fame as great ornithologist-artists, had never met before although, seven years earlier, when Audubon arrived from France, he had settled briefly a few miles from Wilson's school in Milestown. Both were refugees, one from Calvinist Scotland, one from Napoleonic France; one a poet and the other an artist, both floundered for decades before finding themselves through the feathered world; strikingly dissimilar in personality and character, at heart they were both romantics and their geniuses had a common focus. In the light of their future destinies, the chance meeting in March, 1810, in the frontier store on the riverside, though it did not merit attention in Wilson's letters, has for us a dramatic and fateful interest. They were never to meet again.

In respect to the long and heated controversy with all its ramifications, it is sufficient here to observe that it was doubtless natural for Wilson's friends and admirers to feel both resentment and chagrin when Audubon's magnificent *Birds of America* so soon overshadowed Wilson's more modest work, especially since they had good reason to believe that Audubon's opus had its inception on the day that he inspected Wilson's volumes in the Louisville store. Also the great superiority of Audubon's bird masterpieces, as works of art, over Wilson's unpretentious illustrations unfairly obscured the fact that Wilson was not only definitely the pioneer in the field but that he was also, all things considered, much the better and more scientific ornithologist.

From Louisville, Wilson headed eastward toward Frankfort and Lexington, on foot, with only Poll for company. He was soon jolted out of his loneliness and dejection. Near Shelbyville he left the road to examine an abandoned passenger pigeon roost. It was an incredible sight. For miles all the trees were dead, killed by the droppings, and the ground was littered with branches broken under the weight of the roosting birds. The roosting place was "several miles in breadth and was said to be upwards of forty miles in extent! In this tract almost every tree was furnished with nests, wherever the branches could accommodate them."

Wilson learned from the residents of the area the story of the fantastic carnage that followed the appearance of these birds near the haunts of men.

When these roosts are first discovered, the inhabitants from considerable distances visit them in the night, with guns, clubs, long poles, pots of sulphur, and various other engines of destruction. In a few hours they fill many sacks, and load their horses with them. . . . As soon as the young are fully grown and before they left the nests, numerous parties of the inhabitants, from all parts of the adjacent country, came with wagons, axes, beds, cooking utensils, many of them accompanied by the greater part of their families, and encamped for several days at this immense nursery. Several of them informed me, that the noise in the woods was so great as to terrify their horses, and that it was difficult for one person to hear another speak without bawling in his ear. The ground was strewed with broken limbs of trees, eggs, and young squab Pigeons, which had been precipitated from above, and on which herds of hogs were fattening. Hawks, Buzzards, and Eagles were sailing about in great numbers, and seizing the squabs from their nests at pleasure; while from twenty feet upwards to the tops of trees the view through the woods presented a perpetual tumult of crowding and fluttering multitudes of pigeons, their wings roaring like thunder; mingled with the frequent crash of falling timber; for now the axe-men are at work cutting down those trees that seemed to be most crowded with nests, and contrived to fell them in such manner, that in their descent they might bring down several others; by which means the falling of one large tree sometimes produced hundreds of squabs, little inferior in size to the old ones and almost one mass of fat. On some trees upwards of one hundred nests were found, each containing one young only . . . Wagon loads of them are poured into market, where they sell from fifty to twenty-five and even twelve cents per dozen.

As he went on toward Frankfort one of these great and thrilling flights of pigeons passed overhead.

They were flying with great steadiness and regularity, at a height beyond gunshot, in several strata deep, and so close together that could shot have reached them, one discharge could not have failed of bringing down several individuals. From right to left as far as the eye could reach, the breadth of this vast procession extended; seeming everywhere equally crowded. Curious to determine how long this appearance would continue, I took out my watch to note the time, and sat down to observe them. It was then half-past one. I sat for more than an hour, but instead of a diminution of prodigious procession, it seemed rather to increase both in numbers and rapidity; and, anxious to reach Frankfort before night, I rose and went on. About five o'clock, in the afternoon, I crossed the Kentucky river, at the town of Frankfort, at which time the living torrent above my head seemed as numerous and as extensive as ever.

It was after six in the evening before the mighty multitude passed over, and Wilson, who had a particular fondness for mathematical calculations, attempted, from the astounding spectacle he had observed, to arrive at a valid estimate of their numbers.

Let us suppose this column to have been one mile in breadth (and I believe it to have been much more) and that it moved at the rate of one mile in a minute; four hours, the time it continued passing, would make its whole length two hundred and forty miles. Again supposing that each square yard of this moving body comprehended three Pigeons; the square yards in the whole space, multiplied by three, would give two thousand, two hundred and thirty millions, two hundred and seventy-two thousand pigeons! An almost inconceivable multitude and yet probably far below the actual amount.

An amusing instance of this fondness of Wilson's for startling statistics is his estimate that the harbinger of spring, the swift-flying swallow, in a lifetime of living on the wing, catching insects in flight, probably flies over two million miles, an equivalent of more than eighty-seven times around the world.

Although Lexington, Kentucky, his next significant stopping place, was then only a small town, Wilson readily got eleven subscribers for the *Ornithology*. He celebrated by buying one of the fine horses for which the region was already famous. His journey across Kentucky to Nashville was marked by one memorable bird experience after another: the kingfishers, nesting and feeding on the Kentucky River, a new warbler, which he named the Kentucky warbler, the quantities of whippoorwills in the neighborhood of Mammoth Cave, their "Clamours . . . so incessant" that they disturbed his sleep, another new warbler in Tennessee—the Tennessee warbler.

His last stop before Nashville was a rural tavern, where, although he stayed three days, hunting and sketching in the neighborhood, his kindly and perceptive host refused to accept any payment. "You seem to be travelling for the good of the world," he said, "and I cannot and will not take your money."

From Nashville he shipped off to Lawson a sheaf of bird paintings which never arrived. He wrote a long and humorous letter to his dear friend, Sarah Miller, to whom he was probably affianced, in which he made fun of the typical beau of the area "who had neither been washed nor shaved for a month, with three yards of coarse blue cloth wrapped round his legs by way of boots . . . and breathing the rich perfume of corn whisky," his steed a "mule with ears so long they might almost serve for reins."

With characteristic, almost reckless daring, Wilson now set out down the Natchez Trace, the old Indian path, running the ridges through wilderness and sparsely settled Indian territories to Natchez and New Orleans, a wild and dangerous way with a highly unsavory reputation, little used except by flatboatmen traveling on foot in groups on their way back to man new flatboats loaded with the produce of the Ohio region for delivery in faraway New Orleans. Wilson had studiedly chosen this sinister route because he wanted to investigate personally the death of his friend and hero, Meriwether Lewis, who, only a few months earlier, had, under mysterious circumstances, died of gunshot wounds on the Trace.

Lewis and Wilson had become friends in 1803, when the former had been sent to Philadelphia by President Jefferson to study natural history under Benjamin Barton, in preparation for his historic expedition to the Pacific. They renewed their friendship after the expedition, when Bradford and Inskeep undertook the publication of Lewis's account of the historic voyage. Lewis gave Wilson the bird skins he had collected in the Northwest and shared with him his observations of birds along the way. In the *Ornithology*, Clark's crow, named for Lewis's companion, William Clark, and Lewis's woodpecker, for Lewis himself, honor the two great leaders of the famous expedition.

In temperament and interests Lewis and Wilson had much in common, and, as the work on Lewis's two-volume account progressed, they became fast friends. In 1807 Lewis was appointed governor of Louisiana and left for St. Louis to take up his post. It was the time of the plots of Aaron Burr and the chicanery and double-dealing of General James Wilkinson, with wide ramifications throughout the territory and in the adjacent states. On every hand suspicions flourished.

The last months of Lewis's life and the circumstances of his violent death are shrouded in mystery. No one seems to know whether it was something to do with the Wilkinson plots, or a money dispute with the Secretary of War, or political complications involving his administra-

tion, or a combination of these and other difficulties that prompted
Lewis to set out for Washington in September, 1809, taking an in-
explicably circuitous route from St. Louis down to Memphis and back,
northward up the Natchez Trace. In a crude log cabin that served the
Trace as a tavern, Lewis died of gunshot wounds. His death was announced as a suicide, but the long-delayed official report of the facts
surrounding the case was rife with inconsistencies and unanswered
questions. Dissatisfied with the report and grieving for his lost friend,
Wilson determined to visit the scene of his death, to try to answer some
of the questions and at least to mark his friend's wilderness grave.

He fulfilled his mission. He arranged to have Lewis's grave marked
and fenced; he composed an elegy for his dead hero, and he satisfied
himself, at least, that it was murder and not suicide that had taken his
friend's life. He kept a careful account of the Natchez Trace and of
every circumstance of his investigation. It was an arduous and terrible
experience for him, traveling alone along the edge of precipitous cliffs,
down steep canyons, and up the sharp and rocky faces of the gorges,
with, except for the solitary tavern where Lewis had died, no shelter
except an occasional isolated Indian village. At one of these, where he
intended to lodge, he had one of his few bird encounters on the whole
Trace, for he had traveled fast, intent on his sad mission; the story was
appropriately melancholy. He had stopped to listen to a mockingbird,
singing from a nearby tree, when he heard a sudden report and saw the
bird fall, the victim of a young Indian gunner.

I hastened over into the yard, and walking up to him, told him that was
bad, very bad! that this poor bird had come from a far country to sing to
him, and in return he had cruelly killed him. I told him the Great Spirit was
offended at such cruelty, and that he would lose many a deer. . . . The old
Indian, father-in-law to the bird-killer, replied that when these birds come
singing and making a noise, someone will surely die—which is exactly what
an old superstitious German, near Hampton, in Virginia, once told me. . . .

Wilson's decision to set aside the claims of his own demanding
project in order to undertake such a dangerous journey for the honor
and memory of his friend, Lewis, is but one more indication of the
true nobility of his nature. The emotional and physical strain, however,
took its toll in a debilitating illness during the last week on the Trace.
Exhausted, he pushed on grimly to Natchez, arriving there the last part
of May.

There followed a welcome interlude, a pleasant and highly successful month in New Orleans and the Mississippi country between that city and Natchez. Much of that time was spent in "the sweet society" of the William Dunbar family at The Forest, their plantation near Natchez. Dunbar, then an invalid, was a fellow Scot, highly educated, particularly in the sciences, materially successful, the head of a large and attractive family, all of whom, it appears, were enamored of the traveling birdman. Wilson helped the girls of the family with their drawing and their music. The boys joined him in seeking birds, with such enthusiasm that they continued to collect for him after his return to Philadelphia. The children supplied a cage for Poll and hung it on the porch of the plantation house, from which "by its call it soon attracted the passing flocks" who perched upon the trees around the porch, to "converse" with the prisoner.

The Mississippi plantation was an excellent location for an ornithologist, and Wilson found a wealth of birds to study and collect during his few idyllic weeks there. It was while staying at The Forest that he obtained a rare Mississippi kite, which he vividly portrayed in the *Ornithology*. This was a memorable experience on two counts: the bird was a new species, discovered and named by Wilson; in its capture, the kite inflicted with its lethal talons severe wounds on Wilson's hand when he sought (with success) to carry it back to serve as a living model, whose look of implacable hostility and fierceness was effectively caught in his painting.

Largely through Dunbar's influence, but partly because of Wilson's growing reputation, assisted in New Orleans by the volume of the *Ornithology* brought by General Wilkinson from Charleston, subscriptions came easily in New Orleans and from the neighboring plantations—sixty-four with little effort. The latter part of June he embarked by sea for Philadelphia. With him still was his parakeet. He "determined to persevere in her education," but poor Poll, destined for another fate, wrought her way through the cage about daybreak one morning and instantly flew overboard, to perish, presumably, in the Gulf of Mexico.

⌒∾ 5

It was August before he reached Philadelphia, a full six months after he had departed for Pittsburgh on the first leg of this four-thousand-mile journey—a long time to be absent from his position as editor of the *Cyclopaedia*. He had by now become so single-hearted in his exclusive devotion to his *Ornithology* that, on his return home, he took time only to attend to a few details in connection with the progress of the *Cyclopaedia* before going into seclusion for a month or more, devoted entirely to preparing the text and illustrations for Volume Three of his birds. Those on the purple grackle, spotted owl, and meadowlark, and those Western specimens given him by Captain Lewis, had been substantially completed before his journey, but to round out the volume he had many more to cover. Now, working with feverish intensity, he finished memorable descriptions and paintings of the kingfisher and the parakeet, the incomparably colorful little painted bunting, popular as a caged bird in New Orleans, the blue grosbeak, also frequently caged, the Mississippi kite, and many others collected in the Mississippi Valley.

Already highly displeased by Wilson's long absence from his editorial job and by the rapidly mounting costs of producing the *Ornithology*, while receipts lagged, publisher Bradford was in no mood to be tolerant of Wilson's almost total immersion in his own project. Difficulties and disagreements between author and publisher were soon threatening the entire undertaking. To quiet the troubled waters, Wilson resigned his editorial position on the *Cyclopaedia* and plunged into a frenetic effort to speed up the *Ornithology* so that receipts might come to the rescue before Bradford grew yet more disenchanted. Even so, it was February, 1811, before the third volume was off the press and ready for distribution.

This was no signal, however, for the slightest relaxation of effort. He was already deep into Volume Four, working with a steady concentration, almost fey in its intensity, as though heaven had sent him secret warning of the imminence of his death. Even his collecting expeditions were now brief and intense, mostly short journeys to Great Egg Harbor, on the Jersey coast, behind the present Ocean City, one of John Bartram's favorite collecting areas, where, as a boy, William Bartram had helped his father collect pine and lotus seed. There were also visits to nearby Cape May, a productive ornithological region introduced to Wilson by his wealthy Philadelphia neighbor, George Ord, who owned land there. Ord, later to become Wilson's biographer and passionate champion, began to accompany him on his expeditions and was soon absorbed in the undertaking.

During this period Wilson was living much of the time with the

Bartrams, garnering dual benefit from his association with the birds of the botanical garden and the wisdom and experience of the old naturalist himself. He was there in the summer of 1811, when he completed Volume Five and was preparing its introduction:

> In Mr. Bartram's botanic garden, and the adjoining buildings, comprehending an extent of little more than eight acres, the author has ascertained, during his present summer-residence there, that not less than fifty-one pair of birds took up their abode and built nests within that space.

Volume Four includes some fascinating and absorbing descriptions of birds as varied as the ivory-billed woodpecker, the cuckoo, and several owls, an intriguing story of the crow, and a dramatic and poetic account of the bald eagle. Now almost halfway through his tremendous task, Wilson wrote with confidence and authority, in rhythmic prose, lively with personal anecdotes, warm with loving sympathy for his subject.

In the introduction to the fifth volume he refers to the ten thousand miles he had traveled in search of birds, through "woods and fields, unfrequented forests, solitary ranges of mountains and morasses." Actually, however, in spite of his far-flung searches, most of the species included in the fifth and sixth volumes, both of which appeared in 1812, were those found on the Jersey shore, at Great Egg Harbor and Cape May. He was now getting into the realm of the shore birds, most of which he, like Catesby, had left until last.

In spite of persistent financial difficulties Wilson had already finished a substantial part of his *Ornithology*. By the completion of the sixth volume, he was, at long last, experiencing not only success but some measure of real appreciation of the great significance of his work. In a poignant letter to an old friend in Paisley he wrote:

> I was a wanderer when I was in Scotland, and have been much more so since my arrival here. Few Americans have seen more of their country than I have done, and none love it better. Fortune has not yet paid me up all her promises, after all the wild goose chase she has led me; but she begins to look a little more gracious than usual, and I am not without hope.

As the work progressed, his absorption only deepened. In the preface to Volume Five he had written:

> The author of the present work has a thousand times turned, with a delight bordering on adoration, to the magnificent repository of the woods and

fields. . . . *The Grand Aviary of Nature*. In this divine school he has studied from no vulgar copy; but from the works of the *Great Master of Creation* himself; and has read with rapture the lessons of his wisdom, his goodness, and his love, in the conformation, the habitudes, melody, and migrations of this beautiful portion of the work of his hands.

Though the long and concentrated struggle to complete the *Ornithology* must have left him little time for friendship, his devotion to Sarah Miller and hers to him apparently never faltered. In August of 1812, on the eve of one of his countless bird pilgrimages, in his beautiful script he penned Sarah a farewell note, characteristically dramatic and resolute, yet warm and appealing:

I cannot be out tomorrow as I expected. Mr. B[radford] and I having all our accounts to settle. . . . In the meantime do not be alarmed when I tell you that I must now either run the risk of losing all or make one last and very long and expensive journey to collect what is due. . . . There is no other choice left between this and absolute ruin. You will not therefore my dearest friend object to this as on it my whole hopes of happiness depend. Mr. B. has positively refused to advance anything until he receives it and I have as positively told him that I will proceed no farther with the work until I am paid for what I have done. . . .

This prospective journey was, in fact, his last of any consequence. It was an ailing Wilson, traveling only under pressure of necessity, who set out up the Hudson, then on across to Lake Champlain, thence eastward across New England, and back home through the Connecticut Valley. Exhaustion from overwork had brought on a resurgence of tuberculosis, from which his biographers believe he had suffered intermittently since boyhood. In addition he was now handicapped by a heart condition. Nevertheless, he successfully completed the long trip and arrived home buoyed by the resulting financial relief.

Though his health continued to decline during the winter of 1812–1813, he completed Volume Seven, and moved out to Kingsessing in the spring to spend the summer with the Bartrams.

On his return to Philadelphia, after a late summer trip to Cape May in search of shore birds, he fell suddenly ill and died on August 23, 1813. He was forty-seven years old. He had lived barely long enough for the first real taste of scientific recognition—only weeks before his death he was elected to membership in both the American Philosophical Society and the Academy of Natural Sciences.

He had lived long enough, however, to accomplish his own lasting monument and to carve his place in the natural history of his adopted country as the Father of American Ornithology. Years after his death, in his native Paisley, the townspeople erected a memorial statue which portrayed their native son attired for the woods, with his gun slung by straps across his back, a dead bird in his right hand, a pencil in his left. At his feet are his parakeet and sketchbook; only the flute and a book of poems are missing.

Of wider note and greater currency are the ornithological memorials in nomenclature: Wilson's plover, Wilson's snipe, Wilson's warbler, Wilson's bluebird, Wilson's phalarope, Wilson's thrush (veery), and Wilson's tern. These and at least thirty-one other new species were among the 262 species included in the *Ornithology*.

His friend and ardent admirer, George Ord, saw the eighth volume through to completion and prepared a ninth, including in the latter a biographical sketch with this tribute: ". . . When we reflect that a single individual, 'without patron, fortune, or recompense,' has accomplished in the short span of seven years, as much as the combined body of European naturalists have taken a century to achieve, we feel almost inclined to doubt the evidence of our senses."

Chapter 8

MAN AND NATURE

~∞ 1

For anyone traveling the New Jersey Turnpike, crossing the Jersey Meadows is an unpleasant but memorable experience. The pall of polluted air, the stench, the appalling outlook on every hand, dimly seen through smarting eyes, belong to a region from which man has driven nature's God. As the traveler continues south, across the Hackensack River, from time to time, through the tank "farms" and the forests of smokestacks and towers of the refineries, if the haze is not too heavy, he may see the skyline of the city of Newark looming through the murk. It is all but impossible now for him to discover any trace of the lovely meadows that existed there before we sacrificed them on Mammon's altar. Certainly it is difficult for anyone to relate the depressing landscape to the younger Michaux's description of the country when he passed that way in the late spring of 1802: "About nine miles from New York," he wrote, "is a place called Newark, a pretty little town, situated in New Jersey. The fields that encompass it are planted with apple trees; the cider that is made there is accounted the best in the United States."

The young Frenchman's immediate destination was Philadelphia. Without doubt one of the principal attractions there was his father's old friend, William Bartram, and the Bartram's famous farm, where the acres around the stone house and down the slope to the west bank of the Schuylkill were given over to a botanic garden, a place of note on many counts, not the least of which was the romantic figure of the old botanist. It was a place of idyllic pastoral beauty with gardens of astonishing variety, and its view eastward across the peaceful ᴜchuylkill River to the extensive green meadows beyond, "a noble seat to observe fish and passage birds." Here, spring and fall, those limpid waters were crowded with myriads of colorful waterfowl.

All that was a century and a half ago—only a cosmic moment. Now, engulfed by the sprawling city, the old gray stone Bartram home stands in its twenty-seven-acre green island, surrounded by noisy and noisome slums, residential and industrial. Across the river, all over the meadows that gladdened the aesthetic senses of William Bartram and his friend Wilson, a jungle has grown, a gray and smoky jungle of warehouses, railroad yards, oil refineries, and junkyards. The once beautiful and teeming Schuylkill, where the friends spent endless hours watching the feeding waterfowl, is now only superficially a river. In essence it has been converted into a dead thing, its dark, foul, oil-coated waters devoid of birds and fish.

Such are the wages of what we are wont to describe as progress, a part of the price of the "good life" we twentieth-century Americans have so energetically and heedlessly sought and, some think, have found.

More recently, the remains of another famous garden of the period encountered the force of a progress of even more dubious merit with the result that every vestige of it was obliterated. Most of the site of André Michaux's famous Charleston garden is now beneath the runways of the Charleston Army Air Base, beneath its heavy pavements, barred from producing anything, even an earthworm or a blade of grass that might contribute a bit of oxygen to offset, in a meager way, the quantities of carbon dioxide being loosed by the thundering jets streaking across its dead soil.

It was progress of a more beneficent intent, less destructive in purpose and in precious resources, that drowned, far beneath the waters of Clark Hill Reservoir, the Savannah River rapids where Mark Catesby had seen the ponderous sturgeon spawning. There now both rapids and sturgeon survive only in history.

Fifty miles farther south, a wasteful and misguided policy of progress utterly destroyed the superlative forest in north Georgia that William Bartram described with awe. Heedless of the centuries required to reproduce such a magnificent treasure, men wholly cleared away the giant trees to provide land for a few bountiful harvest years before, sterile and exhausted, those once rich, red hills were abandoned to erosion and ruin. It was again something called progress that log-rolled and burned the giants of the parklike Alabama forest, equally admiringly described by William Bartram, farther along his way to Mobile, that the rich black soil could be mined of its fertility and leached of its substance through single-crop farming. Now those exploited and crippled lands nourish again a forest cover of pines, marching line upon line in close formation to their rendezvous with the Moloch maws of the air-and-water-befouling paper mill down on the tidewater.

The rich and varied flora and the teeming wildlife of the American wilderness, in contrast with those of the tamed and relatively thickly populated European countries, instilled a conviction among settlers that the American forest and the wildlife it supported were inexhaustible. Except for a few of the thoughtful and observant, such as the men with whom this book has been concerned, that dangerous fallacy persisted far into the day of lives yet in being. It became a firm national illusion which refused to die until only scraps of the primeval forest and a remnant of its pristine wildlife were left alive.

Mark Catesby, a bare fifty years after the first landings at Charleston, noted that rice fields were already becoming unproductive. Years before that he had seen worn-out and abandoned fields on the Virginia tobacco plantations. Generations passed, oblivious to such warnings. Now to agronomists and ecologists it is patent that fields given over to the cultivation of a single crop, such as tobacco or grain, will sicken and die just as inevitably as would a forest given over to a single species of wildlife. John Bartram recognized this, at least as far as his fields were concerned, and undertook curative measures that made his farm the envy of his neighbors and a showplace of the community.

Eastern America, well endowed by nature and with only a sparse native population of Indians, could and did, for centuries, as we have seen, support an incredibly rich and varied wildlife as long as proper balances between the plant world and the animal world and between predator and victim were maintained. But as fast as the Europeans, piece by piece, wrested the wilderness from the Indians, they proceeded ruthlessly (history permits no kinder word) to disrupt the whole balance of life that the wilderness had effectively maintained for thousands of years.

Even by 1750 results of this folly were plain to observant eyes, such as those of the naturalist Peter Kalm, friend of Catesby and John Bartram, who noted of the New Jersey settlements:

> All those . . . born in America . . . asserted that there were not nearly so many edible birds at present as there used to be when they were children. . . . They even said they had heard the same complaint from their fathers who were born in this locality. In their youth the bays, rivers, and brooks were quite covered with all sorts of waterfowl, such as wild geese, ducks, and the like. About sixty or seventy years ago, a single person could kill eighty ducks in a morning; but at present you frequently waited in vain for a single one. A Swede above ninety years old assured me he had in his youth killed twenty-three ducks at a shot. . . . The wild turkeys, and the birds which the Swedes in this country call partridges and hazelhens, were seen in large flocks in the woods. But at this time a person gets tired with walking before he can start a single bird.

Kalm attributed the decrease in birds in part to excessive slaughter of them and in part to their being frightened away by lack of protection. "In spring the people steal eggs, mothers and young indifferently, because no regulations are made to the contrary. And if any had been made, the spirit of freedom which prevails in the country would not suffer them to be obeyed. But though the eatable birds have been diminished greatly, yet there are others which have been increased . . . since the arrival of the Europeans."

Among those that had increased inordinately in response to environmental changes brought about by the settlers were the grackles "which the English call blackbirds, and the Swedes corn thieves." On the authority of Dr. Franklin, Kalm reported that a similar increase of grackles in New England resulted in an early and important lesson in ecology for the region's farmers. ". . . by means of the premiums which had been paid for killing them in New England, they have been so thoroughly extirpated, that they were very rarely seen, and in a few places only. But in the summer of 1749, an immense quantity of worms appeared on the meadows which devoured the grass, and did great damage so the people repented of their enmity against the corn thieves. . . . But after these enemies were killed off the worms were of course more at liberty to multiply, and therefore they grew so numerous that they did more mischief now than the birds did before. In the summer of 1749, the worms left so little grass in New England that the inhabitants were forced to get hay from Pennsylvania. . . ."

At about the same time, far-ranging and thoughtful John Bartram was already noting the marked and rapid deterioration of the "inexhaustible" resources of the American wilderness. To his friend, Jared Eliot, in Connecticut, he "observed with concern our approaching distress on account of our want of timber for fencing and indeed many other necessary uses."

Even beyond the areas actually settled, wildlife was diminishing at an alarming rate. After his long 1762 journey down the coast as far as Georgia and back, through the mountains as far west as the Ohio River, he had written to Peter Collinson: "I did not see any wild animal in all that journey, except two or three deer; only one tame bear at the Fort; nor so much as a fox or wolf, to be seen or heard, although I lay six nights in the woods on the banks of the Ohio . . . and two nights on the Alleghany Mountains."

The contrast between that report and John Lawson's on the same region sixty years earlier speaks loudly enough of the destruction wrought by the settlers, aided now by the natives whom they had enlisted in the hide and fur trades.

Both Peter Collinson and his son, Michael, were as concerned as Bartram. Michael wrote from Manchester:

Considering the destruction that is perpetually going on, I should not be surprised if the whole race of Bears should become extinct; and still more so with regard to the Beaver, there being an annual sale, here only, of between forty and fifty thousand of their skins.

A few years later, in response to Bartram's continuing anxiety, Michael wrote, with prescient pessimism:

The general remarks you make respecting the extirpation of the native inhabitants of your vast forests are striking and curious, and carry conviction along with them; and, indeed, I cannot help thinking but that, in the period you mention, notwithstanding the amazing recesses your prodigious continent affords, many of the present species will become extinct, and perhaps the Indians, themselves; . . .

The few game laws enacted by the colonial assemblies were almost all negative—bounties for such unwanted creatures as cougars and wolves, on the assumption that "what is not useful is vicious." For example, before the Plymouth Colony was ten years old, a bounty of a penny a head was being paid for killing wolves. A few years later passenger pigeons were being offered in the Boston market at six for a penny, and everywhere in the country wild birds were a common article in the marketplace. To these inducements to killing add the thriving fur trade, with its customers all over the world. When no wild creature with edible flesh, or useful fur or hide, or any predator considered dangerous, or any animal regarded as a threat to crops, was safe from unrestrained attacks, it is easy to see why the "inexhaustible" wildlife of the East precipitately became almost exhausted.

With the close of the American Revolution, when settlers poured westward across the mountains into Tennessee, Kentucky, and the Old Northwest, forest and wildlife destruction, which had become the proud hallmark of the colonist, his very way of life, went with them and spread like a virulent blight all across that vast and unspoiled wilderness between the Appalachians and the great river. It had taken a century and a half to reduce the coastal provinces from a teeming land of magnificent forests to the relative poverty John Bartram reported in 1762. However, the ravaging of this new and vaster wilderness was much more swiftly done. It was already far advanced when André Michaux roamed the region. Then, although bear were still common, elk and buffalo were already scarce. A decade later, when his son traveled across Kentucky and Tennessee, he apparently saw none of these creatures. His concern was for the reckless abandon with which the young country was putting its primeval forests to fire and ax.

When Alexander Wilson crossed the same regions in 1810, he described the pigeon-killing orgies of the inhabitants, but, for the most part, there was little left to subdue in that area of the wilderness. The fur trade had already swept devastatingly over it and passed on westward across the Mississippi, far up into the Missouri country. The glamour was already gone from the land. Daniel Boone, trailblazer and master hunter, is quoted that same year as saying:

Sir, what a wonderful difference thirty years makes in the country! Why, at the time I was caught by the Indians, you would not have walked out in any direction for more than a mile without shooting a buck or bear. There were then thousands of buffaloes on the hills in Kentucky; the land looked as if it would never become poor; and the hunt in those days was a pleasure indeed. But when I was left to myself on the banks of the Green River, I daresay for the last time in my life, a few *signs* of deer were to be seen, and as to a deer itself, I saw none.

The Louisiana Purchase in 1803 opened a vast new area of the American wilderness for conquest. The winning of the West was a two-pronged invasion—by sea and by land, by schooner and prairie schooner —gold rushes to California, land rushes to plow the rich grasslands of Kansas and Nebraska, railroad thrusts to serve the new domains, to bring in the settlers and haul out the timbers that the followers of Paul Bunyan and his blue ox were harvesting in wholesale slashes through the forests of Wisconsin and Minnesota.

Merely incidental to this virulent westward erosion were the accounts of slaughter, told first around the campfires, then on lonely nights in the sod houses on the endless prairies, or in the miners' shacks, and later handed down to children, who only through the imagination of the young could recapture the extravagance of those days. They were tales of slaughter to match the tales of Tamerlane, slaughter of literally millions of buffalo, sometimes for their hides, often for their tongues alone, sometimes simply for the fun of it.

Transcontinental trains stopped in the prairies to permit the passengers the pleasure of slaughtering the buffalo, whose great carcasses were left, unharvested, for wolves and vultures. There were tales of matching the speed and endurance of mustang mounts, the power of gunpowder, and the speed of leaden balls, against tens of thousands of elk and hundreds of thousands of pronghorns, mule deer, and bighorn sheep. Especially exciting were the tales of the great jaguars, the giant grizzlies, the cunning cougars, the packs of wolves—all fair game and no quarter given, so that few of any species survived the force of the great conquest.

Compounding the folly and moral felony of the ruthless destruction of millions of buffalo was the official government sanction, even encouragement, of the slaughter, with the shameful intent of starving the Indians into surrendering their lands for settlement. General Philip Sheridan stated the official policy: "Let them kill, skin, and sell until the buffalo is exterminated, as it is the only way to bring about lasting peace and to allow civilization to advance."

Young Theodore Roosevelt, a rancher in North Dakota in the eighteen-eighties, reports the result:

No sight is more common on the plains than that of a bleached buffalo skull; and their countless numbers attest the abundance of the animal at a time not so very long past. On these portions where the herds made their last stand, the carcasses dried in the clear, high air, or mouldering skeletons abound. . . . A ranchman who at the same time had made a journey of a thousand miles across northern Montana, along the Milk River, told me that, to use his own expression, during the whole distance he was never out of sight of a dead buffalo and never in sight of a live one.

The policy was completely successful. The buffalo and other big-game species were brought to the verge of extinction and the Indian, hungry, cold, and drastically diminished in numbers, was brought to heel. With scarcely a qualm of conscience, he had been treated as just another predator, as indeed he was, part of the wilderness wildlife, to be extirpated with the other beasts that civilization might retrieve the land for constructive purposes. Conscience had little weight in the scale when measured against "progress" in the adolescent, aggressive nation. It all seemed a grand, dramatic, and inspiring demonstration of the American Spirit at its best—dramatic enough to pack movie houses all across the country every Saturday for half a century, with audiences enthralled by violent, amoral heroes, in violent, amoral situations, incident to a violent and amoral facet of our history. Rarely shown on the silver screen were the sad and inevitable consequences. For thousands who destroyed the animals and drove out the Indians from dryer grasslands, the victory quickly proved a Pyrrhic one. A few years of cultivation, a few dry years, and their fertile lands were literally gone with the wind, ruined beyond redemption, with a ruin that bred ruin that was soon magnified in silted rivers, flooded lowlands, reduced rainfalls, falling water tables. For the laws of nature are far more effectively enforced than any made by man. When the rule of nature was overthrown by the extirpation of the native wildlife of the dryer grasslands and the frail and inadequate laws of man were substituted, it took but a few years of overgrazing to turn vast expanses into useless, wind-blown desert areas that a thousand years of persistent care can never redeem.

When the three hundred years of largely fruitless searching for gold in North America was crowned with success by the big strike at Sutter's Mill, few foresaw its terrible cost. For every ounce of sterile and unproductive gold retrieved from the valleys of the West by hydraulic mining, tons of fertile and productive soil were washed away to choke the streams and silt the bottomlands below, a destruction compounded by the soil-deprived, boulder-strewn barrens left behind. Other lands, made vulnerable by the logging operations, were repeatedly devastated by fires, creating yet more man-made barrens.

All that violent depredation of the natural environment was but a variation on an oft-repeated theme in the long history of man. The almost naked and soilless hills of Greece, their counterparts in Italy, the barren sands and desolation of the once bountiful lands of North Africa, Mesopotamia, vast areas of Pakistan, and northern China are ample exhibits of the ignorance, folly, or greed of men of earlier eras. Those lands too were part of our heritage as the whole earth is the heritage of all its creatures, and the lesson implicit in their devastation is there for us to read. The lesson they demonstrate is also part of our heritage. Today that lesson is more urgent than ever, for the margin of the earth not yet despoiled grows ever narrower and narrower, while the weapons of destruction grow ever swifter and more terrible.

Never in all history had anything remotely comparable to the conquest of the American wilderness occurred. Never had so vast a land been seized and tamed in so short a time. And never had a conquest been more violent, thanks largely to guns and plows, simple instruments in the ever mounting arsenal of modern man's potential for violence. Thus did it come to pass that a shockingly maimed and manhandled and badly denuded America, at the turn of the century, was given over to us of the "enlightened" twentieth century.

The early years of the new century, however, brought no new vision. Still the old watchwords prevailed—manifest destiny, laissez faire, development, free enterprise. Reckless destruction of soil and water, forest and wildlife continued unabated. The remnant thousand buffalo shrank to twenty or thirty. The elk, once the widest ranging of any American hoofed animal, was reduced to a single beleaguered herd. The pronghorn antelope was slaughtered to the brink of extinction. And even as the Eskimo curlew was being driven to extinction, in 1914 the last living parakeet and the last surviving passenger pigeon died in their cages.

With no consideration of consequences, rivers, great arteries of the country's life, were treated as little more than convenient sewers. Salmon and sturgeon became casualties of erosion mud, paper-mill wastes, and city sewers. Soil mining continued its heedless devastation. Single-crop farming went on leaching fertility from the black belts of the South. Sterile and gullied red hills became the hallmark of the once fertile Southern Piedmont. Fire and overgrazing cost many a new England hillside its thin soil covering. Dust bowls claimed wider and wider areas in prairies of the West, while the wind took an increasing toll of the soil of the overgrazed dry grasslands. Only in respect to our dwindling forests was there any indication of a change of spirit.

~~~ 2

Actually there had been signs of a rising sense of forest conservation faintly blowing in the wind in the latter quarter of the old century. The seed that gave rise to that new spirit had been planted a generation earlier, in the closing months of the Civil War, when a remarkable book, *Man and Nature*, appeared. *Man and Nature* (the title of which has been borrowed to head this chapter) was essentially a trailblazing work on ecology, although at that time there was no science known by that name. Its author, Vermont-born George Perkins Marsh, was an equally remarkable man, a man of incredible industry and Jeffersonian versatility. Scholar and linguist (he mastered twenty languages before he was thirty), philologist of note, antiquarian, farmer, and naturalist, he was also lawyer, congressman, and ambassador. There had been many witnesses to the destruction of America's resources, but few had perceived the consequences. As Marsh expressed it: "Sight is a faculty, seeing an art." Seeing was an art in which he was a master.

He understood the intricate fabric of life with its complex interdependence:

The larvae of the mosquito and the gnat are the favorite food of the trout in the wooded regions where those insects abound. Earlier in the year the trout feeds on the larvae of the May fly, which is itself very destructive of the spawn of the salmon, and hence, by a sort of house-that-Jack-built, the destruction of the mosquito that feeds the trout that preys on the May fly that destroys the eggs that hatch the salmon that pampers the epicure, may occasion a scarcity of this latter fish in waters where he would otherwise be abundant.

In nature plants and animals in competition with their fellow plants and animals maintain a well-regulated balance. Rarely do wild animals injure their environment, and when they do it is almost always a result of man's tampering with and unbalancing the animal's environment. Extending this truism to primitive man, Marsh observed:

Purely untutored humanity, it is true, interferes comparatively little with the arrangements of nature, and the destructive agency of man becomes more and more energetic as he advances in civilization, until the impoverishment, with which his exhaustion of the natural resources of the soil is threatening him, at last awakens him to the necessity of preserving, if not restoring what has been wantonly wasted. . . . The popular traditions of the simpler peoples recognize a certain community of nature, between man, brute animals, and even plants; and this serves to explain why the apologue or fable, which ascribes the power of speech and the faculty of reason to birds, quadrupeds, insects, flowers, and trees, is one of the earliest forms of literary composition.

Careful observation and well-documented facts give special weight to Marsh's grave warnings to modern man:

But man is everywhere a disturbing agent. Wherever he plants his foot, the harmonies of nature are turned to discords. The proportions and accommodations which insured the stability of existing arrangements are overthrown. Indigenous vegetable and animal species are extirpated, and supplanted by others of foreign origin, spontaneous production is forbidden or restricted, and the face of the earth is either laid bare or covered with new and reluctant growth of vegetable forms, and with alien tribes of animal life. These intentional changes and substitutions constitute, indeed, great revolutions; but vast as is their magnificence and importance, they are, as we shall see, insignificant in comparison with the contingent and unsought results which have flowed from them.

Marsh's conclusion is that "man has too long forgotten that the earth was given to him for usufruct alone, not for consumption, still less for profligate waste." In contravention of this axiom he saw his fellow countrymen absorbed in brazenly "breaking up the floor and wainscoting and doors and windowpanes of our dwelling, for fuel to warm our bodies and seethe our pottage."

To make his case for the preservation of our forests and for the management of them for indefinitely sustained yield, he marched out a veritable phalanx of case histories of societies and civilizations decayed and fallen for want of their forest heritage, which they had consumed. It was a frightening confrontation, even for Americans, long accustomed to take an unfocused, double-vision view of their forests, seeing them at the same time as a nuisance obstacle to agriculture and progress and as an inexhaustible resource. For those who persist in reaping where they have not sown, Marsh warned, ruin lies in wait.

The seeds Marsh planted were slow to germinate. Although *Man and Nature* was well received and had a profound impact in intellectual circles, its views were far too alien to the habitual attitudes of the average American for it to have any immediate effect on public sentiment or practice. In Washington, however, there were those who responded intelligently to Marsh's warnings and moved to do what they could within the limitations of the times. An aggressive group, aided by rising public indignation against the great land grabs and the wholesale timber stealing from public lands, inaugurated drastic legislation to save what was left of the wilderness and the forests. While, except for the new national park system, they failed, their efforts advanced the growing sentiment for some measure of conservation. By 1890 this sentiment had enough support to get from Congress an act authorizing the establishment of forest reserves. Thirteen million acres were immediately set aside, on paper, but left unpatrolled and thus unprotected from depredation. Within a few years this was doubled and steps were taken to supervise these reserves and to establish a conservation-oriented land policy under the supervision of the United States Forest Service.

At least in limited areas, mostly in the West, the comeback trail had been blazed. Soon progress was evident in the elk and buffalo, near the brink of extinction. The two or three dozen buffalo became hundreds. The elk did even better despite persistent poaching—five hundred in a single year to satisfy the market demand of its namesake fraternal order for souvenirs.

However, the war over Western public lands and the fate of the millions of acres involved in the struggle to save at least a remnant of our heritage from exploitation represented but a small part of the nation's total land heritage and an equally small part of its wildlife. Of far greater import for the future were lands in private ownership. These lands, which furnished the bulk of the country's essentials for life, had suffered most at the hands of man, and, because of their extent, it was the abuse of these privately owned lands which most threatened our future welfare and our children's heritage.

For even the beginning of any substantial reform in the care of the vast domain of private ownership the country had to await the long agony of the Great Depression. In retrospect that financial trauma of the thirties has faded into relative insignificance in comparison with its sociological impact. During those years of travail and disillusionment, in America at least, many a fixed and long cherished illusion was shaken and many swept away forever. Doubt was cast on the deeply entrenched faith that industry and free enterprise will inevitably add up to the good life for all. Another casualty was the shibboleth of the inexhaustibility of our natural resources and with it our traditional aversion to public ownership or control of those resources. These changing concepts and the actions that resulted brought to the American general public a degree of understanding of the fundamental dependence of man upon nature and the interdependence of all living things—the science of life: ecology.

A variety of agencies, some born of the great disillusionment, others galvanized into action by the urgency of the times, focused their efforts on mending the terrible depredation that a few heedless generations had wrought in field and forest all across the land. State and federal forest services, the Soil Conservation Service, and the Civilian Conservation Corps attacked the problem of our battered lands on several fronts. Soon, freighted with new hope, young pine plantations were beginning to cover the gashes and gullies of man-made badlands in Georgia's red hills; neat contour terraces and strip-planted fields began to display pleasing topographical patterns on Kentucky's fertile hills; protective shelter belts of green saplings began to interrupt the flat horizon-to-horizon view in the rich farmlands of the Plains States, while in the dust bowls of the Southwest patches of green once again took over custody of what was left of fertility there, beginning the long, slow convalescence of the dry grasslands. Even in that classic example of man-made badlands, that prime exhibit of man's ability to destroy with his chemical wastes every vestige of life on earth from earthworms to trees, the Copper Hill section of southeast Tennessee, where in earlier years of unrestrained exploitation the fumes of copper smelters had killed everything as far as the eye could see, even there bits of green marked the first steps in a formidable redemption process, which is as yet far from assured.

Millions of acres of submarginal farmlands and poor woodlands passed from private to public ownership to be added to existing state and national forests or to form new public forest reserves. Publicly maintained forest-fire protection services had become an accepted government function, like soil conservation activities, and the operation of forest tree nurseries to provide low-cost seedlings to reestablish forests on depleted farmlands. Aid and encouragement of the building of "farm" ponds became yet another ecological government activity.

Although most of these activities were directed toward improvements on privately held properties, the mere existence of those improvements represented an ecological boon to nature emanating beyond and above property bounds—a boon to nature's health in which the public has an interest, of life and death importance.

A concomitant of the activities of all these busy "emergency" agencies was a stream of publicity directed toward justification of such un-precedented "socialistic" activities in the land of laissez faire, publicity that served to introduce the American general public to the simple and fundamental principles of ecology, the capstone of the life sciences. Twentieth-century Americans, despite their man-centered, man-domi-nated, urban-oriented society, were given glimmerings of an awareness of what to their primitive ancestors was evident—the essential importance of nature to their survival.

Here and there all across the country dramatic changes began to appear. Once again blends of soft brown covered the fire-blackened forest floors. The litter of the new forests was soon covering the raw earth with a protective blanket. Relieved of fire's scourge, fruitful for-ests once more offered refuge and sustenance to a rejuvenating popula-tion of wilderness creatures. Most dramatic was the return of the white-tailed deer. Forest protection, closed breeding seasons, and freedom from most of their natural predators, the bobcat, cougar, and wolf, resulted in an enormous resurgence in the whitetail whose numbers in places even exceeded the carrying power of their ranges. Even the black bear was making a modest comeback. For the first time in Amer-ica's recorded history there was a sustained increase in wildlife—albeit a sadly unbalanced wildlife, with its natural checks and balances dis-rupted. With most of their predators extirpated, the rabbit, squirrel, and even the fox populations approached or perhaps even exceeded their pristine numbers.

For birds, especially waterfowl, the picture was far less bright. Among native species, perhaps only blackbirds and robins regained anything like their former numbers. Alien imports such as the rock dove (the common pigeon of our cities), the house sparrow, and the starling provided the only other significant increases in the bird popula-tion, illustrating a well-established, ecological principle. Rarely do alien animals, particularly of the higher orders, find a vacant place in nature's tight-knit web, but if by chance they do find an unoccupied niche it is usually one empty of natural enemies as well, and a population explosion such as that of the British starling in America is apt to occur. Among the rare exceptions is the ring-necked pheasant, a well-adapted but properly restrained immigrant from the Old World.

More and more tightly constricted breeding grounds, oil-coated rivers and coastal waters, and ever increasing numbers of guns awaiting them all along their migration routes continued to keep ducks and other waterfowl to a fraction of what had been their numbers even as late as in Alexander Wilson's day. Hawks and eagles, plovers and herons, turkey and grouse—none regained their former abundance. And, of course, of many other species there were no survivors. Since his arrival in America the white man had already been the active instrument in the utter extermination of twenty species of birds and mammals. Sixty other species had been brought to the verge of extinction.

Even so, the process of mending our battered lands that had been launched and the concomitant partial recovery of its creature world were impressive and visible evidence of what might be done. Tentative steps had been taken along the trail Marsh had blazed four score years before. It is now possible to regard the Great Depression in the light of what it wrought as not wholly evil in its effects; indeed it became the catalyst for reactions essential to the survival of mankind on earth.

3

However, this new wisdom had scarcely begun to make its mark when a large part of the world was plunged into yet another of man's fratricidal orgies, which he tends to excuse as natural in himself, although in nature wild creatures never engage in mass attacks on their own kind. The glorification of the slaughter of one's brother we must shamefully admit is a human perversion of idealism, entirely foreign to nature. World War II proved to be not only the greatest internecine slaughter the world has ever known but also the most extravagant squandering of unrenewable resources, a squandering which the Cold War aftermath continues at such a reckless rate that it is difficult to avoid the feeling that the human race is possessed by a madness inexorably driving it to global suicide.

Any real concern for the earth as a suitable environment for our posterity becomes entirely academic if the human race, like overcrowded laboratory animals or Scandinavian lemmings when their numbers reach an insupportable level, is bent on wholesale self-destruction. If that is also man's fate, it becomes only debatable whether he will destroy himself gradually by poisoning his environment and destroying his natural resources (a denouement already imminent in terms of the age of mankind) or more swiftly through a nuclear exchange, intentional or accidental, which will render the planet uninhabitable by man or beast.

To go on we must believe that somehow salvation is possible. It may be that salvation is inherent in the realization of the simple fact that the clear and present danger from these fearful possibilities has no national boundaries—it is *Everyman*, white, black, and yellow, irrespective of his economic or political persuasion, over whom the sword of Damocles hangs, and by so slender a thread. It is mankind and all life on earth that faces annihilation. And it is becoming blatantly obvious that only if the world can turn from its national rivalries long enough to recognize its immediate and common peril and move hereafter in full awareness of it is there any hope at all. If modern man has arrogated unto himself powers which a generation gone would have thought reserved to God, he has willy-nilly taken unto himself those heretofore reserved to the devil too. At last man, the great extinguisher of species, is squarely confronted with the extinction of yet another: *Homo sapiens* himself.

If, through the intercession of Providence or through some miracle of human intelligence and compassion, man awakens, and, while yet there is time, turns his giant strength and godlike power and intelligence to nuclear control, to the restriction of his atomic genii to constructive purposes, and to a proper care of his natural resources, he can still abide in hope. If an all-destroying holocaust can be averted and the threat of it virtually eliminated, time will be won and energy and intelligence released for mankind to meet the other threats along his way, threats potentially just as lethal but fortunately less imminent and more susceptible to control.

In contrast to the dramatic and obvious horror of a nuclear war, many of the other major threats to human survival are insidious, a quality which increases their latent peril. The most publicized of these is the population explosion. Over the centuries since the dawn of civilization man has to a degree artificially frustrated the natural checks and balances of the wilderness, which otherwise would have kept his numbers relatively constant. Until modern times this was but a moderate frustration with no great impact, permitting only moderate increases in human population. However, with the success of medical science in the control of infectious diseases and other life-saving advances, and through improved means of producing and transporting food, plus the rise of organized charity, public and private, nature's laws for population control among her creatures was virtually suspended for *Homo sapiens*. The forces that had kept him through the ages one of the rarer of earth's creatures were suddenly removed. Demographers think the earth's human population reached a million some 300,000 years ago and, in the ensuing 280,000 years, increased about three million—an increase in those 2800 centuries that approximates the monthly increase in world population today. There were less than a billion people on earth as recently as 1750. Today there are more than three billion. Unless the current rate of increase is checked, the world population will double to more than six billion by the end of this century.

When *Man and Nature* appeared a century ago, there were some thirty million people in the United States directly or indirectly dependent on the land whose exploitation gave Marsh his great concern for the future. Now there are six times that number with far less unspoiled productive land for their support, for, as Marsh feared, vast expanses have gone the way of the ancient fields of North Africa and Mesopotamia and become man-induced deserts. Cities, highways, strip mines, and trash dumps have requisitioned what adds up to very substantial subtractions from the remainder of the productive areas.

Obviously, neither in America nor in the world as a whole can this sort of thing continue indefinitely. If one asks where is the limit beyond which it cannot go, the answer may well be that it has already been reached—even, possibly, long since passed. There may be an oblique answer to that query in another: Is the sum of human happiness greater for two hundred million Americans today than it was for half that number in 1900? Or in another: Will the human society of six billion in the year 2000 be something better than the lot of today's three billion?

A world consensus that the answers to those questions cannot possibly be in the affirmative is becoming more and more apparent. The inescapable logic of the arguments for the application of brakes to the spiraling population growth is being emphatically reinforced by visual illustrations of the consequences of no restraint. On every hand we see those consequences, from the near-starving millions of Calcutta, to the miserable villages of South America, to the restive slums of cities all over the world. World opinion in support of effective birth control is clearly mounting to proportions sufficiently powerful to bring about widespread implementation. It seems, therefore, a fairly reasonable assumption that the human race is not going to emulate blindly the brainless bacteria of the winemaker's fermentation vat and breed himself into extinction in his own lethal residues, or follow the example of cancer cells that by their unrestrained multiplication destroy the whole living organic system that sustains them.

However, even if our population explosion is successfully checked there is a real possibility that by the time this is achieved the world population will have already reached lethal proportions. Indeed it is by no means a frivolous thought that perhaps human numbers have already reached an intolerable and insupportable level. All over the world there is an impatient surge toward better living standards for everyone. Three billion people are striving and agitating for the standard of living now enjoyed by only a few hundred million, largely concentrated in Europe and North America, a standard of living possible only in a sophisticated, highly contrived, highly mechanized society. If such a goal of universal well-being were obtainable, it almost certainly would not be sustainable for any substantial period, and even more certainly not if the way of life to be emulated is that of the average middle-class American. The available resources of the world, even if far more carefully husbanded than at present, simply could not sustain the drain and besides, even if they could, the earth would quickly become untenantable.

Already man is burning the world's candle of life at both ends—this despite the fact that half the people of the earth are consuming only meager pittances of its resources. The resource demands of modern industrial societies are enormous. Although the lives of only a relatively small fraction of the people of the world are geared to such societies, the consumption requirements of that small fraction already far exceed the earth's reproduction of expendable resources. Already with most of the world in serious want and with relatively few bountifully supplied, we are recklessly overspending the earth's resource capital, putting us in the position of life tenants committing waste against our remainder-men—our posterity.

It is essential that people realize that man produces nothing—he only spends. Those who proudly style themselves producers, the farmer, the textile worker, the fisherman, and the miner, are actually nothing more than gatherers or processors. Practically the only earthly production since the Creator produced the cosmos has come from the intricate, sun-powered, synthetic chemical assembly line of the green cells of living plants. Since the few exceptions, such as the utilization of the sun or volcanic heat, water or wind power for chemical synthesis, are relatively inconsequential, it is broadly correct to assert that, to the extent that the sum of all the burning, all the eating, and all the decaying on earth exceeds the calories being concurrently stored by the earth's green plants, we are engaging in deficit living and violating our trusteeship of the earth.

It is here in America where a substantial portion of the population has attained the degree of comfort and artificial living toward which the earth's billions aspire that the candle of stored life energy is burning at both ends most furiously. We in the United States are relentlessly diminishing the real productivity of the country by constantly curtailing our basic manufacturing units, our sun-trapping green leaves, from which we derive the air we breathe, the food we eat, most of our clothing, much of our housing, and the relative moderation of our climate. To obtain almost every other material thing we consume—our motive power, heat, and the products of their application in manufacturing, we tap the stored sunlight trapped by chlorophyll in the cells of plants that flourished millions of years ago, available to us in the "sunlight savings account" of our fossil fuels—the earth's coal and oil reserves. The rate of consumption of those nonrenewable resources necessary to maintain an industrial society such as we have in the United States is so great that, even if our way of life never becomes the way of life of most of the rest of the world, those savings accounts of stored sunlight will soon be reduced to the point of exhaustion of our oil and gas reserves. With little left for those who follow us, we will, in effect, be passing on to our posterity, perhaps within the space of a century, a house so badly wrecked by our riotous occupancy that, if they can live in it at all, it will be at best a poor remnant of the magnificent mansion that was the heritage of our forebears.

Already in the United States we have removed from production to give over to highways as much land as there is in the state of South Carolina, and that does not take into account the Interstate System which, when completed, will have consumed another three thousand square miles; nor does it include the vast aggregate of the highway borrow pits and spoil areas from which the life-giving soils have been removed or deeply buried. When we add all the railroad, pipe line, and power line rights-of-way, which are regularly sprayed with herbicides to ensure nonproductivity of food and oxygen, and the parking lots and airports, largely paved to discourage any chlorophyll-producing trespassers, the total area requisitioned and sterilized to serve transportation alone is enormous. This sacrifice of millions of acres to nonproductive uses is compounded when, to pave the highways and airports against any counter-invasion by the plant kingdom, vast quantities of our limited reserves of bitumens, residues of plants that flourished in eons past, are drawn from these reserves to provide ever more and more facilities for an ever-increasing consumption of our irreplaceable reserves of oil, another strictly limited product of archaic plants that flourished on earth millions of years ago. It is still further disturbing that the consumption of those nonrenewable resources for paving, fuel, synthetic tires, and plastics is increasing at a much steeper rate than is the population, so that population control, if achieved, will not automatically check our spiraling extravagance.

While with bland unconcern we burden the atmosphere with an ever-increasing load of the poisonous garbage ceaselessly streaming from smokestacks, aeration towers, railway and motor vehicle exhausts, with equal unconcern, at least until quite recently, we have imposed a killing burden upon our flowing waters. The double burden of the liquid refuse of industry and the sewer outfalls of our cities has already effectively killed the once living and productive waters of thousands of miles of our Eastern waterways, largely eliminating their once very significant food production capacity, and upsetting nature's balance in forest and field now washed by poison waters. The cost of those foul waters in terms of human recreation is immeasurable.

Trash and garbage, the most blatant and offensive aspects of the desolation which is the hallmark of modern urban-industrial living, present an accelerating disposal problem that is already reaching stupendous proportions, and it, too, is a problem that inexorably tends to grow much more rapidly than population. Of all the problems caused by urban concentrations none exceeds that of garbage and trash disposal. Traditionally cities have selected conveniently located swamps and marshes (places where for ages past nature has been at her busiest, producing oxygen and water vapor for the air and food for the support of animal life) to receive the appalling mess, to burn the burnable, to leave the decomposable to rot and abandon the hard-core residue for posterity to contend with—yet another example of our burning the candle of life at both ends: the conversion of the life-giving swamps and marshes to poison-exuding, oxygen-consuming wastelands.

It is thought by biological historians that it was plant life that altered the chemistry of the world to permit the higher forms of animal life to flourish on earth, but that now, ironically, man, life's zenith production, is himself altering the earth so drastically that he may well end by setting in motion an irresistible reversal of the process of which he is the end product. It is thought that when the earth was young and devoid of life its atmosphere lacked both oxygen and carbon dioxide, the two essential atmospheric building blocks of life, that such atmosphere as existed was made up of water vapor, methane, and ammonia until the first primitive plant cells began releasing free oxygen into the air. It has been calculated that the present oxygen content of the air is the product of two thousand years of photosynthesis at the plant growth rate of this geological age before man began his considerable reduction of the earth's plant life. Obviously, then, man is now in the process of mining and consuming not only his stored reserves of coal, iron, and oil, but his oxygen reserves as well. Modern man is asking of the atmosphere not only the necessary oxygen to consume the current production of the plant world but sufficiently more to burn vast amounts produced in the lush ages of the carboniferous period of millions of years ago. To put it a bit more graphically, we of this petroleum- and coal-powered industrial age are requisitioning from the atmosphere the oxygen released into the air by the rank fern forests of which those fuels are the fossil remains.

Just as the building up of oxygen in the atmosphere permitted evolution of the earth's higher forms of life, withdrawing it and locking it back into water and carbon dioxide will surely diminish higher life. However, it is likely that long before man is gasping for oxygen the increased carbon dioxide content of the atmosphere and man's machinations with the earth's surface will have already made the world too inhospitable for his survival. His manipulations of the earth are taking on the proportions of a geological force, perhaps comparable to an ice age. Some scientists take the view that the changes man is making, especially in the atmosphere, will, through what is known as the greenhouse effect, melt the remaining ice at the poles and flood much of the earth's dry land. Others believe that our air pollution and a reduced oxygen content will insulate the surface of the earth from the sun's heat and bring on another ice age.

The burden of this long jeremiad is that man through his modern civilization and the vast human population it has permitted has opened a veritable Pandora's box of destructive forces that threaten him with extinction. Unless heroic measures are taken, man will inevitably call down upon his own head the wrath of nature reserved for those creatures that have lost their places in the ecological symphony. To fend off this fate, we must set about placating nature and determine to treat her with the awe, respect, and tender care due her as the supreme provider, the earth mother from whom all blessings flow.

~~~ 4

That his days may be long in the lands of his fathers (assuming that he has accomplished the obvious prerequisites of reducing his fecundity and confining beyond all chance of escape his atomic genii) man will have to succeed in rejoining nature's ecological symphony. After his latter-day devotion to a cacophony of discord he must learn to conduct his entire life on earth in a melody and rhythm in complete harmony with nature's laws.

Man's hope of survival then depends upon his understanding of and obedience to the organic rules of life. One primary essential is that man shall once again *feel* a oneness with nature, and that he shall be continuously aware of its continuity and of the transience of his own place in the fabric. The direct relationship between his survival and his physical environment was taken for granted by the wilderness Indian for whom oneness with nature was inherent in his daily life, but for modern man in his treeless urban warren this awareness must often depend on artificial insemination.

A massive, sustained educational program to inculcate in all human beings everywhere a high degree of ecological wisdom, the consciousness of the intimate kinship of all protoplasmic life, plant and animal, and the mutual interdependence of all life, is certainly the logical first step and is, without question, the basic essential for man's survival. This massive educational program should not be limited to those now involved in the formal educational processes. We are already too far afloat on disastrous seas to wait until the ecologically uneducated loose their hold on the tiller. This wholesale, world-wide dissemination of ecological principles must be so thorough that man's sense of oneness with nature will be not only common knowledge but an emotional faith deep in the bones of every individual. He must be thoroughly embued with an ecological conscience. For only with such an ethos firmly and universally implanted will mankind be able to give priority to the urgent problem of the survival of his species on earth. Only then will he be able to turn away from the pettiness of nationalism and political quarrels, the insanities of the arms race, the brutal stupidities of war, and recognize that his plight is desperate and the time is now.

Man, destroyer and wastrel, is also *Homo sapiens,* a thinking reed, a creature made in the image of God, and if it is true that his plight is desperate, so also it is true that he has cause for hope, and even, since his survival is synonymous with a world-wide renaissance of peaceful, compassionate, and rational effort, he has cause for hope of a brighter world than he has ever known.

But the problems are myriad, the task gigantic. Here it will be possible to suggest only a few of the more obvious and immediate aspects. It is obvious, of course, that we cannot go back to the primitive state of nature, however great our wilderness nostalgia. The American landscape of the Indian or that our wilderness naturalists described is not compatible with the support of an industrial society of two hundred million people. Laments for the slaughter of the buffalo are fitting, but to wish them back again in all their millions, grazing in the wheat fields of Nebraska, would be fatuous. Though we regret the loss of passenger pigeon and are shocked by tales of its brutal slaughter, would we, even were it possible, bring back its hundreds of millions, with their capacity to consume all the crops of a county in one single day? But, though we cannot and probably would not wish to cover the plains again with buffalo or darken the skies with pigeons, we can and should restore as nearly as possible the balance of nature which we have so dangerously disturbed. Even today the country, with all the demands upon its resources, could still, with enlightened practices, easily support a much more varied and far more numerous fauna, whose addition would be at least a step forward toward a better world.

One of the more fundamental ecological principles is that the more complex the life fabric, the greater its stability. In less well-rounded environments, imbalances often result in selective, runaway populations, sometimes severely damaging the entire environment. Army worm and grasshopper invasions are familiar examples. Among the larger animals, the classic illustration of the ease with which a relatively simple ecological web may be torn and in consequence the whole environmental fabric unraveled is the case of the Kaibab Reserve. In the early years of the century, to encourage the deer there on the north rim of Grand Canyon, the numerous wolves and cougars were extirpated. Within two decades the deer population far exceeded the carrying capacity of the range. Thousands were starving and had to be killed to save the overgrazed range, which by then was already so badly damaged that it has not yet fully recovered. Although it is not quite the relationship of the wolf dwelling with the lamb, visualized in Isaiah's millennium, it is akin, in a way, that cougar and deer cannot survive in nature without dwelling together.

Unquestionably a reintroduction of bobcat, cougar, and bear into the deer ranges in the East would be beneficial. Man is no substitute for the cougar's natural function in keeping a deer herd healthy and strong. Unlike the cougar, a gun does not selectively eliminate the slow, the sick, and the aged. Perhaps the lack of the larger predators and the resulting free reign of the fox helps to account for the failure of wild turkey to thrive today where once they prospered mightily. Other examples of the imbalance caused by man's indiscriminate destruction are legion.

Only when civilized man's enmity toward many natural creatures has been wholly supplanted by empathy with nature will the fauna of the forest be able to approach in numbers and variety its full potential. Such empathy would make more stringent game laws acceptable and would encourage more adequate conservation and refuge areas. Pressures against widespread chemical warfare on insects, fraught with all manner of possible hazards as it unquestionably is, would become irresistible, forcing the substitution of a greater reliance on biological warfare within the ecological framework to keep specific insect pests under control.

Only if imbued with an empathy with nature will man be able to fill the role incumbent upon him by virtue of his intelligence, that of serving as wise physician to the whole body of nature instead of limiting his efforts to treating minor symptoms of its illness, popular illustrations of which are the disproportionate emphasis on programs to save the whooping crane and the California condor.

Turning from the wild creatures to the green world, or what is left of it, the prospect is equally grim. A century and a half ago François André Michaux, observing the rapidity with which the American forests were being destroyed, declared it of "imperious necessity" that the government set aside extensive areas for forest preservation. He had seen that in the Old World most of the remaining productive forest areas were owned by the crown or government. He thought the same policy would prove necessary in America. He did not foresee the vast timberland holdings of pulp and paper companies, lumber companies, and others intent on protecting them in the interest of an indefinitely continuing timber production. But neither did he foresee the twenty-fold population increase that would take place in the ensuing century and a half. Nor could he have foreseen the land-consuming propensities of modern industrial societies. Consequently, though conditions are very different from those he expected to prevail, his "imperious necessity" continues to be equally valid.

To respond to that necessity, and respond we must, calls for massive additional accumulation of public lands, focused especially on areas which might serve to relieve the pressure on such overvisited national parks as Yosemite, Yellowstone, and the Great Smokies. Considering the rate that the nation's remaining lakeshores, seashores, and beaches are being preempted for private development, there is an even greater urgency for extensive additions to the pitifully meager portions of our shorelines publicly owned and protected from commercial development.

But susceptibility to recreational use should be only a minor consideration in other extensive acquisitions in which priority might be given to submarginal forest areas, river swamps, and marshes. In addition to such direct acquisitions, much of the vast holdings of the paper and lumber industries might, through tax incentive plans or cooperative arrangements, be permanently committed to forest and wildlife, with its wood production continuing to feed the raw-material requirements of its industrial owners.

Perhaps of even greater importance in assuring the preservation of at least a minimum of our environmental requirements is the establishment of a new rationale in respect to private property—one that gives more consideration to the rights of generations unborn. Existing concepts of private property, evolved in a world of surplus land, are becoming increasingly inadequate for a world where the productive burdens on land are reaching critical levels. As a matter of fact, a new rationale of land ownership is already in process. In this century, in accommodation to the exigencies of urban-industrial life, we have seen landowners lose the right to forbid air traffic over their property. Zoning laws now often restrict the uses to which they may put their property. In many jurisdictions their pristine rights to water flowing through their properties have been restricted and the pumping of water or oil from beneath their lands regulated. However, far more modification of the rationale of absolute ownership is essential if the enjoyment of the land is to be assured to our "heirs and assigns forever," the expressed intent of a fee simple title (legal jargon for absolute ownership). In the literal sense, a far more conservative rationale (using "conservative" in its primary sense of "having the power to preserve in a safe state") has become yet another facet of "the imperious necessity" of the day.

Viewed in that light, measures that may seem radical, measures that subordinate traditional absolute prerogatives of landownership to the general welfare of both today's society and that of posterity, become conservative. This new conservative rationale must reflect our new-found knowledge and wisdom—that the fabric of life extends over the countryside without regard for the metes and bounds set forth in legal titles. And the converse of that proposition provides that the use of any piece of land spreads its effects through the fabric of life far beyond its metes and bounds.

In the instance of marshes, especially salt marshes, the case for a new rationale of ownership is an even more obvious ecological essential and at the same time more juridically sustainable under existing legal principles. Since, as we are now aware, salt marshes are the cradle areas of the life of coastal waters, it clearly follows that the public has a vital interest in every acre of marshland regardless of its ownership. That being so, the new rationale must restrict private use of marshes to activities which are not deleterious to the public interest in their cradle activities. Ownership of a piece of marshland must no more entitle the owner to fill or pollute it than the ownership of a stream entitles one to pollute it to the detriment of life in the river below.

In short, this new rationale, essential to our posterity, must regard landowners as trustees holding their lands for the use and benefit of themselves *and* their heirs and assigns forever, without the right to un-limited use of the corpus of his trust, or the unfettered right to employ his trust property in any way substantially injurious to his neighbors or to the public generally. Only through such restraints on profligacy and greed can we properly protect the axiomatic equal right of our children and their children's children, all the way into the most remote future, each to use and enjoy the limited bounty of this earth. The new rationale of private property must reflect the truism that the only permanent wealth is in renewable resources, the reproduction of which no one should have an unrestrained right to subvert.

Once we recognize the moral right of our children's children to an unspoiled earth and the obverse obligation of human kind in every era to refrain from despoiling or unduly squandering its resources, it follows as a most obvious corollary that a primary moral necessity facing modern man, most especially twentieth-century Americans, is an immediate and drastic curtailment of our waste of the earth's limited store of fossil fuels. Obviously any substantial move in that direction is so pregnant with consequences that only an ecologically wise and basically just constituency, one with an ecological conscience, would provide the requisite consent of the governed to effect it. Nevertheless such action is both an imperious moral duty owed to posterity and at the same time a mounting necessity for ourselves, our immediate posterity, and our fellow creatures. Thus, despite the dislocations and discomforts inherent in the action, and despite the screams of protest that will rise from those who by purely fortuitous circumstances claim (and exercise) the right to dig, pump, and sell the earth's severely limited multi-million-year-old cache of "fixed sunlight," we must for the sake both of ourselves and posterity quickly and severely reduce our consumption of coal and oil. This giant conservation step must be taken for the sake of the very breath of life and the health of the living world. It is even more imperative for the sake of our children's children and their children's children in order that they may not, through our greed and thoughtlessness, receive from us the mere residue of an embezzled trust, an earth plundered of these valuable minerals.

If one considers the obvious—that before very long shrinking oil supplies will, of necessity, bring about drastic curtailment, the suggestion that such a curtailment be voluntarily accomplished in our time should not seem a very radical proposal. Such action now would have the virtue of being forward looking, intelligent, and conservative—attributes that would be entirely lacking if the world awaits the inevitable forced restriction when there is little left to conserve.

This proposed conservation of fossil fuels can be effected largely through positive and progressive movements and minimally by restrictive actions. Chief among the positive steps should be government assistance to the extent necessary to substantially convert our electric-utility-generating facilities from fossil fuels to atomic fuels, sun heat, earth heat, and water power, to produce power and heat at rates sufficiently low to induce homeowners everywhere to convert home heating systems to electricity. Another positive potential is the development and the introduction of acceptable steam and electric motor vehicles. Negative actions to accomplish such a mammoth fossil-fuel conservation program should include step-by-step restrictions of oil and coal production, gradual discouragement of the continued use of internal combustion engines, by increasing their fuel costs and eventually by prohibiting their use in population centers (with appropriate exceptions, of course, for vehicles such as heavy machinery and aircraft, pending a breakthrough, not yet apparent, in powering them by other than internal-combustion engines).

A drastic limitation of the use of fossil fuels, though essential to man's ecological survival, is, of course, only one step in the solution of a huge and complex problem, some facet of which is presented in almost every aspect of our daily lives. A step of equally vital importance which concern for our environment must demand is the reprocessing of sewage, garbage, and trash. This expensive but entirely feasible process will not only rescue from pollution the waters, swamps, and marshes now sacrificed as dumping grounds, and clear the air now poisoned by the fumes of burning refuse, but will recover for reuse a fabulous wealth of irreplaceable resources, and, last but by no means least, remove the ugly blot of our present disposal sites with their degrading effect, aesthetic and spiritual, on urban life.

A responsible and enlightened electorate, ecologically aware, would cry out in angry protest against the shame of our befouled rivers, lakes, and estuaries and insist upon the adoption of a nationwide program of restoration of the diseased and dying waters to radiant biological health and natural beauty. Costly? Yes. Perhaps as much as three, four, or even five months of the Vietnam war.

Cities free of smog and garbage dumps, fresh clean air to breathe, flowering parks to walk in, rivers of pure and living waters, a country of productive farms, green fields, forests full of wildlife—this is no utopia, impossible to attain, but the natural and inalienable right of mankind. It is only within reach, however, if man develops the ecological wisdom to stop burning the candle of life at both ends and exerts effort to live in harmony with his physical environment. If man can learn to counterpoise his almost godlike power over nature with a corresponding responsibility for her welfare, and a constant awareness that all life on earth is a unity, then indeed, in peace and harmony with his environment and his fellow creatures, it may be the high privilege of the family of man to survive on down through the ages toward the attainment of its infinite potential in the realm of nature's God.

SELECTED BIBLIOGRAPHY

Allen, Elsa Guerdrum, *The History of American Ornithology Before Audubon, Transactions of the American Philosophical Society*, New Series, Vol. XLI, No. 3, 1951, pp. 387–591.

Audubon, J. J., *Audubon and His Journals*, edited by Maria R. Audubon, 2 vols. New York, Dover Publications, Inc., 1960.

Bakeless, John, *Lewis and Clark*. New York, William Morrow and Co., 1947.

Bartram, John, *Diary of a Journey Through the Carolinas, Georgia, And Florida, From July 1, 1765, to April 10, 1766*. Annotated by Francis Harper, *Transactions of the American Philosophical Society*, New Series, Vol. XXXIII, Part 1, Philadelphia, December, 1942.

——, *Observations on inhabitants, climate, etc. . . . Made by Mr. John Bartram, in his travels from Pennsylvania . . . to Canada*. London, 1751.

—— and William, *John and William Bartram's America*. Edited by Helen Gere Cruickshank, American Naturalists Series. New York, The Devin-Adair Co., 1957.

Bartram, William, *Travels Through North and South Carolina, Georgia, East and West Florida . . .* Philadelphia, 1791.

——, *The Travels of William Bartram*. Naturalist's Edition, edited with commentary and annotated index by Francis Harper. New Haven, Yale University Press, 1958.

Bates, Marston, *The Forest and the Sea*. New York, Random House, 1960.

Berkeley, Edmund, and Berkeley, Dorothy Smith, *John Clayton*. Chapel Hill, University of North Carolina, 1963.

Berrill, N. J., *Inherit the Earth*. New York, Dodd, Mead & Co., 1953.

Bonaparte, Charles Lucien Jules Laurent, *American Ornithology*. Philadelphia, Carey, Lea & Carey, 1825–33.

Bourne, E. G., editor, *The Voyages of Columbus and John Cabot*. New York, Scribners, 1906.

Brett-James, Norman G., *The Life of Peter Collinson*. London, Dunstan and Co.

Brooks, Maurice, *The Appalachians*. The Naturalist's America Series. Boston, Houghton Mifflin Company, 1965.

Byrd, William, *The London Diary and Other Writings*, edited by Louis Wright and Marion Tinling. New York, Oxford University Press, 1958.

——, *The Prose Works of William Byrd*. Cambridge, Mass., Harvard University Press, 1966.

——, *The Secret Diary of William Byrd of Westover, 1709–1712*, edited by Louis B. Wright and Marion Tinling. Richmond, Va., Dietz Press, 1941.

——, *William Byrd's Natural History of Virginia, or the Newly Discovered Eden*, Berne, 1737. Richmond, Va., Dietz Press, 1940.

Cantwell, Robert, *Alexander Wilson*. Philadelphia and New York, J. B. Lippincott Company, 1961.

——, "A Legend Comes to Life: Mark Catesby," in *Sports Illustrated*, Vol. 13, No. 18, October 31, 1960, pp. 70–80.

Carson, Rachel, *Silent Spring*. Boston, Houghton Mifflin Company, 1962.

Catesby, Mark, *Hortus Britanno-Americanus* . . . London, 1763.

——, *The Natural History of Carolina* . . . *By the Late Mark Catesby, F.R.S. Revised by Mr. Edwards* . . . London, 1754.

——, *The Natural History of Carolina, Florida, and the Bahama Islands,* . . . *By the Late Mark Catesby, F.R.S. Revised by Mr. Edwards* . . . London, 1771.

Cheston, Emily Read, *John Bartram*. Philadelphia, The John Bartram Association, 1953.

Chinard, Gilbert, *André and François-André Michaux and Their Predecessors, Proceedings of the American Philosophical Society*, Vol. 101, No. 4, August, 1957.

Coker, W. C., *The Garden of André Michaux*. Journal of Elisha Mitchel Scientific Society, Vol. XXVII. Chapel Hill, N.C., 1911.

Core, Earl L., *Plant Taxonomy*. Englewood Cliffs, N.J., Prentice-Hall, Inc., 1955.

Darlington, William, *Memorials of John Bartram and Humphrey Marshall*. Philadelphia, Lindsay & Blakiston, 1849. Facsimile, New York, Hafner Publishing Co., 1967.

De Leuze, M., *A Brief Narrative of the Life and Travels of André Michaux. City Gazette*, Charleston, S.C., July 20–27, 1804.

Dillon, Richard, *Meriwether Lewis*. New York, Coward-McCann, 1965.

Dunlap, William, *A History of the American Theatre*, 2 vols. London, Richard Bentley, 1833.

Fletcher, Stevenson W., *John Bartram, Farmer-Botanist*. Issued by The John Bartram Association, Philadelphia, Pennsylvania.

Frick, George Frederick, and Stearns, Raymond Phineas, *Mark Catesby*. Urbana, Ill., University of Illinois Press, 1961.

Frome, Michael, *Strangers in High Places*. Garden City, N.Y., Doubleday & Company, 1966.

Grosart, Rev. Alexander B., *The Poems and Literary Prose of Alexander Wilson*, 2 vols. Paisley, Alex. Gardner, 1876.

Harshberger, J. W., *The Botanists of Philadelphia*. Philadelphia, 1899.

Herbst, Josephine, *New Green World*. New York, Hastings House, 1954.

Jefferson, Thomas, *Notes on the State of Virginia*. Chapel Hill, University of North Carolina Press, 1955.

———, *The Writings of Thomas Jefferson*, collected and edited by Paul Leicester Ford. New York, G. P. Putnam's Sons, 1895.

Kalm, Peter, *Peter Kalm's Travels in North America*. New York, Dover Publications, 1966.

Lachicotte, Alberta Morel, *Georgetown Rice Plantations*. Columbia, S.C., State Printing Company, 1955.

Lawson, John, *A New Voyage to Carolina*. London, 1709.

———, *A New Voyage to Carolina*, edited with an introduction and notes by Hugh Lefler. Chapel Hill, University of North Carolina Press, 1967.

Laycock, George, *The Alien Animals*. New York, American Museum of Natural History, 1966.

Leslie, Charles Robert, *Autobiographical Recollections*, edited by Tom Taylor. Boston, Ticknor and Fields, 1860.

Locy, William A., *The Story of Biology*. Garden City, N.Y., Garden City Publishing Co., 1925.

Lowenthal, David, *George Perkins Marsh*. New York, Columbia University Press, 1958.

Marsh, George Perkins, *Man and Nature*, edited by David Lowenthal. Cambridge, Mass., Harvard University Press, 1965.

Mathiessen, Peter, *Wildlife in America*. New York, The Viking Press, 1959.

Michaux, André, *Flora Boreali-Americana*. Paris, 1803. (Copy annotated by John Drayton.)

———, *Flora Boreali-Americana*. Paris, 1820. (Copy annotated by Asa Gray.)

———, *Journal de André Michaux, Proceedings of the American Philosophical Society*, Vol. XXVI, 1889, pp. 1–145.

———, *Journals of Travels into Kentucky, 1793–1796*. Published in translation in *Early Western Travels*, edited by Reuben Gold Thwaites. New York, AMS Press, Inc., 1966.

———, Letters by André Michaux and François André Michaux, published in *Les Botanistes Français en Amérique du Nord Avant 1850*. Paris, Centre National de la Recherche Scientifique, 1957.

Michaux, André, *Histoire des Chênes de L'Amérique ou Descriptions et Figures de Toutes les Espèces et Variétés de Chênes de l'Amérique Septentrionale*. Paris, 1801.

Michaux, François André, *The North American Sylva*. Paris, 1819.

——, *Memoire sur la naturalisation des arbres forestiers de L'Amérique Septentrionale*, etc. . . . *comparés avec ceux que produit la France*. Paris, 1805.

——, *Travels to the West of the Alleghany Mountains*. Published in *Early Western Travels*, edited by Reuben Gold Thwaites. New York, AMS Press, Inc., 1966.

Morison, Samuel Eliot, *Christopher Columbus, Mariner*. Boston, Little, Brown & Company, 1942.

Peattie, Donald Culross, *Green Laurels*. Garden City, N.Y., Garden City Publishing Co., 1938.

Petersen, Roger Tory, and Fisher, James, *Wild America*. Boston, Houghton Mifflin Company, 1955.

Plate, Robert, *Alexander Wilson*. New York, David McKay Company, 1966.

Rourke, Constance, *Audubon*. New York, Harcourt, Brace and Co., 1936.

Schramm, J. R., *Influence—Past and Present—of François-André Michaux on Forestry and Forest Research in America, Proceedings of the American Philosophical Society*, Vol. 101, No. 4, August, 1957.

Stewart, George R., *Not So Rich As You Think*. Boston, Houghton Mifflin Company, 1968.

Storer, John H., *The Web of Life*. New York, The Devin-Adair Co., 1953.

Sutton, Ann and Myron, *The Appalachian Trail*. Philadelphia, J. B. Lippincott Co., 1967.

Swem, E. G., *Brothers of the Spade*. Correspondence of Peter Collinson, of London, and of John Custis, of Williamsburg, Virginia, 1734–1746. Published in the *American Antiquarian Society Proceedings*, No. 58, 1948.

True, Rodney H., *François-André Michaux, Proceedings of the American Philosophical Society*, Vol. 78, No. 2, December, 1937.

Udall, Stewart L., *The Quiet Crisis*. New York, Holt, Rinehart, and Winston, 1963.

Wilson, Alexander, *The Foresters*. Philadelphia, Bradford and Inskeep, 1809-10.

——, *American Ornithology*, 9 vols. Philadelphia, Bradford and Inskeep, 1809–14.

Wilson, James Southall, *Alexander Wilson, Poet Naturalist*. New York, Neale Publishing Company, 1906.

INDEX

A Note About the Author

As soon as Henry Savage, Jr., could write a label to identify *Carabidae, Cecropia,* or *Coquina,* he began to collect almost every production of nature. He even learned taxidermy, with something less than workmanlike results, to add glamour to his "museum."

Born and raised in Camden, South Carolina, he left that fair town only long enough to earn his Bachelor of Science and Bachelor of Law degrees, along with a Phi Beta Kappa key, at the University of Virginia. Then he returned home, was accepted into the law firm of Savage, Royall and Kinard, married a charming girl from Columbia, South Carolina, and began raising their family of seven children.

Among his public services were a ten-year stint as Mayor of Camden and one term as President of the South Carolina Municipal Association. He is currently a member of the Board of Trustees of the Medical University of South Carolina and that of the Ashley Hall School.

As attestation for his lifelong consuming interest in things of the outdoors, Mr. Savage was chairman of the regional soil conservation organization and of the county forest protection association. He now serves as President of the South Carolina Forestry Association.

In addition to *Lost Heritage,* he is the author of *America Goes Socialistic, Seeds of Time: The Background of Southern Thinking,* and *River of the Carolinas: The Santee.*

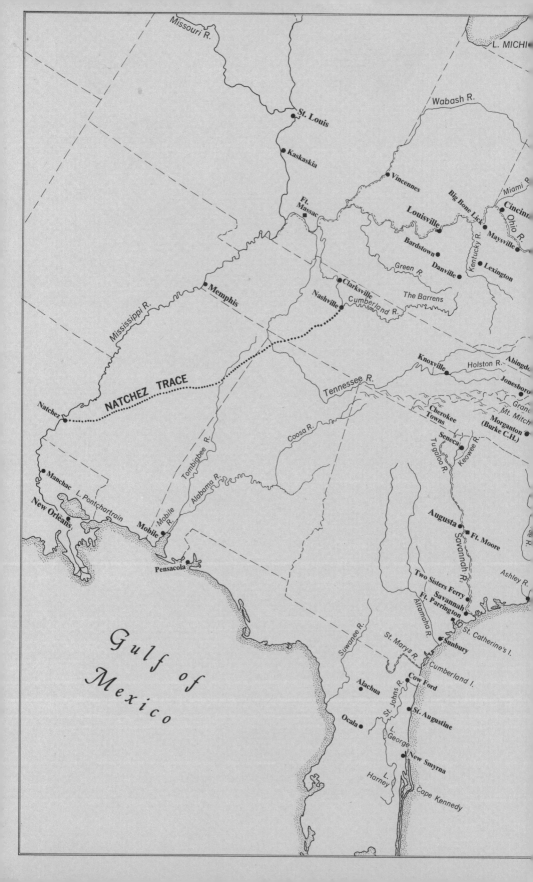